W. T. Barnwell
313 N. University
Phone 1439-W

Materials of Const
White, Johnson

MECHANICS OF MATERIALS

BY THE SAME AUTHORS

Properties and Mechanics of Materials
353 pages; 262 figures; cloth.

PUBLISHED BY

JOHN WILEY & SONS, Inc.
New York

MECHANICS OF MATERIALS

BY

PHILIP GUSTAVE LAURSON, M.S.

Associate Professor of Engineering Mechanics,
School of Engineering of Yale University
M. Am. Soc. C. E.

AND

WILLIAM JUNKIN COX, C.E.

Commissioner of Highways
State of Connecticut
and recently
Assistant Professor of Engineering Mechanics,
School of Engineering of Yale University
M. Am. Soc. C. E.

NEW YORK
JOHN WILEY & SONS, Inc.
London: CHAPMAN & HALL, Limited
1938

Printed in U. S. A.   8/39

Printing	Composition	Binding
F. H. GILSON CO.	TECHNICAL COMPOSITION CO.	STANHOPE BINDERY
BOSTON	BOSTON	BOSTON

PREFACE

This text is designed for courses in Mechanics of Materials (Strength of Materials) as offered in any of the basic engineering curricula. The first fifteen chapters may perhaps be regarded as a minimum course for engineering students. The remaining eight chapters contain slightly more advanced or more specialized material, many parts of which will be included in most courses but any part of which may be omitted. The book has been written to give a maximum of flexibility in this respect. It will be obvious to teachers that the chapters on combined stresses may be taken up earlier in the course if desired, and that the chapters *Continuous Beams, Beams of Two Materials* and *Beams — Additional Topics* may be assigned before columns are studied.

Every effort has been made to present material in such form that students will have no unreasonable difficulty in grasping the principles involved. Extreme conciseness, while admirable in a reference handbook, is not desirable in a first text for undergraduates in any subject. Clear statements with ample explanations and a free use of solved illustrative problems are needed.

The physical behavior of stressed bodies has been emphasized, as well as the mathematical expression of this behavior. The ultimate purpose of a course in mechanics of materials is to prepare the student for an eventual clear understanding of machine and structural design. From the beginning, therefore, the student is encouraged to think of the realities of the situations with which he is called on to deal. Unusual attention has been given to outlining the principles which govern the determination of allowable stresses.

In addition to developing as clearly as possible the simplified expressions on which most engineering design rests, the limitations of these expressions have also been carefully noted and discussed throughout.

Both the double integration of the elastic curve and the area-moment method of deflection have been fully presented, so arranged that either method may be omitted, in whole or in part.

The important recent advances in the theory of columns and in column design have been included. It is believed that the material on columns has been more logically organized than has sometimes been the case.

A feature of the text is the large number (more than five hundred) of carefully designed problems. To stimulate the student's interest many of these problems have been based on actual well-known engineering structures and machines. The problems are graded as to difficulty. Where a new principle is encountered for the first time, there are at least some problems that illustrate the new principle very simply. These are followed by more difficult problems illustrating the same principle alone or in combination with naturally related principles. Then, under each topic, the effort has been made to include one or two problems that even the best students will not find easy. The problems culminate in a group of "comprehensive problems" which form the final chapter. The solution of each of these problems requires the application of a number of principles drawn from different parts of the text. The solution of such problems forms the best possible review of the subject. The authors feel very strongly that no textbook in this subject can be superior to the problems it presents, and they have given very careful attention to making the problems suitable and adequate in every way.

The unusually complete tables are sufficient for the solution of all problems in the text so that the use of a steel handbook may be dispensed with if desired.

The authors gratefully acknowledge their debt to many who have contributed to this book and especially to Professor C. J. Tilden of Yale for advice and encouragement and to Professor Dana Young of Connecticut State College who critically read the manuscript while it was in the plastic state and offered innumerable constructive criticisms. Professor J. P. Colbert, of the University of Nebraska, made many helpful suggestions and Professor M. B. Hogan, of the University of Utah, read and criticized the manuscript. Valuable assistance in preparing the articles on welded joints was given by Mr. Henry Malcolm Priest of the Research Department of the United States Steel Corporation. Mr. P. R. Paladino, Yale 1938, read proof and helped in many other ways. The New York City Board of Water Supply, several industrial organizations, and Mr. Harry G. Acres, of Niagara Falls, Ontario, furnished photographs and data for problems.

P. G. L.
W. J. C.

New Haven, Connecticut
    July, 1938.

CONTENTS

CHAPTER I

CHAPTER II

CHAPTER III

CHAPTER IV

CHAPTER V

CHAPTER VI

CHAPTER VII

CHAPTER VIII

CHAPTER IX

CHAPTER X

CHAPTER XI

CHAPTER XII

CHAPTER XIII

CHAPTER XIV

CHAPTER XX

CHAPTER XXI

CHAPTER XXII

CHAPTER XXIII

APPENDIX A

APPENDIX B

APPENDIX C

MECHANICS OF MATERIALS

CHAPTER I

STRESS AND DEFORMATION

1. Introduction. The forces which hold a body in equilibrium have two additional effects on the body: they deform it, and they cause other forces to act *within* it. Mechanics of materials is the science which establishes the relationships between the forces applied to a body, the resulting deformation of the body, and the intensity of the *internal* forces that are produced by the applied external forces.

To a very large extent all engineering design rests on mechanics of materials. A structure such as the beam and supporting tie rod (Fig. 1) is to support some known load — the weight of a machine, perhaps. This load causes forces to act on the beam, on the hanger, and on the pin connecting them. The amounts of these forces can be determined by applying the principles of statics, which the student is assumed to know. The principles of mechanics of materials may then be used to determine the size which each of the members must have in order to

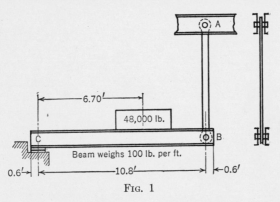

Fig. 1

perform its function satisfactorily, and other principles of mechanics of materials may be used to ascertain how much the tie rod will be stretched by the forces on it, and how much the beam will be deflected or bent. Other illustrations of the application of the principles of mechanics of materials are the determination of the diameter of a shaft to transmit a given amount of power, the required thickness of the shell of a boiler or tank to withstand a given steam or water pressure, etc. By means of mechanics of materials also may be determined the maximum loads which may be applied to existing structures without causing excessive deformations or internal stresses.

2. Stress. Since mechanics of materials is concerned with the *stresses* and *deformations* of bodies, it is desirable to get clearly in mind what is meant by these terms.

Consider the " eyebar " AB shown in Fig. 1. For the loads shown on beam CB, the force which the eyebar AB has to exert on the beam at B to hold the beam in equilibrium is found by the principles of statics to be

$$\frac{1,200 \times 5.40 + 48,000 \times 6.70}{10.8} = 30,400 \text{ lb.}$$

A free-body diagram of AB is shown in Fig. 2a with the axial forces of 30,400 lb. at A and B. Now suppose that a transverse plane be imagined to cut AB into two parts at any point D, and consider the portion BD as shown in Fig. 2b. It is obvious that

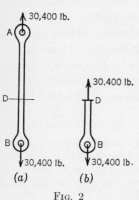

FIG. 2

equilibrium requires a force of 30,400 lb. on BD at D. This force is exerted on BD by the rest of the member, and since D may be taken at any point between A and B, it follows that any segment of AB is exerting a force of 30,400 lb. on the other segment. The *stress* in AB is said to be 30,400 lb.

What has been spoken of as the stress in AB is often called the *total stress* in the member, to distinguish it from the *intensity of stress* or the stress per unit of cross-sectional area, or more simply, the *unit stress*. To illustrate this distinction, if AB is a steel bar 1 in. by 4 in. in cross-section, the total stress of 30,400 lb. in it is distributed over 4 sq. in. of metal. Then the intensity of stress or the *unit stress* in the bar is 30,400/4 or 7,600 lb. per sq. in. If the bar were round, with a diameter of 2 in., the total stress in it would be 30,400 lb. as before, but the unit stress would be 30,400/3.1416 = 9,680 lb. per sq. in. Evidently, whenever a total stress P is uniformly distributed over a cross-section A, the unit stress S on the cross-section is given by the equation $S = P/A$.

It should be noted that total stress is a *force*, expressed in the units of force, usually pounds in the United States. Intensity of stress, however, is expressed in units of force divided by units of area — almost always pounds per square inch in this country. It is a somewhat loose, but convenient and very general, practice to refer to both total stress and unit stress simply as " stress " if the context makes clear whether total stress or intensity of stress is meant.

3. Kinds of Stress. The stresses which occur in bodies are of three kinds, or are combinations of these kinds. These three fundamental stresses are tension, compression, and shear. Tension and compression will be considered in this section, leaving shear for later consideration.

Tensile stress or tension is the kind of stress that exists on cross-sections of a prismatical bar subject to a pair of axial (and consequently collinear) forces which are directed away from one another. The stress in the bar AB of the preceding article was a tensile stress.[1] Forces which cause tensile stress in a body also *lengthen* the body.

Compressive stress or compression is the kind of stress that exists on cross-sections of a prism subject to a pair of axial forces directed *towards* one another, and consequently *shortening* the member. Tensile and compressive stresses act perpendicularly or normally to the surfaces on which they act, and for this reason they are often called " normal stresses." If the lines of action of the collinear forces that cause normal stress pass through the centroid of the cross-section of the body, the stress is uniformly distributed over the cross-section. There are many important examples of this sort of stress distribution. There are also many important instances in which loads do not pass through the centroid of a cross-section, and then a non-uniform stress distribution results. Such cases will not be considered, however, until later.

PROBLEMS

1. Kent's " Mechanical Engineers' Handbook " gives the breaking load for a steel piano wire 0.029 in. in diameter as 237 lb. What tensile unit stress does this load cause? *Ans.* $S_t > 300,000 < 400,000$ lb. per sq. in.

2. A piece of 3-in. standard steel pipe (see Appendix C for dimensions) 6 in. long stands on end on a flat steel surface. What is the unit stress in the pipe when an axial load of 3,000 lb. is placed on its upper end?

3. What load can be carried on the upper end of a $5\frac{1}{2}$-in. $\times$ $5\frac{1}{2}$-in. wood post if the average compressive unit stress is not to exceed 1,400 lb. per sq. in.?

4. In Fig. 3 a weight W is suspended by two wires, AB and AC, of equal length. $L = 5\ d$ and $W = 400$ lb. (a) Calculate the required diameter of wire if the unit stress is not to exceed 15,000 lb. per sq. in. (b) Assume $L = 10\ d$ and calculate the required diameter for the same unit stress. (Neglect weight of the wire in both cases.) *Ans.* (a) $D = 0.214$ in.

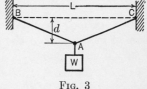

Fig. 3

---

[1] Other combinations of forces often cause tensile stresses in *parts* of a member. For example, there is tension at some points in a bent beam. Tension is most simply produced as stated above, however, and consideration of a loaded bar like AB gives the clearest idea of what tension is.

5. A tank which weighs 42,000 lb. when filled is carried on a framework that has four legs, each made of a 3-in. × 3-in. × ¼-in. steel angle. This frame is supported on a concrete floor, the unit compressive stress in which is not to exceed 600 lb. per sq. in. In order to distribute the pressure from the legs of the frame, a steel bearing plate is placed under each leg. Find the necessary area, and suitable dimensions for these plates, assuming that the force exerted by them on the floor is uniformly distributed.

6. Each cable of the Golden Gate Bridge over San Francisco harbor consists of 27,572 steel wires, each having a diameter of 0.192 in. What is the total stress in the cable when the unit stress in each wire has the value used in design, 82,000 lb. per sq. in.?

4. Deformation or Strain. A body made of any material will be deformed if forces act on it and stress it. In bodies made of some materials (such as rubber) small loads produce relatively large deformations. But bodies made of even the most nearly rigid materials, such as steel, are deformed by any forces producing stress.

Deformation as used in engineering is the change in any linear dimension of a body. This is often spoken of as " total deformation " to distinguish it from unit deformation. Unit deformation is the total deformation in a given length divided by the original length, or it is the deformation per unit of length. The word " strain " in engineering has the same meaning as deformation.

Unit deformation is sometimes thought of as a ratio, but the units are $\frac{\text{Length}}{\text{Length}}$. In engineering work, unit deformation (or unit strain) is expressed in inches per inch. Whenever the deformation of a body is stated, it should also be indicated whether the unit deformation is an increase or decrease in length. The symbol δ, the Greek small d (pronounced " delta "), is generally used to represent unit deformation. Total deformation is represented by Δ, the Greek capital D. Evidently, $\Delta = L \times \delta$, in which L is the length of the body.

Example. A bar 100 in. long is subject to tensile forces at the ends which cause it to change in length $\frac{1}{10}$ in. What is the unit deformation?

Solution: Unit deformation $= \dfrac{\text{Change in length}}{\text{Length}} = \dfrac{\frac{1}{10}}{100} = \dfrac{1}{1,000}$ in. per in. of length. Since the forces are tensile forces, the rod increases in length.

PROBLEMS

1. How much will a steel wire 60 ft. long lengthen if the unit deformation is 0.00055 in. per in.? *Ans.* $\Delta = 0.396$ in.

2. A steel rail 33 ft. long is shortened 0.450 in. by forces acting on the ends. What is the unit deformation of the rail, assuming that it is held straight by transverse supports?

3. What is the unit deformation of the rail if expressed in " feet per foot "?

5. Shearing Stress. Let AB in Fig. 4 be a bolt or bar of steel projecting from a substantial support. Let a vertical force F be applied
to AB. Now consider as a free body a part of AB cut off by any vertical plane. This part is in equilibrium, and ΣV, the sum of the vertical
forces, equals zero. Hence there is an upward force on the cut surface

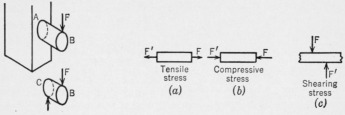

FIG. 4   FIG. 5.   Diagrammatic representation of stresses.

also equal to F. This upward force is exerted by the rest of AB on the
part taken as a free body and is a *stress*. It will be noticed that this is
different from tensile or compressive stress in that it acts *parallel* to the
section, whereas tension and compression are *normal* stresses and are
often so called. This parallel stress is called " shearing stress " because
the force tends to " shear " the bar in two. Fig. 5 shows the conventional methods of representing tensile, compressive, and shearing forces
acting on bodies. It will be noticed that the forces in (*c*) are not in
equilibrium, and it must be assumed that the body is held in equilibrium
by other forces not shown. This is true also of the body CB in Fig. 4.
It is held in equilibrium by a tensile stress developed in the upper half
of the face C and an equal compressive stress developed in the lower
half. These stresses are not uniformly dis-
tributed and therefore will not be discussed
until later.

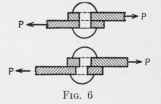

FIG. 6

As another example of shear, when two
plates are held together by a rivet as in
Fig. 6 and tensile forces are applied to the
plates, as shown, the plates tend to slide
past one another and to shear the rivet at
the plane of their adjoining surfaces. Note that in this case the shear
is exerted only on one particular cross-section of the rivet. This differs
from the example given in Fig. 4 in which the shearing force was shown to
act on *any* plane between the load and the wall.

Like tensile and compressive stress, *shearing stress* may refer either
to the total internal shearing force or stress acting on a section through
a body, or it may refer to the intensity of the stress. Total shearing

stress is usually designated by the letter V, and is frequently called *shear*. The expression " shearing stress " generally refers to shearing unit stress, but the context will make clear which is meant. The symbol which will be used in this work for shearing unit stress is S_s.

Shear may frequently be considered to be uniformly distributed over a cross-section; under such circumstances the relation $S_s = V/A$ holds true. Hence, if, in Fig. 6, the pull applied to each of the plates is P lb. and the diameter of the rivet is d in., the total shear on the cross-section of the rivet is P lb. and the unit shearing stress is $\dfrac{4P}{\pi d^2}$ lb. per sq. in.

FIG. 7. Shearing deformation.

Shearing stresses cause a shearing deformation just as tensile stresses cause elongation. In Fig. 7 the distance Δ_s is the shearing deformation in the originally rectangular body A. The unit shearing deformation is the total deformation Δ_s divided by the length L. It is the deformation per unit length.

Shearing deformation is often regarded as an angle. Note that, in Fig. 7, $\delta_s = \Delta_s/L = \tan \phi$. If ϕ is small (as it is for most materials), $\Delta_s/L = \phi$, where ϕ is expressed in radians.

Example. A short $\frac{3}{4}$-in.-square steel rod is held firmly in a vise with one end projecting horizontally. A weight of 200 lb. is suspended from the rod. What is the unit shearing stress in the rod, assuming the shearing stress to be uniformly distributed over the cross-section?

Solution: The total shearing force is 200 lb. and the unit shearing stress is
$$\frac{200}{\frac{3}{4} \times \frac{3}{4}} = \frac{200}{\frac{9}{16}} = 356 \text{ lb. per sq. in.}$$

PROBLEMS

(In solving these problems, assume all stresses to be uniformly distributed.)

→ **1.** A and C of Fig. 8 are two flat bars of steel attached to an overhead structure. The bar B is pinned to A and C by a 2-in.-diameter steel pin D. If B is midway between A and C, what is the shearing unit stress in D?

Ans. $S_s = 1,910$ lb. per. sq. in.

2. A white oak specimen held in holders, as shown in Fig. 9, failed under a total pull, P, of 4,430 lb. by shearing off the upper ear of the specimen. (*a*) What was the shearing unit stress at failure? (*b*) What was the tensile unit stress in the shank?

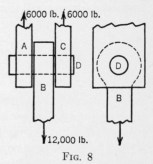

FIG. 8

3. A punch whose diameter is 1 in. punches a hole in a $\frac{3}{8}$-in. steel plate with a force of 47,000 lb. (*a*) What is the shearing unit stress in the plate? (*b*) What is the compressive unit stress in the punch?

→ **4.** A thrust of 18,000 lb. on a shaft is supported by a collar bearing, as shown in Fig. 10. What is the shearing unit stress on the cylindrical surface where the collar joins the shaft? *Ans.* $S_s = 5,240$ lb. per sq. in.

5. A hand crank 15 in. long is keyed to a $1\frac{1}{2}$-in. shaft by a key 2 in. long, $\frac{5}{16}$ in. wide, and $\frac{1}{4}$ in. thick, as shown in Fig. 11. When the pull on the handle of the crank is 65 lb., what is the shearing unit stress in the key?

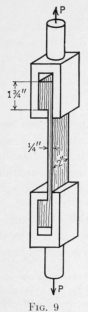

$1\frac{3}{4}''$

$\frac{1}{4}''$→

$2''$

P

FIG. 9

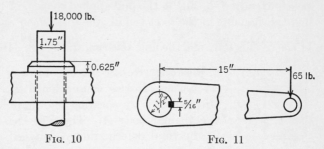

FIG. 10   FIG. 11

6. The Relation between Unit Stress and Unit Deformation. For many important engineering materials there is a constant ratio of unit stress to unit deformation, so long as the unit stress is not too great. If a bar of steel, for example, is subjected to axial tensile loads, it is found that the elongation produced by 10,000 lb. of load is just twice that produced by 5,000 lb. This fact, that "strain is proportional to stress," was first stated by Robert Hooke (1678) and is known as *Hooke's law.* Most wrought metals obey this law very closely; many other materials follow it so closely that its application to them does not involve important error.

It follows from Hooke's law that if loads P_1 and P_2 act on a member made of some material that obeys Hooke's law, and produce unit stresses of S_1 and S_2, accompanied by unit deformations of δ_1 and δ_2, respectively, then

$$\frac{S_1}{\delta_1} = \frac{S_2}{\delta_2} = \frac{S}{\delta} = \text{a constant}$$

This constant is known as the *modulus of elasticity* of the material in question (or sometimes as Young's modulus, after Thomas Young who is credited with having first defined it in 1802). The symbol E is commonly used for modulus of elasticity. The modulus of elasticity for all grades of steel is about 30,000,000 lb. per sq. in.[1] For some species of timber, however, it is only 1,000,000 lb. per sq. in., or less. For most

[1] Since S is lb. per sq. in., and δ is in. per in., it follows that E, like S, is lb. per sq. in.

other materials of engineering importance it lies between these extremes. The experimental determination of values of the moduli of elasticity for different materials will be discussed in the next chapter. That chapter will also consider the stress limits within which the constant ratio holds. Here it is desired merely to bring out the fact that, for many important materials and at the stresses ordinarily used in design, there is such a constant ratio. Values of the moduli of elasticity of a number of the more important materials are given in Appendix C.

If this constant ratio of unit stress to unit strain did not exist (exactly, or at least closely enough to be assumed) a great deal of engineering design would be much more difficult and less exact. Therefore the equation $S/\delta = E$ is one of the most important in the mechanics of materials.

For almost all materials the modulus of elasticity is the same in tension as in compression. But for any material the ratio of *shearing* stress to shearing deformation is different from the corresponding ratio for normal stresses. The unqualified term "modulus of elasticity" always implies normal stresses. The shearing modulus of elasticity is sometimes called the *modulus of rigidity*. The symbol for it is E_s. For all materials the modulus of rigidity is less than the modulus of elasticity, as is demonstrated in Chapter XVI.

Since the modulus of elasticity of steel is about 30,000,000 lb. per sq. in., if a bar of steel 100 in. long is stressed in tension to 20,000 lb. per sq. in., the unit deformation is

$$\delta = \frac{S}{E} = \frac{20,000}{30,000,000} = 0.00067 \text{ in. per in.}$$

The length of the 100-in. bar, therefore, is increased 0.067 in., or a little more than $\frac{1}{16}$ in.

PROBLEMS

1. A cylinder of structural steel is 2 in. in diameter and 20.000 in. long.   (*a*) What force applied axially to the end will stress it up to 28,000 lb. per sq. in.?   (*b*) If the stress is compressive, what will be the change in length of the cylinder?   (*c*) How long will the cylinder be when the load is 60,000 lb.?   *Ans.*   (*a*) $P = 88,000$ lb.

2. Heat-treated steel bolts 2 in. in diameter and 22.5 in. long are used for clamping the cable bands onto the $28\frac{3}{4}$-in.-diameter cables of the San Francisco–Oakland Bay Bridge.   Each bolt was designed to have 68,000 lb. of stress in it when fully tightened. To determine the amount of tightening necessary, the stretch of a bolt due to a 68,000-lb. load was calculated.   The bolt was then tightened until its stretch (measured with calipers as shown in Fig. 12) reached the calculated value.   What was this value?

3. A homogeneous prismatical bar hangs vertically.   Its cross-sectional area is A sq. in., its length L ft., its weight w lb. per ft., and its modulus of elasticity E lb.

per sq. in. What is the total elongation of the bar due to its own weight? (*Hint:* Set up an expression for the elongation of an elementary length dx at a distance x from the lower end of the bar, and integrate.)

4. A bar of steel ($E = 30,000,000$ lb. per sq. in.) and a bar of cast iron ($E = 12,000,000$ lb. per sq. in.) have dimensions as shown in Fig. 13. The load P causes

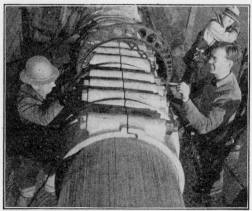

Courtesy, American Bridge Co.

FIG. 12. An application of Hooke's law (Problem 2).

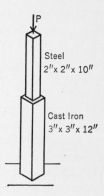

Steel
2″x 2″x 10″

Cast Iron
3″x 3″x 12″

FIG. 13

the total length of the two bars to decrease 0.008 in. Calculate P, assuming a uniform distribution of compressive stress over all cross-sections of both bars. Is the load so computed greater or less than the actual load required to cause the given shortening? *Ans.* $P = 41,100$ lb.

5. Two collinear brass bars ($E = 17,000,000$ lb. per sq. in.) each $\frac{1}{2}$ in. in diameter are connected to one another by means of a turnbuckle (Fig. 14). The threaded

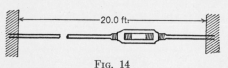

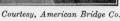

20.0 ft.

FIG. 14

ends are " upset " so that the half-inch diameter is maintained at the root of the thread. The turnbuckle has 11 threads per inch. The outer ends of the bars are maintained at a fixed distance of 20.0 ft. apart. The turnbuckle is tightened until the initial stress in the bars is 500 lb. per sq. in. What additional unit stress is caused by a quarter turn of the turnbuckle? (Assume the elongation of the turnbuckle to be the same as that of an equal length of bar.)

7. Poisson's Ratio. When a prism or other body of elastic material is subjected to compressive loads, not only do the dimensions in the direction of the loads decrease, but also the transverse dimensions increase. If the loads are tensile the length increases and the transverse dimensions decrease. For stresses within the range for which S/δ

is a constant (E), the ratio of the transverse *unit* deformations to the longitudinal unit deformations is a constant for a given material. This constant is called Poisson's ratio. The symbol m is used for this constant in this book.

Values of Poisson's ratio vary considerably, but those given below are common:

Aluminum alloys	0.36
Brass, bronze, copper	0.33
Monel metal	0.25–0.26
Steel	0.25–0.28
Concrete	0.10–0.18

Poisson's ratio for steel is commonly taken as $\frac{1}{4}$.

Example. A steel eyebar 2 in. by 6 in. in cross-section is stressed in tension by a total pull of 300,000 lb. What is the change in the 6-in. dimension?

Solution: $S_t = 300,000/12 = 25,000$ lb. per sq. in. The unit longitudinal deformation is $\delta = 25,000/30,000,000 = 0.000833$ in. per in. The transverse unit deformation is $m\delta = \frac{1}{4} \times 0.000833 = 0.000208$ in. per in. In width of 6 in. $\Delta = 6 \times 0.000208 = 0.00125$ in.

These transverse deformations which accompany axial stress do not result from transverse stress and do not cause transverse stress. This

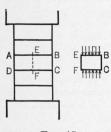

Fig. 15

may be shown by considering a pile of smooth rectangular blocks (Fig. 15) loaded in compression. The transverse dimensions, such as AB, of each block increase. If part of the block $ABCD$ cut off by a plane EF at any point is considered as a free body, there can be no resultant force on the face EF (and consequently no stress) since there are no horizontal forces on BE, BC, or CF to balance such a force on EF.

Stresses will result, however, if this transverse deformation is *prevented*, as for instance it would be if AD and BC were in contact with rigid surfaces before the loading was applied.

This transverse change in length is somewhat analogous to temperature expansion or contraction which does not cause or result from stresses, but which causes stresses if prevented. It is apparent that the complete stress analysis of a confined or restrained body may involve the use of Poisson's ratio.

An important relation between the constants E, E_s, and m for a given elastic material is expressed by the formula

$$E_s = \frac{E}{2(1 + m)}$$

This formula is derived in Chapter XVI.

For $m = \frac{1}{4}$, as in steel, this gives $E_s = \frac{2}{5}\, E$, or about 12,000,000 lb. per sq. in., a value commonly used for steel.

8. Triaxial and Biaxial Stress and Deformation. The rectangular solid shown in Fig. 16 is subject to stresses in three directions. This condition of stress is known as " triaxial " stress. The vectors represent the unit stresses, any one of which may be either tension (as shown) or compression. The change in length of the dimension parallel to one of the stresses is the algebraic sum of the three deformations in that direction produced by each of the unit stresses. This unit deformation along the x axis may be expressed by the formula given below:

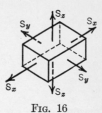

FIG. 16

$$\delta = \pm \frac{S_x}{E} \mp \frac{S_y}{E}\, m \mp \frac{S_z}{E}\, m$$

in which the upper sign in any term is to be used if the corresponding unit stress is tensile stress. If one of the unit stresses is zero, the case is one of biaxial stress.

Cases of biaxial stress and triaxial stress are met with in the design of certain types of structures and pressure containers.

PROBLEMS

1. A rectangular bar made of an aluminum alloy is 1 in. by 3 in. in cross-section. Tensile forces of 50,000 lb. each are applied to the ends, and compressive forces of 40,000 lb. each are distributed over opposite 10-in. lengths of the 1-in. wide faces. Calculate the changes in length and in width of this 10-in. portion.

2. A round rod of steel 1.250 in. in diameter and 14 in. long was subjected to loads of 33,750 lb. in a testing machine. It was observed that a gage length of 2 in. near the midpoint of the rod increased in length 0.0018 in. and the diameter of the rod decreased 0.00024 in. Calculate the modulus of elasticity and Poisson's ratio for this steel.   *Ans.* $m = 0.21$.

3. A cube, the length of each side of which is L, is subjected to compressive stresses due to forces applied to two opposite faces and causing a unit shortening of δ. Show that, if terms involving δ^2 and δ^3 are neglected, the volume change is $L^3\delta(2\, m - 1)$.

GENERAL PROBLEMS

1. A weight of unknown magnitude is suspended from a steel wire ($E = 30,000,000$ lb. per sq. in.) which when unstressed is 10 ft. long and $\frac{1}{16}$ in. in diameter. The total deformation that results is 0.06 in. The same weight is then suspended from a copper wire, 6 ft. long and $\frac{1}{8}$ in. in diameter. The total deformation is 0.0152 in. What is the modulus of elasticity of the copper?

2. A block of steel (Fig. 17) is supported by a steel rod $2\frac{1}{4}$ in. in diameter. If two loads of 22,000 lb. each are applied to the block as shown, calculate the tensile and shearing unit stresses in the rod.

3. A $7\frac{1}{2}$-in.-by-$7\frac{1}{2}$-in. timber post rests upon a 12-in.-by-12-in. steel bearing plate on top of a concrete pier as shown in Fig. 18. The base of the concrete pier is 3 ft. 0 in. square. If the total load carried by the post is 64,000 lb., find (a) unit stress in the timber post, (b) bearing stress on concrete at top of pier, and (c) unit pressure on foundation. Neglect the weight of the concrete pier.

Ans. (b) $S = 445$ lb. per sq. in.

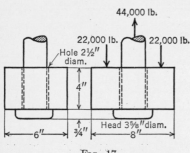 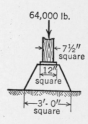

Fig. 17   Fig. 18

4. (a) What force will be required to punch a square hole 1 in. by 1 in. in a $\frac{5}{8}$-in. plate of steel for which the ultimate strengths are: tension = 70,000 lb. per sq. in., shearing = 50,000 lb. per sq. in.? (b) What is the compressive unit stress in the punch? (c) A punch is made of steel with an ultimate strength of 150,000 lb. per sq. in. in compression. What is the greatest thickness of plate (with strengths as above) in which it can punch a 1-in.-by-1-in. square hole? (d) What is the smallest square hole that a punch of this material can punch in the $\frac{5}{8}$-in. plate?   *Ans.* (a) $F = 125,000$ lb.

5. A tension member in a 374-ft. railroad bridge consists of six eyebars 12 in. by 2 in. and two eyebars 12 in. by $2\frac{3}{8}$ in. The panel length is 34 ft. 0 in. One of the $2\frac{3}{8}$-in. thick bars has the pin holes drilled 0.025 in. too close together. The total load on the tension member equals 3,200,000 lb. (a) What is the unit stress in the short bar? (b) In the other bars? (c) What would be the unit stress if all bars were exactly the same length?   *Ans.* (b) $S = 15,700$ lb. per sq. in.

6. A steel tape for measuring distances is 0.30 in. wide and 0.015 in. thick. It is exactly 100 ft. long when supported throughout its length and pulled with a force of 12 lb. What will be its length if the chainmen pull with a force of 50 lb.?

7. In a laboratory test of its properties a cypress block $1\frac{3}{4}$ in. by $1\frac{3}{4}$ in. in cross-section and 10.00 in. long was loaded on the ends with 5,880 lb. The shortening in a length of 6 in. was measured and found to be 0.0127 in. What was the modulus of elasticity of this piece of cypress?   *Ans.* $E = 907,000$ lb. per sq. in.

8. In Fig. 19, A and B are steel blocks $1\frac{1}{2}$ in. by 2 in. by 9 in. which rest upon two supports E and F. D is a steel bar 1 in. by $1\frac{1}{2}$ in. by 6 in. which passes through a 1-in.-by-$1\frac{1}{2}$-in. slot in C and which rests upon A and B. The steel bar C is 4 in. by $1\frac{1}{4}$ in. and carries a load P of 12,000 lb. D is midway between E and F. A and B are in contact with C. Calculate: the shearing unit stress and maximum compressive unit stress in A and B; the shearing, compressive, and maximum tensile unit stress in C; and the shearing stress and maximum compressive stress in D.

9. A weight of 1,000 lb. is to be suspended by a steel wire 25 ft. long. The maximum allowable unit stress in the wire is 20,000 lb. per sq. in., and the total deformation must not exceed 0.18 in. What is the required diameter of the wire?

Ans. $D = 0.266$ in.

10. Three steel wires, a, b, c, each 0.0400 sq. in. in cross-sectional area, connect two rings as shown in Fig. 20. The lengths of the wires, unstressed, are: $a = 100.00$ ft., $b = 99.950$ ft., $c = 99.900$ ft. Calculate the elongation of wire a and the unit stress in wire a when a load of 2,500 lb. is hung on the lower ring.

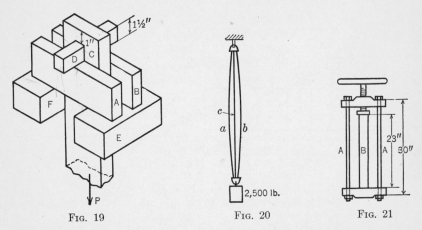

FIG. 19   FIG. 20   FIG. 21

11. A straight steel bar is 12 ft. long and has a rectangular cross-section which varies uniformly from 1 in. by 1 in. to 1 in. by 5 in. What change occurs in its length when it is subjected to an axial load of 20,000 lb.?

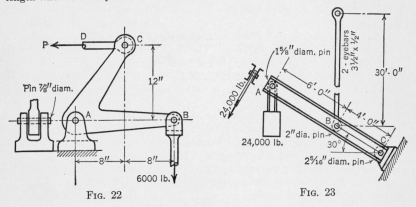

FIG. 22   FIG. 23

12. A screw press has the dimensions shown in Fig. 21. The rods marked A are of steel 1.00 in. in diameter. The pitch of the screw thread is 0.125 in. A brass tube B with outside diameter 2.50 in. and inside diameter 1.50 in. is placed in the press. What part of one turn is required for each increase of 1,000 lb. per sq. in. stress in the brass tube? (Assume no deformation of the upper and lower heads of the press, nor of the screw.)

13. In the bell-crank mechanism shown in Fig. 22, determine the necessary cross-sectional area of CD if the tensile unit stress in it is to be $\frac{4}{5}$ the shearing unit stress in the pin at A. $Ans.\ \ A = 0.721$ sq. in.

14. In the structure shown in Fig. 23, find the tensile unit stress in the eyebars and the shearing unit stresses in pins A, B, and C.

15. In the truss shown in Fig. 24, the member DE is made of two square rods, each 1.25 in. $\times$ 1.25 in. in cross-section. Calculate the unit stress caused by the loads shown.

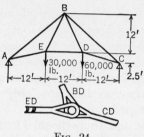

Fig. 24

16. A balcony 120 ft. long is 6 ft. wide. One side is supported on a horizontal sill attached to a wall. The other side is hung from vertical steel rods spaced at 20-ft. intervals along its length. The balcony is designed to carry a " live load " of 125 lb. per sq. ft. The " dead-load " weight of the balcony is an additional 20 lb. per sq. ft. The ends of the rods are threaded, and the tensile unit stress in the rods at the root of the thread (see Appendix C) is not to exceed 18,000 lb. per sq. in. (a) What is the necessary area of a rod at the root of the thread?   (b) What size rods should be used?   (c) How much will the rods elongate under full load if they are 28 ft. long?

CHAPTER II

MECHANICAL PROPERTIES OF MATERIALS

9. Introduction. *Mechanical* properties of materials relate to the resistance a material offers to forces applied to it. From the standpoint of this treatise, such properties are the most important that a material may possess. Mechanical properties include elasticity, stiffness, strength, ductility, malleability, brittleness, toughness. This chapter will define those properties, explain how they are determined, and comment on their importance.

10. Elasticity: Elastic and Proportional Limits. Elasticity is that property which enables a body deformed by stress to regain its original dimensions when the stress is removed. This, the technical definition, has a somewhat different meaning from the word as frequently used in everyday speech in referring to a material like rubber, which is capable of deforming *greatly* under stress, and of regaining its approximate original dimensions when the stress is removed. In a mechanical sense the criterion of elasticity is not the amount of deformation, but the completeness with which the original dimensions are regained when the stress is removed. From this standpoint, both steel and glass are highly elastic since they have the ability to go back to their original dimensions when relieved of stress.

The opposite quality to elasticity is plasticity. That is, a perfectly plastic body is one which does not make any recovery of its original dimensions upon the removal of a stress. No material is perfectly plastic. Similarly, no body is wholly elastic *at all ranges of stress.* Even steel can be stressed so greatly that some deformation remains after the stress has been removed. It is only up to a certain unit stress that steel is an elastic material. Above that stress it is partially elastic and partially plastic. This limiting unit stress above which a material cannot be stressed without causing a permanent deformation is called its *elastic limit.* The deformation which remains when a body is stressed above the elastic limit and the stress is then removed is called *permanent set.* Fortunately, most of the important engineering materials are elastic, or very nearly elastic, over considerable ranges of stress.

Many materials possess the property of *proportionality of stress and deformation.* This property, as expressed by Hooke's law, " Stress varies as strain," was discussed in Art. 6. In no material, however,

15

does a constant ratio between unit stress and unit deformation hold throughout the entire range of stress which the material can resist.   As the unit stress is increased, eventually a value is reached at which the same increment of stress causes a different (usually larger) increment of strain than those previously observed.   The stress value at which unit strain ceases to be proportional to unit stress is called the *proportional limit* of the material.   For most materials the proportional limit appears to be the same as the elastic limit; that is, when the material ceases to be elastic, it also ceases to follow Hooke's law.   There is a proportional limit corresponding to each of the three kinds of stress.

11. Stiffness.   Stiffness is the property which enables a material to withstand high unit stress without great unit deformation.   Steel is said to be very stiff because a load which causes a large unit stress produces only a small unit deformation.   Wood is much less stiff because a greater deformation accompanies a much lower stress.   In everyday speech, stiffness is associated with resistance to *bending*.   There is no such restriction in the technical use of the term, however.   Stiffness is resistance to any sort of deformation.   The definition of stiffness shows that this property is evidently measured by the modulus of elasticity of a material.

Values of the moduli of elasticity of several common materials are given below.   The moduli of elasticity of steel and Duralumin vary between rather close limits, so that the values given here are applicable to all grades of these materials.   For different species of wood, different " mixes " of concrete, different compositions of cast iron and brass, however, there are wide variations in the value of E.   The values given below are average or typical.

Steel	30,000,000 lb. per sq. in.
Brass	16,000,000 " " " "
Cast iron	12,000,000 " " " "
Duralumin	10,000,000 " " " "
Concrete	2,000,000 " " " "
Yellow pine (along grain)	1,600,000 " " " "

12. Strength.   The *strength* of a material is the property which determines the greatest unit stress that the material can withstand without fracture or excessive distortion.   Brittle materials actually break into pieces when the load on them becomes excessive.   Ductile materials, however, especially under compressive loads, though also under tensile and shearing loads, may distort excessively and thus lose their usefulness without actual fracture.   In such cases, the unqualified term, strength, becomes somewhat vague.   More useful concepts of strength are *elastic strength, yield strength, ultimate strength, fatigue* *strength,* and *creep strength.* These are more limited and more exactly definable quantities. They will be defined and discussed in later articles.

Any material has tensile, compressive, and shear strengths, corresponding to the three kinds of stress.

13. Ductility, Malleability, and Brittleness. Ductility is the property which enables a material to undergo plastic deformation under tensile stress. Ductile materials are commonly defined as those which can be readily drawn into wires.

Malleability is the property which enables a material to undergo plastic deformation under compressive stress. Malleable materials are those readily beaten into thin sheets. Most materials which are very ductile are also quite malleable.

Brittleness is the absence of plasticity. A brittle material is neither ductile nor malleable.

Ductility and malleability are important properties in any member to which severe loads may be applied suddenly, particularly if the consequences of sudden failure would be serious. For example, a crane hook should be made of a ductile rather than a brittle material.

Even in uses where impact is not to be anticipated, it is often important that materials be not too brittle. This is because there is always a degree of approximation in saying that a stress is uniformly distributed over a cross-section. Even in a tension member of the same nominal cross-section throughout and of material as nearly homogeneous as can be obtained, although the stress under an axial load will have very nearly the average value over almost the entire cross-section, there will be minute areas where the stress will be decidedly above the average. These will be points where there are slight flaws in the material, or where there are sudden small changes in cross-section, such as might be due to an accidental tool mark or scratch in the surface of the member. In a ductile material under a steady load this condition of minute areas with relatively high stresses is of small consequence.[1] Further increase in load simply causes the minute area of overstressed metal to yield plastically, instead of fracturing. But if the material is brittle rather than ductile, it may crack instead of flowing. The end of the crack will be a point of high stress concentration, which may cause the crack to spread until failure of the entire member results. Therefore it is advantageous to use materials possessing a fair degree of ductility. If brittle materials must be used, precautions should be taken to reduce points of high stress concentration to the minimum.

[1] However, in situations where "fatigue" must be considered, it may be very important. See Art. 22.

14. Toughness. Toughness is the property of a material which enables it to endure shock or blows. When a blow is struck on a body, some of the energy of the blow is transmitted to the body and absorbed by it. In absorbing this energy, work is done on the body. This work is the product of the deformation and the average stress while the deformation is being produced. Consequently, a body which can be both highly stressed and greatly deformed will withstand a heavy blow and is said to be tough.

The single term " toughness " is used to indicate either *elastic* toughness or *plastic* toughness. Elastic toughness is measured by the amount of energy which a body can absorb without the production of a stress which exceeds its elastic limit; plastic toughness, by the amount of energy which can be absorbed without causing fracture. Elastic toughness is generally called resilience, the term " toughness," if unqualified, usually being understood to mean plastic toughness. Resilience and " energy loading " of members will be discussed in Chapter XVII.

15. The Determination of Mechanical Properties — Testing. The mechanical properties of materials are most readily ascertained by subjecting the materials to appropriate tests in laboratories equipped for the purpose and called materials-testing laboratories. Such tests are made from two standpoints. They may have as their aim research on a material to discover additional facts concerning one or more of its properties; or they may be made in order to determine whether the properties of a given *lot* of material meet the standard specified for the use for which that particular material is intended.

Most of the important basic tests, including all the routine tests for determining the quality of a given lot of material, have been evolved over a period of years, and the procedure for each has been carefully worked out and standardized so that the results of different laboratories may be comparable. The American Society for Testing Materials (abbreviated A.S.T.M.) is an organization which is engaged in determining the best procedure for each test. It publishes directions for making such tests and specifies the limits within which certain results should lie if the material for any particular use is to be regarded as acceptable.[1]

16. Static Tensile Test. The static tensile test is one of the simplest tests which can be made, and for a large number of engineering materials, including most of the metals, it is the most informing. It may be used to determine the elasticity, stiffness, strength, ductility, resilience, and toughness of the materials.

In this test, a specimen (usually a round or rectangular bar) is placed

---

[1] A collection of some important specifications of the A.S.T.M. is published under the title " Selected A.S.T.M. Standards for Students in Engineering."

in a " testing machine " which stretches it, thus subjecting it to tensile forces. The stretching, done at a slow and uniform rate, sets up stresses in the specimen which eventually result in its failure. Fig. 25 shows a common form of specimen for this test.

A record of the static tensile test is kept by observing at frequent intervals the total stress in the specimen as measured by the " weighing " device of the machine and simultaneously observing the elongation as measured by a strain gage or " extensometer." These simultaneous readings are recorded opposite one another. The observed

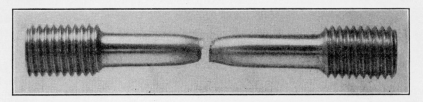

Fig. 25. Above: test specimen of ductile steel broken in tension (about ¾ full size).

Right: fracture of same specimen (enlarged).

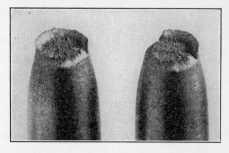

values are completed by taking the specimen from the machine after it has been broken, fitting the ends closely together, and measuring the final length between gage points. The diameter at the cross-section of failure is also measured. A record of these measurements constitutes the " log " of the test.

17. Stress-Strain Diagram. The data of a static tensile test are often shown graphically by means of a curve, of which the ordinates are the apparent unit stresses and the abscissas the corresponding unit elongations. Such a curve is called a *stress-strain diagram*.

The upper curve of Fig. 26 is a stress-strain diagram representing a test of " mild " or ductile steel. The test specimen was cylindrical, the original diameter being 0.619 in. The final diameter of the fracture was approximately 0.38 in. Deformations were measured in a *gage length* of 8 in. When the specimen broke, this had increased to 10.16 in. Points on the curve represent simultaneous values of unit stress and unit deformation computed from the observed loads and the *original* dimensions. A *smooth* curve is drawn, rather than one which passes through every plotted point. It is probable that the true behavior of the specimen is represented by a smooth curve and that the slight deviations of the plotted points from the smooth curve are mostly due to small errors of the instruments and of observation. The origin is a point on the curve, since for zero unit stress there is zero unit deformation.

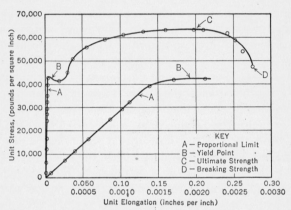

Fig. 26.   Stress-strain diagram for ductile steel.

Until the unit stress exceeds the proportional limit, the " curve " is a straight line *OA*, since the unit stress and unit deformations are proportional. For the upper curve a scale was chosen which would permit the entire diagram to be shown. Plotted to this scale, the part of the curve below the proportional limit is nearly vertical. The lower curve shows this part of the diagram drawn to a scale of unit deformation which is 100 times as large as the scale of the upper curve.

Somewhere near the point *A* on the diagram, the deviation of the curve from a straight line indicates that the material is no longer conforming to Hooke's law.[1] The unit stress corresponding to the upper end of the straight line is the *proportional limit*. It could be shown that this stress

---

[1] The statement that the proportional limit is " somewhere near the point *A* " is intentionally indefinite. The reason for this is that, the more accurate the measurements of stress and strain are, the lower the proportional limit is found to be. Lack of proportionality of unit stress and unit strain commences *very gradually* and has probably existed through a stress range of several thousand pounds per square inch before it can be detected even by the most exact measuring devices which have been devised. This indefiniteness of the proportional limit is not of great practical importance, however, because, so long as lack of proportionality of unit stress and unit strain is too small to be detected, its consequences are ordinarily too small to be serious.

is also the *elastic limit*, at least for all practical purposes. The elastic limit also measures the *elastic strength* of the material.

A short distance above the proportional limit the curve is seen to be horizontal. This indicates that the specimen is stretching without any increase in the load. This unit stress is the *yield point*. The unit elongation which occurs at the yield point may be 2 per cent, or more, of the gage length — 20 or 30 times as great as the elongation produced in stressing the specimen up to the proportional limit.[1] When the yield point has been reached, the curve dips downward for a short distance representing a period of the test during which the specimen transmits less load as it stretches. Then there follows a long length of the curve rising continuously, but becoming flatter until the maximum ordinate is reached, at which point the curve is again horizontal. The unit stress represented by the maximum ordinate is the *ultimate strength*.

Further stretching is produced by a *decreasing* force. During this stage of the test the observer notices that somewhere along the length of the specimen, throughout a short length, the specimen begins visibly to decrease in diameter and to increase in length. This is called *necking*. It progresses rapidly until at this reduced section the specimen suddenly pulls apart with a loud report. While this necking is in progress, the load which the specimen transmits decreases because the cross-sectional area is rapidly decreasing. The unit stress at which the specimen actually breaks is called the *breaking strength*.[2]

In addition to the proportional limit, yield point, ultimate strength, and breaking strength, the stress-strain curve indicates the modulus of elasticity. This is the *slope* of the straight part of the curve from the origin to the proportional limit. The lower curve shows that a unit deformation of 0.001 in. per in. corresponds to a unit stress of 30,000 lb. per sq. in. The slope of the line is the ordinate divided by the

---

[1] The existence and significance of the yield point are strikingly brought out by a simple experiment. Let a length of ten or a dozen feet of soft " iron " wire of about 1/30-in. diameter be unwound from a small coil, and let one end be firmly attached to a hook or nail. If the other end is held in one's hand and pulled slowly and steadily, the sudden increase in length that occurs without increase in load can be very clearly felt. Before the wire is pulled, moreover, it will not be straight, but will be crooked or wavy, as a result of its having been unrolled from the coil. A light pull on the wire will keep it straight, so long as the pull is applied; but the wire will return to its crooked condition when the pull is released. However, after the pull has been increased until the yielding of the wire is felt, the wire remains straight when the pull is released.

[2] A compressive stress-strain diagram of a short specimen of *ductile* material would show no ultimate and breaking strengths. The unit stress (computed from the original cross-section) would simply increase indefinitely until the capacity of the testing machine was reached.

abscissa, or

$$\text{Slope} = \frac{30,000 \text{ lb. per sq. in.}}{0.001 \text{ in. per in.}} = 30,000,000 \text{ lb. per sq. in.}$$

Since these are simultaneous values of S and δ below the proportional limit, it is apparent that this slope is S/δ, which equals E.

The *percentage of elongation* is 100 times the total change in length divided by the original length. This is a measure of ductility. It is usually calculated even when the curve is not drawn. For this specimen the calculation is

$$\text{Percentage of elongation} = \frac{10.16 - 8}{8} \times 100 = 27 \text{ per cent}$$

Another index of ductility is usually calculated. This is the *percentage of reduction of area*. For the specimen described, the diameter of the fracture was found to be approximately 0.38 in. This is approximate because the fracture is not a perfect circle. The reduction of area in square inches equals the area of a circle 0.619 in. in diameter minus the area of a circle 0.38 in. in diameter. This is $0.301 - 0.113 = 0.188$ sq. in. The percentage of reduction of area is equal to $\frac{0.188}{0.301} \times 100 = 62$ per cent. For a given grade of steel this percentage of reduction of area is less dependent on the gage length than is the percentage of elongation.

18. True and Apparent Unit Stress. The stresses shown by the stress-strain curve drawn as described in Art. 17 are evidently smaller than the stresses which actually exist in the specimen. An axial tension produces a lateral contraction (Art. 7), and the stressed cross-sections of the member are therefore smaller than the unstressed cross-section used in computing the plotted unit stresses. The stresses calculated from the original cross-section of a specimen are called " apparent unit stresses." These stresses have greater practical value for most purposes and are much more easily determined than the true unit stresses, and they are the stresses usually determined. There is very little difference between true and apparent stresses until the yield point of the material has been passed, and the principal difference between the two stresses occurs after necking has begun. During this period of the test the minimum cross-section is decreasing faster than the load so that although the apparent stress is decreasing the true stress is rising rapidly.

19. Stress-Strain Diagram of a Brittle Material. Brittle materials do not have a sharply defined yield point as described in the foregoing

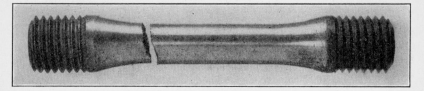

Fig. 27. Tensile fracture of cast iron.

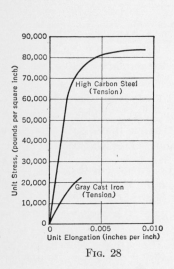

Fig. 28

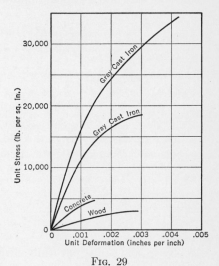

Fig. 29

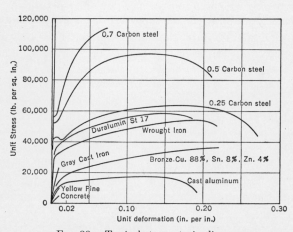

Fig. 30. Typical stress-strain diagrams.

test.   Instead, the stress-strain curve merely deviates gradually from the tangent when the proportional limit is reached.   Since brittle materials are those which are incapable of much plastic deformation, they do not draw down or neck before failure, but snap without warning (Fig. 27).   When a stress-strain diagram is drawn for such a material, it ends before it becomes horizontal, the ultimate strength and the breaking strength being the same.   Fig. 28 shows stress-strain diagrams for brittle steel, and for cast iron under tension.   For such materials the true and apparent unit stresses are evidently very nearly the same.

Figs. 29 and 30 show typical stress-strain diagrams for a variety of common engineering materials, each of which varies greatly in physical properties.

PROBLEMS

1. The log of a tensile test of hot-rolled steel is given below. Calculate unit stresses and corresponding deformations and draw the stress-strain curve, using scales of 1 in. = 10,000 lb. per sq. in. and 1 in. = 0.05 in. per in. Also replot the curve up to the yield point, using a scale of 1 in. = 0.0005 in. per in. Start this curve at the same origin. Determine and state values for (a) proportional limit, (b) modulus of elasticity, (c) yield point, (d) ultimate strength, (e) breaking strength, (f) per cent elongation, (g) per cent reduction of area.

TENSILE TEST OF HOT-ROLLED STEEL

Gage length, 2 in.			
Diameter of specimen, 0.496 in.			
Load (lb.)	Elongation (in.)	Load (lb.)	Elongation (in.)
0	0.00000	7,500	.03800
1,600	.00056	8,700	.08000
2,400	.00081	9,400	.11000
3,600	.00122	10,000	.15000
4,600	.00164	10,500	.18000
6,400	.00221	11,200	.45000
7,200	.00254	10,800[2]	.64000
8,000	.00320	10,200	.73000
7,500[1]	.00480	8,700[3]	.76000
7,300	.01700		

[1] Strain-gage removed. Subsequent elongations measured with dividers and steel scale.
[2] Necking begins to show.
[3] Specimen broke. Final diameter at fracture = 0.28 in.

2. The log of a tensile test of gray cast iron is given below. Calculate unit stresses and corresponding unit deformations, and draw the stress-strain curve, using scales of 1 in. = 8,000 lb. per sq. in., and 1 in. = 0.004 in. per in.   Determine the value of E when the stress is 4,000 lb. per sq. in.; when the stress is 8,000 lb. per sq. in.

TENSILE TEST OF GRAY CAST IRON

Gage length, 2 in. Diameter of specimen, 0.761 in.			
Load (lb.)	Elongation (in.)	Load (lb.)	Elongation (in.)
0	0.00000	7,000	.00400
1,000	.00028	8,000	.00520
2,000	.00074	9,000	.00690
3,000	.00120	10,000	.00920
4,000	.00170	11,000	.01300
5,000	.00234	11,500	.01580
6,000	.00300	11,800	

3. A bar of the above cast iron is 48 in. long and $\frac{7}{8}$ in. square.   How much will it lengthen when the load on it is increased from 4,000 lb. to 5,000 lb.?   When the load is increased from 10,000 lb. to 11,000 lb.?

20. Toughness Indicated by Stress-Strain Diagram.   The stress-strain diagram is a " force-distance " diagram, and the area under the curve represents the average value of the work done per unit volume of the material and is therefore a measure of the toughness of the material.   The area under the straight sloping part of the curve[1] represents the average value of the work done per unit of volume in stressing the specimen to the proportional limit and is therefore a measure of the elastic toughness or resilience of the material.

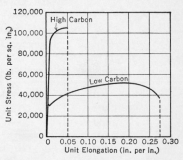

FIG. 31.   Toughness indicated by stress-strain diagrams.

Fig. 31 shows that a " mild " (low-carbon) steel possesses greater toughness than a high-carbon steel, even though the latter is much stronger under a static load.   This lack of toughness of brittle materials is confirmed by impact experiments.   On the other hand, since both the steels whose properties are pictured have the same value of E, the

[1] This area equals $S^2/2\,E$, in which S is the proportional limit of the material. The value of $S^2/2\,E$ for a given material is called the *modulus of resilience* of the material and is discussed in the chapter on elastic energy in Arts. 206 and 207. These two articles may be studied at this time.

" strong " steel is seen to be much more *resilient* than the more ductile steel. Springs, axles, etc., which are ruined if permanently deformed by shock loads, are therefore made of strong steels.   On the other hand, for such objects as crane hooks, the rupture of which would be much more serious than the permanent distortion only, weaker but more ductile and therefore tougher steels are used.

21. The Effect of Overstress: Cold Working.   The properties of a material are largely, but not entirely, fixed by its chemical composition. Even after the material has been incorporated into the machine or structure of which it is to form a part, many of its mechanical characteristics may be greatly changed.   This fact can be illustrated as follows:

If two specimens of mild hot-rolled[1] steel are cut from the same bar, their chemical composition and the manufacturing processes to which they have been subjected are identical, and therefore the mechanical properties of the two specimens should be very nearly the same.   Fig. 32a represents the stress-strain diagram for one such specimen, tested

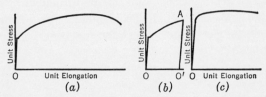

FIG. 32.   Effect on ductile steel of stress above elastic limit.

to failure in the usual manner.   In Fig. 32b, OAO' represents the stress-strain diagram of a similar specimen, loaded to a unit stress A well above the elastic limit and then unloaded.   As the unit stress is decreased, the unit elongation decreases and $A-O'$ is a straight line with a slope equal to the modulus of elasticity of the material.   The distance $O-O'$ represents the permanent set which has been given to the specimen.   If this specimen, after having been stressed above the elastic limit and then unloaded, is again tested, this time to failure, the stress-strain curve is found to be as represented in Fig. 32c.   The modulus of elasticity is unchanged.   The proportional limit, however, has been raised to practically the value of the maximum unit stress to which the specimen was subjected in its first test.[2]   The ultimate strength (com-

---

[1] Hot-rolled steel is rolled into bars or other shapes between grooved rolls, the final " passes " being completed before the steel has cooled below a red heat.   Cold-rolled steel is subjected to additional rolling after it has cooled.

[2] This increase in the tensile proportional limit is accompanied, however, by a roughly corresponding decrease in the compressive proportional limit.   Conversely, overstress in compression raises the compressive proportional limit, but lowers the tensile proportional limit.

puted on the basis of the *original* cross-section) is found to be slightly greater than the strength of the specimen which was tested to failure without unloading. The ultimate elongation is found to have been decreased by approximately the amount of the permanent set which was given the specimen the first time it was tested.

22. The Effect of Repetitions of Stress: Fatigue. The specimen described in Art. 17 was tested to failure under a gradually increased load. This failure consisted of eventual rupture preceded by marked distortion extending throughout the specimen. That is typical of the failure of a ductile material under a gradually applied load. On the other hand, a specimen or member, even though of a ductile material, may fail very suddenly without any visible distortion having occurred, if subjected to a great many *repetitions* of stress.

Many machine and structural parts are acted on by loads that are applied and removed a great number of times. Percussion drills, the plungers of rivet hammers, connecting rods of engines, spokes of bicycle wheels, blades of water wheels and steam turbines are subjected to millions and in some cases to billions of loadings. Sometimes (as in the connecting rod of a gas engine, where pressure acts only on one face of the piston) the stress in the member fluctuates only between a larger and a smaller value (or zero) without any change in the *kind* of stress. In other members, however (the piston rod of a " double-acting " steam engine is one), the stress varies from a maximum in compression to a maximum in tension and back to a maximum in compression again. Both of these are illustrations of stress *repetition*. The second is an example of stress *reversal* as well; that is, the connecting rod of the double-acting steam engine is said to be subject to *repetitions or cycles of reversed stress*.

The failure resulting from a very great number of repetitions of stress (reversed or not reversed) is called a " fatigue failure." The exact nature of this failure is imperfectly understood. However, the failure apparently results from the fact that (as noted in Art. 13) even though the calculated stress in the member is within the elastic limit there are minute regions where the " localized stress " (discussed further in Chapter IV) is far above the average stress. If the deformation in these minute regions is inelastic, after a very large number of repetitions a small crack forms. The boundaries of this minute crack are regions of still higher stress, and this causes the fracture to spread gradually until eventually the cross-section of the member is so reduced that it suddenly snaps. Throughout the failure, however, the region of high stress has always been so small that the deformation does not extend through a sufficiently large volume of the material for it to become visible. A very large proportion of the failures of machine parts are "fatigue" failures of this sort.[1]

The effects of repeated stresses are studied by means of "fatigue tests." The results of a series of such tests on any given material may be shown by what is called an *S-N* (stress-number) diagram (Fig. 33).

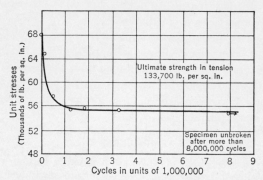

FIG. 33.   *S-N* curve for a chrome-nickel steel.

The abscissa of a point on an *S-N* curve is the number of repetitions causing failure when the calculated value of the repeated stress is that indicated by the ordinate of the curve. The lower the value of the stress, the larger the number of repetitions before failure. For most metals such a curve eventually becomes horizontal as *S* decreases. Obviously the ordinate to the horizontal part of the curve is the value of the computed stress which can be repeated an indefinitely great number of times without causing failure. This stress value is called the *endurance limit* of the material. Tests of this sort are most often carried out with stresses which are "completely reversed"—that is, which vary from a maximum in tension to the same maximum in compression. They may, however, be carried out for stresses varying between a maximum and some smaller value or zero, or from a maximum in tension to a smaller maximum in compression, and vice versa. The unqualified term *endurance limit*, however, ordinarily refers to the endurance limit for a completely reversed normal stress.

Under repetitions of shearing stress, especially if the direction of the shear is reversed, fatigue failures sometimes occur. Materials that have an endurance limit under normal stress also appear to have a shearing endurance limit. For wrought ferrous metals under completely re-

[1] The term "fatigue" dates from a time when the nature of the failure was not known and it was believed that stress repetition caused a "crystallization" of the material composing the specimen. The term "gradual fracture" which has been proposed is much more accurately descriptive, but has not come into wide use.

versed shearing stress, the shearing endurance limit is about 55 per cent of the endurance limit under completely reversed normal stress.

The endurance limits of materials show more correlation with ultimate strength than with other mechanical properties. For rolled steel the endurance limit under completely reversed normal stress is about one-half the ultimate tensile strength. For most other metals it is less than half; in many cases decidedly less.[1]

Under stresses which are not completely reversed, the endurance limit is higher than when the reversal is complete. The smaller the range of stress, the more nearly the endurance limit approaches the ultimate strength of the material. For a very small fluctuation in stress, the endurance limit may be nearly as large as the ultimate strength as determined by static loading.

PROBLEM

The fatigue tests, the results of which are pictured in Fig. 33, were made on a machine that produced 1,200 cycles of stress per minute. Assuming that an average delay of 12 hours occurred between the breakage of a specimen and the start of the next test, how much time was required for assembling the data presented in the figure?

23. Creep. When an elastic material, such as steel, is loaded at ordinary temperature, it deforms in proportion to and almost simultaneously with the loading. Thereafter the load may apparently act on the material for an indefinitely long period without causing any further appreciable change in dimensions. Even if the material is stressed above its elastic limit, after an immediate deformation there appears to be no further change in dimensions until there is some change in load.

At elevated temperatures, however, the behavior is quite different. If steel at a temperature of 700 or 800° F. (temperatures which are not at all uncommon in modern boilers, steam turbines, and other apparatus) is subjected to long-continued stress, so long as this stress acts there is a very slow continuous yielding of the material. This slow yielding under steady load and high temperature is called *creep*. Its existence is very important in the design of machines and structures which must resist high temperatures for long periods of time. In order to keep the creep rate sufficiently low, it may be necessary to use stresses much less than those which would otherwise be satisfactory.

[1] For values of the endurance limits of various materials, and a fuller discussion of this topic, see reports of the Research Committee on Fatigue of Metals, *Proceedings, American Society for Testing Materials*, Vol. 30, Part 1 (1930), and Vol. 32, Part 1 (1932). See also H. F. Moore, " The Fatigue of Metals — Its Nature and Significance," *Transactions, American Society of Mechanical Engineers, Applied Mechanics Journal*, March, 1933.

For some materials, such as asphalt, and very soft metals like lead, creep is present at ordinary temperatures. For most metals, however, creep is either not present at ordinary temperatures, or the rate of creep is so extremely slow that it has not been detected with the measuring equipment available. It is not yet known definitely which is the case.

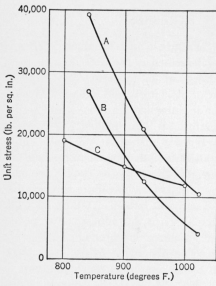

Fig. 34. Creep curves for three low-alloy steels.

It is also unknown whether, at a temperature at which creep is known to exist under high stress, there is any limiting stress below which no creep occurs. It is known that, at temperatures high enough for creep to occur, the higher the temperature, the greater is the rate of creep produced by any given stress intensity. Conversely, at any given temperature, increasing the stress increases the rate of creep. A given rate of creep may therefore be produced in any material by an infinite number of combinations of temperature and stress. Fig. 34 shows the combinations of temperatures and stress which cause several different kinds of steel to deform at the rate of 1 per cent in 100,000 hours of load application.[1]

The maximum stress which can be continuously applied to a material at some specified temperature without causing a specified deformation to be exceeded in a given period of time is called the *creep limit* for that material, temperature, and rate of creep. Thus the creep limit of steel A, Fig. 34, at a temperature of 900° F. and for the specified rate of creep is 26,000 lb. per sq. in.; for steel B, it is 16,500 lb. per sq. in.

PROBLEM

Tabulate the creep limits of steels A, B, and C, Fig. 34, at the given rate of creep and at each of the following temperatures: 850°, 920°, 1,000° F.

[1] One hundred thousand hours corresponds to a "life" of somewhat more than ten years (11.4) of continuous service. One per cent in 100,000 hours is a rate of creep which has frequently been considered suitable.

Data for curves of Fig. 34 are from "Symposium on Effect of Temperature on Metals," pp. 370, 371, joint publication of *Am. Soc. for Testing Materials* and *Am. Soc. of Mechanical Engineers*, 1931. See also H. F. Moore, Materials of Engineering, 1936.

CHAPTER III

ALLOWABLE STRESSES

24. The Nature and Causes of " Failure " of a Member. When a specimen is " tested to failure " as described in the preceding chapter, " failure " ordinarily means the breakage of the specimen. On the other hand, a member of a structure or machine is said to have " failed " when it ceases to be able to perform its intended function satisfactorily.

If a member made of a ductile material is " overloaded," it ceases to function satisfactorily because of excessive distortion. A water tank, for example, as the pressure is increased excessively, generally begins to leak because of distortion in the neighborhood of the rivet holes long before there is any marked fracture. This type of failure through distortion at ordinary temperature has been termed " failure through *elastic breakdown*." It is the principal source of failure in overloaded *structures*, and in some machine frames where any pronounced bending of the frame leads to a lack of precision of movement too large to be tolerated. On the other hand, in brittle materials the breakdown of elastic properties usually results in *fracture* before the amount of distortion has become important.

Where loads fluctuate and are repeated a great many times, as in many machines, failure of ductile as well as of brittle materials generally results from fracture unaccompanied by visible distortion. As was stated in Art. 22, this type of failure by gradual fracture is called " fatigue."

At high temperatures (as stated in Art. 23) the *very gradual* continuous flow of material, resulting from too high a stress, may, after a long time, render a member useless for further service. Failures of this type are called *creep failures*.

Parts of structures or machines may fail in any one of these three ways, depending on the conditions of their use.

25. The " Usable Strength " of a Material. From what has gone before, it should be apparent that the fraction of the *ultimate strength* of a material which can be utilized practically is not entirely determined by the material itself. A stress perfectly satisfactory under a static load at ordinary temperature might result in a fatigue failure under repetitions of load, or in a creep failure under high-temperature

31

loading.   Under steady loads at ordinary temperatures, the *yield-point* stress is ordinarily the stress limiting the usefulness of wrought iron and the milder grades of steel.   So long as the stress remains below the yield point, distortion will generally not be excessive; as soon as the stress reaches the yield point, however, the deformation may become twenty times what it was at a slightly smaller stress, and be too great. Only wrought iron and the milder grades of steel have a definite yield point, however.   In reference to other metals, the expression " yield strength " is often used to denote the stress accompanying the maximum amount of distortion that may be considered admissible.   For aluminum and other non-ferrous alloys the yield strength has often been taken as the stress accompanying a permanent set of 0.2 per cent in a specimen of the material.   For steady loading at ordinary temperatures, the usable strength of a ductile material may therefore generally be considered to equal its *yield point* (if it has one) or its *yield strength*; the usable strength of a brittle material equals its ultimate strength, since fracture occurs before distortion has become pronounced.

Under high-temperature loading, it has been brought out that the maximum stress which can be considered satisfactory is affected by the temperature to be resisted and by the allowable rate of creep, and that this stress is called the *creep limit*.   The creep limit therefore fixes the usable strength of a material used at high temperature.   If the temperature is sufficiently high, or if the rate of creep must be very small, the usable strength may be a very small fraction of the ultimate strength of the cold material.

Under repetitions of stress, the *endurance limit* may be taken as the usable strength of the material, since stresses less than this may be repeated an indefinitely great number of times without causing failure. The ratio of the ultimate strength to the endurance limit is called the " fatigue ratio " of the material.

Depending on conditions of use, therefore, the yield point or yield strength, the creep limit, or the endurance limit may be said to determine the usable strength of a material.

26. Allowable Stress and Working Stress.   The *allowable unit stress* or simply the *allowable stress* is the unit stress value specified or selected as proper for use in calculating the dimensions of a member which is to carry any stated load, or for calculating the maximum load which should be applied to any given member.   Since members may be designed to resist tension or compression or shear, there are allowable tensile, compressive, and shearing unit stresses.   Allowable stresses are either specified by some authority (such as a bridge engineer of a railroad, or the building department of a city) or selected by a designer of competent judgment after careful consideration of the materials to be used and the conditions of service of the machine or structure.

The *working unit stress* is the unit stress (as calculated) which results in a given member from the loads actually carried or assumed to be carried. When the loads on a structure are variable, the working stress is a variable stress. In this respect it differs from allowable stress, which, once selected for a given member, has a fixed value. The working stress may be at times only a small fraction of the allowable stress. The working stress should not exceed the allowable stress, although it does in structures which carry loads greater than the " design loads."

The allowable stress used in design is sometimes called the " allowable working stress," and sometimes this latter term is shortened to " working stress." In such usage the term " working stress " has the same meaning as " allowable stress " as used in this book. It is preferable, however, to reserve the term working stress for the actual unit stress in the member under whatever load it may be carrying, and to speak of the design stress as the " allowable stress."

27. Determination of Allowable Stresses. It should be evident that the unit stress in a member should not exceed the usable strength of the material of which the member is made. To accomplish this, the allowable stress used in the design of the member must be considerably less than the usable strength of the material. This difference between the allowable stress and the usable stress constitutes a " margin of safety" which is necessary to provide for the following possibilities:

1. Actual loads may exceed design loads. This may be a consequence of a deliberate increase in loading in the future, or of careless or accidental overloading.

2. Stresses calculated by ordinary accepted procedures may be less than the actual maximum stresses. This may be due to simplifying assumptions made in stress calculations,[1] or to the effects of shocks, vibrations, etc., which are indeterminate.

3. The actual usable strength of the material may not be as great as that assumed. This may be because of uncertainties inherent in the material or because of defects in the member which escape inspection.

4. Through corrosion, weathering, or decay the effective cross-section of a member may be appreciably lessened with the passage of time. For example, unless kept well painted, steel members may lose appreciable strength by rusting away; wooden members may rot.

For a simple case of loading where the stress could be computed with

---

[1] For example, the assumption that members of riveted trusses are subjected to axial loads only, although it is known that they are subjected to relatively small bending forces as well.

perfect accuracy, and with a type of load which could never be greater than that assumed, and such that no shocks or vibrations could ever be caused by the loading, and with a perfect material known to be free from defects and used under such circumstances that deterioration would be absolutely prevented, it might be permissible to use an allowable stress *almost* equal to the usable strength, but this is an ideal combination which never occurs.

The necessity for a margin of safety having been considered, some of the conditions that together influence its size may be discussed. These include:

1. Exactness with which loads are known.

2. Nature of loads — whether steady or variable.

3. Accuracy with which stresses due to known loads can be calculated.

4. Reliability of material.

5. Resistance of material to corrosion and deterioration.

6. Nature of material from standpoint of whether or not it gives warning of failure.

7. Seriousness of failure if it occurs.

8. Other practical considerations which sometimes limit the margin of safety. In the design of a dirigible frame all conditions would indicate the desirability of a large margin of safety. Practical requirements of lightness result in a design in which, for certain parts, the difference between the design stress and the usable strength is probably much less than in any other important structure.

It is not customary to specify the margin of safety, but rather to specify the allowable stresses for the materials to be used in a structure. Such specifications must, of course, take into consideration the variables enumerated above. A given material such as structural steel, for example, may have allowable stresses for some certain use very different from its allowable stresses for some other use. Hence there are allowable stresses " for structural steel for buildings " which are, in general, considerably higher than the allowable stresses for the same steel in machines where shock and vibration may be caused by the loads, and where high localized stresses (which would be unimportant in a building frame) would probably result in fatigue failure.

28. Allowable Stress Values. In designing machines — locomotives, automobile engines, steam shovels, lathes — many different materials, with widely different mechanical properties, are used. Also the conditions under which these various machines are employed differ greatly in severity. For these reasons it is not feasible to attempt to give here any general tables of allowable stresses for materials as used in ma-

TABLE I

ALLOWABLE STRESSES

(All stresses are given in pounds per square inch.)

STRUCTURAL STEEL FOR BUILDINGS

	A	B	C
Tension on net section of rolled steel	20,000	18,000	16,000
Compression on short lengths (not columns)	20,000	18,000	16,000
Shear on pins and power-driven rivets	15,000	13,500	12,000

Values specified in column A are in the 1936 " American Institute of Steel Construction Specifications for the Design, Fabrication and Erection of Structural Steel for Buildings," and are permitted by a number of cities in their building codes. Values in column B are in the 1938 " Building Code of New York City " and in the building codes of many other cities. Both of these values are based on an ultimate tensile strength of 72,000 lb. per sq. in. for structural steel which is now the standard. Values specified in column C were given from 1900 to 1930 in numerous bridge specifications and building codes. They were based on steel having an ultimate strength of 65,000 lb. per sq. in.

CAST IRON

(American Association of State Highway Officials, 1935 Specifications for Highway Bridges)

Tension 3,000   Compression ... 12,000   Shear 3,000

BEARING ON BRICK MASONRY

(New York City Building Code, 1938)

Kind of Mortar:

Portland cement ... 325   Cement-lime 250   Lime 100

(For brick having an ultimate strength greater than 4,500 lb. per sq. in., higher stresses are allowed.)

BEARING ON CONCRETE AND STONE MASONRY

(American Railway Engineering Association, 1935 Specifications for Steel Railway Bridges)

Granite masonry (portland cement mortar)	800
Sandstone and limestone masonry (portland cement mortar) ...	400
Concrete masonry	600

LUMBER

(Based on Stresses Recommended by the United States Forest Products Laboratory, Madison, Wisconsin)

NOTE: Appendix C gives nominal and actual sizes of commercial lumber.

	Compression on Short Lengths						Shear		
	Parallel to Grain			Perpendicular to Grain			Parallel to Grain		
	I	II	III	I	II	III	I	II	III
Southern pine (dense)									
Select	1,280	1,170	990	380	260	230	130	130	130
Common	1,030	930	790	380	260	230	100	100	100
Spruce									
Select	800	750	650	250	150	120	85	85	85
Common	640	600	520	250	150	120	70	70	70
Oak, white or red									
Select	1,000	900	800	500	375	300	125	125	125
Common	800	720	640	500	375	300	100	100	100

Stresses in columns I, II, and III are for different conditions of use, as follows: I. Continuously dry. II. Occasionally wet but quickly dried. III. More or less continuously damp or wet.

chines. The design department of each manufacturing organization generally decides on the stresses which will be used in its own designing, basing them on the materials to be utilized and on the purpose of the product.

In structural work, however, the variety of conditions encountered is much narrower and the range of materials ordinarily used is much less, so that allowable stresses in structural work can be more nearly standardized. Various bodies of engineers from time to time prepare specifications which include allowable stresses for material that meets certain strength standards. For example, the American Railway Engineering Association, the American Society of Civil Engineers, and the American Institute of Steel Construction are typical organizations which at one time or another have prepared specifications that include allowable stresses for structural carbon steel for bridges or for buildings. In addition to stating the allowable stresses, such specifications also include the physical characteristics of the material to be used, and cover the more important aspects of design, fabrication, and erection, so.as to insure that the stresses used shall be consistent with the conditions of material and of use that were presupposed in the preparation of the specification. The tables of allowable stresses presented on page 35 consist of extracts from such specifications, but are limited to the simple stresses that have so far been considered in this book. In Appendix C will be found a much more comprehensive set of tables which include allowable values for bending and other stresses.

PROBLEMS

1. A short spruce post which measures $7\frac{1}{2}$ in. by $7\frac{1}{2}$ in. bears against an oak sill, as shown in Fig. 35. What is the allowable load on the post? (Wet location.)

Ans. $P = 16,880$ lb.

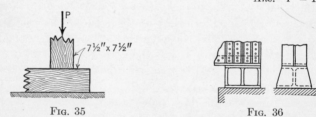

FIG. 35   FIG. 36

2. A cast-iron bridge " pedestal " (Fig. 36) carries a load of 325,000 lb. It rests on a concrete pier. The dimensions in contact with the concrete are 22 in. by 22 in. Does this comply with the specifications of the American Railway Engineering Association, 1935?

3. A tension member in a roof truss in New York is composed of two angles which together have a net section of 9.46 sq. in.   (*a*) What total load is permissible for the member?   (b) If the total tension in the member is 165,000 lb., what is the working stress?   *Ans.* (b) $S = 17,440$ lb. per sq. in.

4. A pump rod, a, is $1\frac{3}{4}$ in. in diameter. It is attached to another section of the rod by a cottered joint (Fig. 37).   A slot is cut through the enlarged end of the rod for a cotter $\frac{1}{2}$ in. thick and $2\frac{3}{4}$ in. deep.   If allowable tensile stress is 6,000 lb. per sq. in. and allowable shearing stress is 4,500 lb. per sq. in., what is the allowable load on the rod?   With this load, what is the minimum value of the dimension l as limited by shearing stress?

5. A small sprocket chain is made of links of steel as shown in Fig. 38.   The links marked a are $\frac{1}{2}$ in. wide and $\frac{3}{16}$ in. thick.   The pins are $\frac{1}{4}$ in. in diameter.   If allowable stresses are: tension, 8,000 lb. per sq. in.; shear, 5,000 lb. per sq. in., what is the greatest allowable load on the chain?

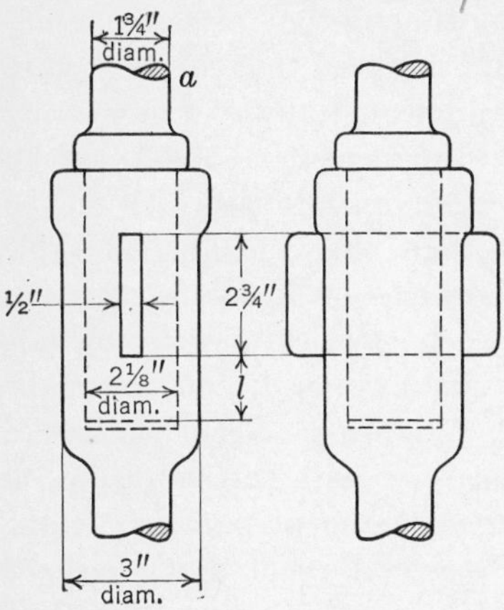

FIG. 37

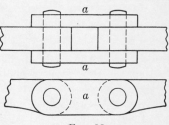

FIG. 38

29. Factor of Safety.

" Factor of safety " is a term denoting the ratio of the greatest load a member or structure could carry, to the design load.   For instance, if the tensile load which would cause fracture of a tensile member is known (on the basis of the specified minimum strength of the material composing the member) to be at least 80,000 lb., and if the member is designed to carry a tensile load of only 20,000 lb., its factor of safety is said to be at least 4.   This is a *design* factor of safety.   The *working* factor of safety is the ratio of the load causing fracture to the load actually being carried.   The working factor of safety can evidently be greater or less than the design factor of safety, depending on whether the load being carried is less or greater than the design load.

In most structural and machine parts, the maximum stress is evidently proportional to the load.[1]   In such cases the design factor of safety is evidently given by dividing the *ultimate strength* of the material by the allowable stress; the working factor of safety is obtained by dividing the ultimate strength by the working stress.

[1] Columns are an exception to this rule, the maximum stress increasing more rapidly than the load.

The concept of a factor of safety is of especial value in examining a structure that has its different parts subjected to different kinds of stress (tension, compression, or shear) in order to ascertain which part would be likely to give way first, in the event of an excessive load. The term " factor of *safety* " is misleading, however. There are few structures that could have the loads increased in the ratio of the design factor of safety without *failing* long before the loading was completed. This is because, as pointed out, failure under steady loads results more frequently from excessive distortion than from actual fracture or collapse; and under repeated loads it results from fatigue. Nevertheless, the concept has its uses, particularly in comparing the strengths of different parts of a structure.

Example. A steel eyebar carries a load of 100,000 lb. and is $1\frac{1}{2}$ in. by 4 in. in cross-section. The end of the bar is held by a pin, arranged as shown in Fig. 39. Assuming that the shearing stress is uniformly distributed over the cross-sections of the pin, what is the proper diameter of the pin to make its factor of safety in shear equal to the factor of safety of the eyebar in tension? Ultimate strengths of the material composing bar and pin are: tension, 60,000 lb. per sq. in.; shear, 45,000 lb. per sq. in.

Solution: S_T in eyebar = 100,000/6 = 16,700 lb. per sq. in.

Therefore, F.S. of eyebar in tension = 60,000/16,700 = 3.59.

Hence S_S in pin for same factor of safety = 45,000/3.59 = 12,500 lb. per sq. in.

Therefore the necessary area to support shear in pin = 100,000/12,500 = 8.00 in.²

The shearing stress is distributed over two cross-sections of the pin. Therefore the required cross-section of pin = 4.00 in.²

Whence, required pin diameter = 2.26 in.

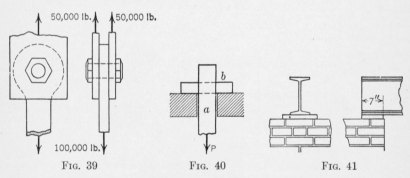

FIG. 39   FIG. 40   FIG. 41

PROBLEMS

1. In Fig. 40, a is a steel rod 1 in. square which carries a load P. A steel pin, b, $\frac{1}{2}$ in. square is driven through a hole in a as shown. The ultimate tensile strength of the steel is 64,000 lb. per sq. in. and ultimate shearing strength is 48,000 lb. per sq. in. If the factor of safety is not to be less than 4, what is the greatest allowable load P? Is the factor of safety in this problem a design or a working factor of safety?   *Ans.* $P = 6,000$ lb.

2. If the pin in Problem 1 is $\frac{5}{8}$ in. square and the load P equals 3,500 lb., what is the factor of safety? If the factor of safety is not to be less than 4, what is the maximum allowable value of P?

3. What should be the size of a square pin, b, to pass through the rod, a, if the factor of safety of the pin in shear is to be just equal to the factor of safety of the rod in tension?

GENERAL PROBLEMS

1. An I-beam (Fig. 41) rests on a brick wall laid with portland cement mortar. The maximum end reaction of the beam is 15,700 lb., and the beam projects 7 in. over the wall. Find the width of bearing plate required. *Ans.* $b = 6.9$ in.

2. Fig. 42 shows a bell-crank lever such as those used in various mechanisms to change the direction and magnitude of a force. Determine the sizes of pins B and C so that the factor of safety of each pin in shear shall equal the factor of safety of rod D in tension. Tensile ultimate strength of the steel is 70,000 lb. per sq. in. Shearing ultimate strength of the pin steel is 50,000 lb. per sq. in. Diameter of D is 1.20 in.

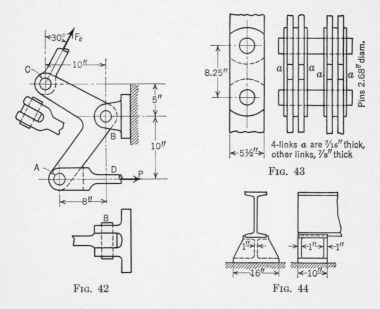

FIG. 42

FIG. 43

4-links a are $\frac{7}{16}''$ thick, other links, $\frac{7}{8}''$ thick

FIG. 44

3. Chain used in operation of the spillway gates at the Ft. Peck dam has links and pins with the dimensions shown in Fig. 43. These links and pins are of chrome-nickel steels, heat treated. Assuming uniformity of stress distribution, find the maximum tensile unit stress in the links and the maximum shearing unit stress in the pins under a load of 600,000 lb. Why are links of different thicknesses used?

4. A steel beam in a bridge rests on a cast-iron pedestal of the dimensions shown (Fig. 44). The pedestal rests on a pier of sandstone masonry. It is proposed to move over the bridge an exceptionally heavy load which would cause a reaction of 86,000 lb. at the end of the beam. (*a*) Calculate the unit compressive stress which this load would cause in the masonry. (*b*) Does this comply with the American

Railway Engineering Association specifications? (*c*) Would you allow this load to be moved over the bridge?

5. A southern pine beam (dense select grade), with dimensions as shown in Fig. 45, is supported at the ends on brick walls laid up with portland cement mortar. It carries a load at the midpoint of 35,000 lb. (*a*) Calculate the required length, *a*, of the center steel bearing plate. (*b*) Find the minimum length, *b*, of beam on the wall bearing plate. (*c*) Find the width, *c*, of the wall bearing plate. (Assume location to be continuously dry.) *Ans.* (*c*) *c* = 11.1 in.

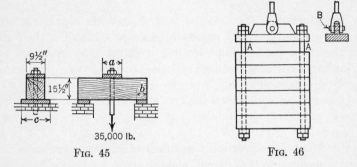

FIG. 45   FIG. 46

6. An elevator counterweight, constructed as shown in Fig. 46, weighs 6,000 lb. If the elevator is braked while ascending, the descending counterweight is accelerated upward. An assumption for this acceleration, in accordance with modern elevator practice, is 5 ft. per sec.[2] What should be the diameter of the threaded rods, *A*, and the pin, *B*, if tensile and shearing stresses are limited to 8,000 and 5,000 lb. per sq. in., respectively?

CHAPTER IV

STRESSES DUE TO AXIAL LOADS

30. Introduction. This chapter will discuss the stress caused by loads the resultant of which passes through the centroid of the area on which the stress exists. Such loading is called *axial* loading. Truly axial loading is not often realized in engineering practice. For example, the loads on a bolt which holds two flanges together are not truly axial unless the surfaces with which the bolt head and the nut are in contact are *exactly* parallel to one another. In most cases, the surfaces are not exactly parallel. Nevertheless, they are so nearly parallel that an axial loading of the bolt is invariably assumed to exist in such cases. The loading is idealized to that extent, and the stress analysis is based on an assumed perfect loading. As noted in the preceding chapter, one of the reasons why a margin of safety is provided between the usable strength of a material and the allowable stress is to take care of uncertainties that result from working assumptions of this sort which may not be absolutely true.

This chapter will consider stresses in bars which have a straight axis but different cross-sectional areas at different points along their lengths; it will consider stresses due to temperature changes, stresses on oblique planes through axially loaded prisms, stresses in certain members made of more than one material, and stresses in thin-walled pressure containers. The loading will invariably be assumed " axial " as defined at the beginning of this article.

31. Stresses in Members of Variable Cross-Section; Localized Stress. When a prism of rectangular cross-section is loaded axially, it is believed that the stress distribution is very nearly uniform over sections which are some distance away from the points where the loads are applied. The assumption of uniformity of distribution of such stress is always made. Suppose, however, that at some cross-section of the bar there is a cylindrical hole, as in Fig. 47a. In this case, the stress is not uniformly distributed over the cross-section through the hole, but reaches a maximum value immediately adjacent to the hole, as shown. The stress decreases rapidly so that the average stress on the cross-section is reached not far away from the hole. A similar situation exists in a bar notched at the sides, as shown in Fig. 47b, or in a bar

41

in which two portions of different widths are joined with a " fillet " (Fig. 47c).

The ratio of the maximum stress to the average stress is affected by the ratio of the radius of the hole, notch, or fillet to the width of the bar. For a circular hole in a plate of indefinitely great width (or an indef-

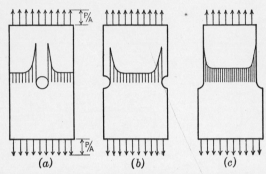

$$(a) \qquad (b) \qquad (c)$$

FIG. 47. Ordinates of curves are unit stresses on reduced sections.

initely small hole in a bar of finite width) it can be shown mathematically that the maximum stress in an " ideal " material is three times the average. If the diameter of the hole bears a finite relation to the width of the bar, the ratio of maximum to average stress is less. The same situation exists with respect to notches in the side of a bar.

In cases of this sort where, because of a change in shape of the member, the maximum stress over a small area is above the average stress, the ratio of maximum to average stress is called the *stress concentration factor* for that change in shape.

The mathematical analysis of cases of this sort frequently becomes very complex. Because of this, a number of experimental procedures for the study of stress concentrations and the determination of stress concentration factors have been developed.[1] Fig. 48 shows graphs giving stress concentration factors for three types of change in cross-section.[2] These stress concentration factors were determined by the experimental procedure known as photoelastic analysis.

Inspection of Fig. 48 shows that, for each of the changes in cross-section, a very small hole, notch, or fillet causes a much larger stress concentration than does a hole, notch, or fillet of somewhat greater radius.

[1] For a simple and clear description of some of these, see F. B. Seely, " Advanced Mechanics of Materials," page 191. For mathematical analysis see S. Timoshenko, " Theory of Elasticity," McGraw-Hill Book Company, 1934, page 75.

[2] " Factors of Stress Concentration Photoelastically Determined," M. M. Frocht, *Transactions, A.S.M.E.*, Vol. 57 (1935), page A-67.

Considering the member with a hole, for example, if the hole has a diameter of only one-tenth the width of the " net " cross-section through the hole ($r/d = 0.05$), the maximum stress, immediately adjacent to the hole, is 2.7 times the average. If, however, the diameter of the hole equals the net width ($r/d = 0.5$), the maximum stress is only 2.1

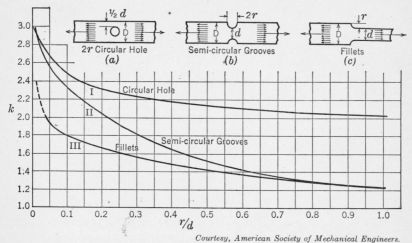

FIG. 48. Stress concentration factors (flat bars).

times the average. In the cases of the notch and the fillet, the gain in stress uniformity as r increases with respect to d is even more pronounced. In all these cases, however, it is evident that the stress as calculated from $S = P/A$ is much too low.

In some situations this fact is important; in others it is not. In a member made of material with a pronounced yield point and subjected to " gradually applied " or steady loading, the maximum stress on the reduced cross-section is much above the average so long as the maximum stress is below the yield point. However, as the load is increased, this stress differential diminishes. The maximum stress reaches the yield point of the material long before the average stress does, but increase in load thereafter causes no increase in the maximum stress. Instead there is only a flow of metal in a region adjacent to the hole. As this region is very small, the plastic deformation of the member is without serious consequences. Before the " usable strength " (Art. 25) of the material is approached, most of the inequality of stress has disappeared; when the full usable strength has been developed, all the stress inequality has disappeared. Consequently, in structural practice no allowance is made, for example, for the stress concentration immediately adjacent to the root of the thread of a bolt subjected to tension, or adjacent to holes in axially loaded steel tension and compression members. In this case, the minute deformation is unimportant, and most of the stress inequality disappears before a dangerous load is reached. Generally speaking, therefore, in designing in the milder grades of steel (or other ductile materials), and for loads which do not fluctuate rapidly, no account is taken of such local stresses.

In using more brittle materials, stress concentrations are much more serious. Under the high local stress, a crack is likely to start because of the inability of the brittle material to deform plastically. Under repeated loads, also, localized stresses are important, because under repeated loads a stress above the endurance limit, even though it exists only on a very small area, tends to start a fatigue crack. Therefore, in designing members of brittle materials and members subject to reversals of stress, where changes in dimension are unavoidable the effort is made to minimize the non-uniformity of stress distribution by means of fillets, the avoidance of sharp notches, etc., and to employ the stress concentration factor in making proper allowance for such localized stress as remains.

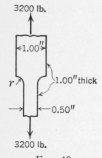

FIG. 49

Example. A steel bar of rectangular cross-section and subjected to complete alternations of tensile and compressive stress has a reduced portion as shown in Fig. 49. The endurance limit of the steel is 40,000 lb. per sq. in., and the maximum computed stress in the bar is not to exceed $\frac{1}{4}$ of the endurance limit. If the load on the bar is 3,200 lb., what is the minimum size of fillet that may be used?

Solution: Area of reduced section = 0.5 sq. in. Therefore average stress on reduced section = 6,400 lb. per sq. in. Allowable computed stress = 10,000 lb. per sq. in. Therefore allowable stress concentration factor = 10,000/6,400 = 1.56. Therefore, from Fig. 48, required $r/d = 0.35$, whence required radius of fillet = 0.175 in.

PROBLEMS

1. The head of a standard structural-steel eyebar is joined to the shank by a fillet the radius of which is equal to the width of the shank. Assuming the graph given in Fig. 48 for stress concentration due to fillets to apply to this case, what is the ratio of the stress where the fillet begins, to the stress at the midlength of the eyebar, all stresses being within the proportional limit of the material?

2. Fig. 25 shows a standard form of static tensile test specimen of mild steel. Fig. 27 shows a tensile test specimen of cast iron. From the standpoint of stress concentration, discuss the difference in their shapes.

32. Temperature Stresses. Most substances expand when they are heated and contract when they are cooled. The rate at which this change in dimension takes place as the temperature changes is expressed by a number called the *coefficient of thermal expansion*, for which the symbol C is used.

This quantity is the unit change in dimension per degree change in temperature, temperature usually being expressed on the Fahrenheit scale in this country.

Commonly assumed values of the coefficients of thermal expansion (per degree Fahrenheit) for a few materials are:[1]

Steel	0.0000065
Cast iron	0.0000062
Copper	0.0000093
Concrete	0.000006
Wood	0.000003

In many forms of construction, allowance must be made for this expansion and contraction. For instance, a concrete road slab should be laid with joints at intervals. Otherwise, as it cools and contracts in winter weather, the contraction will set up tensile stresses in the material which may cause it to crack.

When some constraint prevents the deformation normally accompanying change in the temperature of a body, the resulting stress equals $E \times \delta$, where δ is the unit deformation which is prevented from occurring.

Example. A steel bar 1 in. square is held between rigid supports exactly 10 ft. apart. There is no stress in the bar when its temperature is 50° F. What is the unit stress in it when its temperature is 0° F.?

Solution: The change in temperature while the bar is constrained = 50°. $C =$ 0.0000065. Therefore $\delta = 0.0000065 \times 50 = 0.000325$ in. per in. Since $S = E\delta$, $S = 30{,}000{,}000 \times 0.000325 = 9{,}750$ lb. per sq. in., tension.

It should be noted that in a body in which *all* temperature deformation is prevented, the unit stress set up by a change in temperature is wholly independent of the length of the body. Nor is the total force which the body exerts on the constraints at its ends affected by its length, but only by its cross-sectional area, its modulus of elasticity, and its temperature change. However, in a body which undergoes some change in dimension with change in its temperature, but not the entire change which would normally occur, the stress is affected by the length of the body.

Example. A railroad track is laid in winter at a temperature of 15° F., with gaps of 0.01 ft. between the ends of the rails. The rails are 33 ft. long. If they are prevented from buckling, what stress will result from a temperature of 110° F.?

[1] For a more comprehensive list see A.I.S.C., " Steel Construction," or other handbooks.

Solution: The normal change in length of a 33-ft. rail when its temperature increases 95° = 0.0000065 × 95 × 33 = 0.0204 ft. The change in length prevented = 0.0204 − 0.01 = 0.0104 ft. Therefore, the unit deformation which is prevented is δ = 0.0104 ÷ 33 = 0.000315 ft. per ft. Since $S = E\delta$, $S = 30{,}000{,}000 \times 0.000315$ = 9,450 lb. per sq. in.

An alternative method of solution of this problem is to find how much temperature change occurs without constraint of the rails and then to compute the stress which results from the subsequent change in temperature.

PROBLEMS

1. A surveyor's steel tape is 0.050 in. thick and 0.250 in. wide and is exactly 100.000 ft. long at 70° F. with a pull of 15.0 lb. What pull will be required to make it 100.000 ft. long at 20° F.? *Ans.* $P = 137$ lb.

2. A copper bar, 20 ft. long, is cooled from 212° to 32° F. At 107° the ends are suddenly gripped and further contraction prevented. What is the stress in the bar when 32° is reached? ($E = 17{,}000{,}000$ lb. per sq. in.; $C = 0.0000095$.)

3. A tube of Invar steel 5 sq. in. in cross-section and 20.000 in. long at 32° F. and a tube of brass which has the same dimensions at the same temperature, are placed end to end. Their temperature is then raised to 232° F. while a pressure is exerted on their ends to keep them exactly 40.000 in. apart. At 232° F. what is the total force exerted on the end of each block, and what is the length of each block? (C for Invar steel = 0; for brass = 0.0000104; E for Invar steel = 29,000,000 lb. per sq. in.; for brass = 14,500,000 lb. per sq. in.)

33. Fastenings Utilizing Temperature Stress. Certain types of fastenings used in machinery rely on the shrinkage due to cooling to

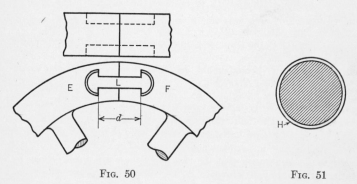

Fig. 50　　　　　　　　　　　　　Fig. 51

set up the tensile stress desired in them. *L*, Fig. 50, is a link, two of which are used at each joint to hold together two parts, *E* and *F*, of a flywheel. The length between the heads of *L*, when the link is unstressed, is made slightly less than the distance, *d*, between the shoulders in *E* and *F*. If *L* is heated until its length has increased to a point where the link can be slipped into the slot, as it cools the tendency of its length to decrease will set up a tensile stress in the link thus creating a force which will hold E and F tightly together. The amount of the force is evidently the product of the cross-sectional area of the link and the unit stress set up in it by the prevention of its shortening. The heating of the link merely affords a simple and easy way of lengthening the link until it can be entered in the slot.

H, Fig. 51, is a hoop or band " shrunk on " a solid cylinder. The inside diameter of the hoop is made slightly less than the outside diameter of the cylinder. The hoop grips the cylinder just as a rubber band grips when stretched and placed around a roll of paper. The temperature expansion affords an easy means of " stretching " the hoop so that it can be placed on the cylinder. Tires are " shrunk " on locomotive wheels in this way, and collars are sometimes shrunk on shafting.

Sometimes a bolt is heated and the nut tightened while the bolt is hot. The contraction of the bolt while cooling will then cause stresses greater than could be effected by tightening the nut on the cold bolt.

Two numerical examples of the utilization of temperature stresses follow:

Example 1. A steel hoop $\frac{1}{4}$ in. thick and 1 in. wide is to be shrunk on a solid shaft 10 in. in diameter. How much smaller should the inside of the unstressed hoop be if the unit stress in the hoop is to be 20,000 lb. per sq. in. and if any compressive deformation of the shaft is disregarded?[1]
Solution: The length of the hoop may be taken as π times the mean diameter = 10.25 π.
The total elongation of this length to produce the specified stress = 10.25 π × 20,000/30,000,000.
The original length should be 10.25 π − 10.25 π × 20,000/30,000,000.
The original diameter of the hoop should be this length divided by π, or 10.25 − 10.25 × 20,000/30,000,000.
The diameter of the hoop should be less than that of the shaft by 10.25 × 20,000/30,000,000 = 0.00683 in.

Example 2. Two cast-iron flanges each $1\frac{1}{2}$ in. thick are bolted together with a 2-in.-diameter bolt. The bolt is 50° F. hotter than the flanges. The nut is tightened until the bolt has an initial stress in the body of the bolt of 2,000 lb. per sq. in. What will be the unit stress when the bolt has cooled?
Solution: On the assumption that the cast-iron flanges are not deformed by the tension in the bolt the unit deformation in the bolt which is prevented as the bolt cools is 50 × 0.0000065 = 0.000325 in. per in. This causes a unit stress in the bolt of 0.000325 × 30,000,000 = 9,750 lb. per sq. in. To this must be added the initial stress due to tightening the nut, making a total tensile unit stress of 11,750 lb. per sq. in. This is the unit stress in the body of the bolt. At the root of the thread the

---

[1] In a similar case but with a thicker hoop the deformation of the shaft would not be negligible.

unit stress equals the total tension in the bolt divided by the area at the root of the thread.

$$S = \frac{11,750 \times 3.142}{2.300} = 16,050 \text{ lb. per sq. in.}$$

Actually, the unit stress in the bolt is less than that calculated above. The true condition of stress in bolt and flanges is difficult to determine but, if some assumptions are made, approximate values can be found for the stresses in bolt and flanges.

FIG. 52

The "long diameter" of a hexagon nut for a 2-in. bolt is given in handbooks as $3\frac{5}{8}$ in., and the "short diameter" is $3\frac{1}{8}$ in. It might be assumed that the forces exerted by the nut and the head of the bolt compress a cylinder of cast iron (Fig. 52) about 3.4 in. outside diameter with a 2-in.-diameter hole (for the bolt). The cross-sectional area of this hollow cylinder is $9.08 - 3.14 = 5.94$ sq. in.

Let δ_c equal the unit shortening of the hollow cast-iron cylinder. If the bolt shortened freely owing to cooling 50° there would be in the bolt a unit shortening of $50 \times 0.0000065 = 0.000325$ in. per in.

The amount of this unit shortening which is prevented by the cast iron equals $(0.000325 - \delta_c)$ in. per in.

The total stress in the bolt will be $3.14(0.000325 - \delta_c)30,000,000$ lb.

The total stress in the cast iron will be $5.94 \ \delta_c \times 12,000,000$ lb. These two opposing forces must be equal.

$$3.14(0.000325 - \delta_c)30,000,000 = 5.94 \ \delta_c \times 12,000,000$$
$$30,600 - 94,200,000 \ \delta_c = 71,400,000 \ \delta_c$$

$$\delta_c = \frac{30,600}{165,600,000} = 0.000185 \text{ in. per in.}$$

The unit stress in the cast iron equals $0.000185 \times 12,000,000 = 2,220$ lb. per sq. in.

The unit stress in the steel bolt equals $(0.000325 - 0.000185)30,000,000 = 4,200$ lb. per sq. in.

To this must be added the initial stress of 2,000 lb. per sq. in., due to tightening of the nut, making a total stress in the body of the bolt of 6,200 lb. per sq. in., and at the root of the thread of 8,470 lb. per sq. in. This initial stress in the bolt increases the stress in the cast iron by an amount which equals

$$\frac{2,000 \times 3.14}{5.94} = 1,060 \text{ lb. per sq. in.}$$

so that the total stress in the cast iron is 3,280 lb. per sq. in.

PROBLEMS

1. For "shrunk-link-joints" as illustrated in Fig. 50, Kent's "Mechanical Engineers' Handbook" recommends that the length of the link be 0.999 of the sum, d, of the thicknesses of the two parts to be joined by the link. If the link is steel and if the material of the flywheel is assumed *absolutely rigid*, what unit stress results in a link made in accordance with this recommendation? How many degrees Fahrenheit must the temperature of the link be above that of the flywheel castings in order to place it in the slot? *Ans.* 154° F.

2. A thin steel collar is shrunk onto a steel post. It just slips on when heated to 200° F., the post then being at 100° F. and 8.000 in. in diameter. What is the unit stress in the collar when it and the post are at 0° F.?   Given, $C = 0.0000065$. Assume all the strain to be in the collar.

34. Shearing Stresses Caused by Tension or Compression.

In a body subject to tensile or compressive stress in one direction there will be shearing stress on any plane neither parallel nor perpendicular to the normal stress. The maximum value of this shearing stress is one-half the normal stress, and it occurs on planes inclined 45° to the normal stress.

Proof: The body shown in Fig. 53*a* is a prism subject to tensile stress, the resultant force being P. In *b* is shown one segment of this prism cut off by a plane *m–n* making an angle θ with a plane perpendicular to the direction of the tensile stress. This segment is in equilibrium, one force being the external load P and the other force being the equal and opposite force P exerted by the rest of the body on the inclined face. This force on the inclined face may be resolved into two com-

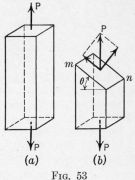

Fig. 53

ponents: one parallel to the face and equal to $P \sin \theta$, and one normal to the inclined face and equal to $P \cos \theta$. The area of the inclined face is $A/\cos \theta$ if A is the area of the cross-section of the prism.

The parallel component causes shearing stress, the unit stress being

$$S_s = \frac{P \sin \theta}{A/\cos \theta} = \frac{P}{A} \sin \theta \cos \theta = \frac{P}{A} \frac{\sin 2\theta}{2}$$

The maximum value of S_s occurs on a plane for which $\sin 2\theta$ is a maximum. The maximum value of $\sin 2\theta$ is its value when $\theta = 45°$ or $135°$ and is 1.

When $\sin 2\theta = 1$, $S_s = P/2A$ which is one-half of the normal unit stress. There is also tensile stress on any inclined plane, its value being

$$S_t = \frac{P \cos \theta}{A/\cos \theta} = \frac{P}{A} \cos^2 \theta$$

S_t is a maximum when $\theta = 0$.

Example. A specimen of Duralumin, 0.500 in. in diameter (Fig. 54), failed under a tensile load of 11,500 lb. The plane of failure was found to be at 48° with the cross-section. What was the average shearing unit stress at failure? What was the average tensile stress on a cross-section?

Solution: $A = \pi r^2 = 0.196$ sq. in.

$$S_s = \frac{P}{2\,A} \sin 2\,\theta = \frac{11,500}{2 \times 0.196} \sin 96° = 29,100 \text{ lb. per sq. in., average}$$

shearing stress

$$S_t = \frac{P}{A} = \frac{11,500}{0.196} = 58,700 \text{ lb. per sq. in., average tensile stress}^1$$

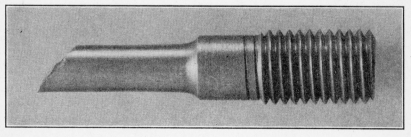

Fig. 54.   Failure of Duralumin under tension.

The propositions stated and proved above illustrate the important fact that at any point in a body subject to stress there are different stresses (or combinations of stresses) on planes in different directions.[2]

Fig. 55.   Failures of concrete and cast iron under compression.

[1] The tensile strength of a material is defined as the tensile unit stress on a cross-section of the material when failure occurs, irrespective of whether the failure was due directly to tension on a cross-section or to shear on an oblique plane. The tensile strength of the above specimen of Duralumin would therefore be said to be 58,700 lb. per sq. in. Brittle materials ordinarily have shearing strengths much less than the compressive strength, so that when compressive loads are applied, they fail in oblique shear. The compressive strength, however, is defined as the value given by dividing the ultimate load by the area of the cross-section.

[2] The equations given above for the stress on an oblique section disregard the friction that exists between particles of the material when it is subjected to *compressive* forces. This friction reduces the stress on an oblique section and has the

The relationships between these different stresses, and applications of the relationships, will be considered in Chapter XV. In ductile materials, or brittle materials under tensile loads, however, the stresses on planes perpendicular or parallel to the loads are generally more serious than any others. Most of the cases considered in the earlier chapters of this book are of that sort.

PROBLEMS

1. Table I, Art. 28, gives the following allowable stresses for dense southern pine, common grade, in a dry location: compression on end of grain, 1,030 lb. per sq. in.; compression on side of grain, 380 lb. per sq. in.; shear parallel to grain, 100 lb. per sq. in. (a) What is the allowable load on the end of a 8-in.-by-8-in. (nominal size, see Table X) post? (b) If this load is placed on the end of a post in which the grain of the wood makes an angle of 20° with the axis of the post, what is the resulting shear along the grain? Compression on the side of the grain? Are these within the specified values? *Ans.* (a) $P = 58,000$ lb.

2. A brass bar $\frac{1}{2}$ in. by $\frac{1}{2}$ in. in cross-section has grooves 0.1 in. deep on opposite faces, in a plane which makes an angle of 40° with the other two faces of the member. If the shearing strength of the material is 0.6 the tensile strength, which is more likely to occur when the bar is acted on by tensile forces: a tension failure on a cross-section, or a shear failure on the 40° plane?

35. Shearing Stresses on Mutually Perpendicular Planes. If, at a point within a body subject to stress, there exists a shearing unit stress along one plane, there must also be an equal shearing unit stress along a perpendicular plane through that point.

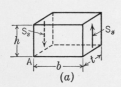

(a)

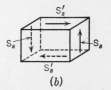

(b)

Fig. 56

Proof: Fig. 56a shows a small rectangular particle taken from a point in a stressed body where a shearing unit stress of S_s lb. per sq. in. is known to exist along vertical planes. This small body will then have

effect of causing failure to take place on a plane making a greater angle with the cross-section than 45°. For brick and concrete, it is nearer 60°. (See Fig. 55.) An analysis of this behavior, taking internal friction into account, yields results close to those given by experiment. (See "Materials of Engineering," by J. B. Johnson, 3rd edition.) In the example worked out above, the specimen failed on a plane not quite at 45° with the axis because of some condition of the material that made it a little *weaker* on the 48° plane than on the 45° plane. The unit stress, of course, was slightly greater on the 45° plane, where it was 58,700/2, or 29,350 lb. per sq. in.

shearing stresses of S_s lb. per sq. in. on two opposite vertical faces, as shown in a.

It is apparent that, since the body is in equilibrium, the sum of the moments of the forces acting on the body is equal to zero, and other forces than those shown in a must be acting on the body. Such additional forces do exist and are supplied by shearing unit stresses of S_s' lb. per sq. in. acting on the horizontal faces of the body as shown in b.

The sum of the moments of all the forces on the body with respect to A (or any other point) equals zero. Therefore

$$(S_s \times ht) \times b - (S_s' \times bt) \times h = 0$$

whence $S_s = S_s'$, as was stated at the beginning of this article.[1]

The existence of equal shearing unit stresses on mutually perpendicular planes will be further discussed in connection with shafts and beams.

36. Axial Stresses in Members of Two Materials. When a known axial force acts on a member made of two materials, symmetrically arranged, the unit stress in each material can usually be determined, provided the modulus of elasticity of each material is known. In such cases, the total deformation (shortening or lengthening) of each material in the member is the same. Therefore the unit deformation of each material is the same if the lengths are the same, or in any event, the unit deformations bear a known relationship to one another. Since $S = E\delta$, it follows that the ratio of the unit stresses in the two materials is known, or in other words, the unit stress in one material can be expressed in terms of the unit stress in the other material. The total load is equal to the sum of the products obtained by multiplying the cross-sectional area of each material by the unit stress in it. Consequently, if the areas are known an equation can be written with the unit stress in one material as the only unknown. Or an equation can be written with the unit deformation as the only unknown; and this unit deformation can be solved for and used to determine the unit stresses.

Example. In Fig. 57, A and A' are steel bars 2 in. by 6 in. by 12 in. B is a cast-iron block 5 in. by 6 in. by 12 in. A load of 200,000 lb. is applied on the end as shown. What is the unit stress in the steel?

Solution: Let the unit deformation in each material be δ. Then the unit compressive stress in the steel is 30,000,000 δ, and in the cast iron is 12,000,000 δ. The

---

[1] The presence of uniformly distributed tensile or compressive stresses on the faces of this block does not affect the soundness of the above reasoning; nor does the presence of non-uniformly distributed normal stresses, provided the dimensions of the block are infinitesimal.

total stress in the three blocks equals 200,000 lb. Therefore

$$30,000,000 \, \delta \times 24 + 12,000,000 \, \delta \times 30 = 200,000$$

$$\delta = \frac{1}{5,400}$$

Hence the stress in the steel = 30,000,000/5,400 = 5,550 lb. per sq. in.

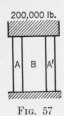

Fig. 57

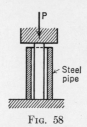

Fig. 58

PROBLEMS

1. Three wires, each having the same cross-section and the same unstressed length at 60° F., hang side by side in the same plane. The middle wire, equidistant from each of the others, is steel. The outer wires are copper. (*a*) If a weight of W lb. is hung from the three wires, what part of the load is carried by each? (*b*) What must the temperature become for the entire load to be carried by the steel wire? (*c*) For the three wires to be loaded equally?

2. The aluminum bar shown in Fig. 58 has a cross-section of 3 sq. in. and a length of 10.0015 in. when unstressed. The steel pipe has a cross-section of 3 sq. in. and a length of 10.00000 in. when unstressed. E equals 30,000,000 lb. per sq. in. for steel and 10,000,000 lb. per sq. in. for aluminum. What is the axial load, P, which will cause the same unit stress in each material? (Assume rigid supports.)

STRESSES CAUSED BY INTERNAL PRESSURE

37. Rupturing Forces in Pressure Containers. The pressure of a liquid or of any confined gas acts normally to the surface of the container in which the pressure exists. This normal pressure sets up stresses in the walls of the container and tends to rupture them. The design of such a container, or the investigation of the stresses set up in one by a given unit pressure, includes two distinct steps: first, the determination of the force which tends to rupture the container along the surface or surfaces where rupture is most likely to occur; second, determination of the stresses which result from the action of this force. Determination of the *force* will be considered in this article.

The resultant force *in any given direction* which a liquid or gas exerts on the interior surface of a container is equal to the force exerted on a plane surface taken perpendicular to the given direction and equal in area to the projection of the interior surface on that plane. As an illustration, consider the spherical tank shown in Fig. 59. If it contains a gas at a unit pressure of R lb. per sq. in., the resultant upward force exerted on the part of the tank above the plane a–a is $\pi x_1^2 R$; the resultant upward force exerted on the part of the tank above the plane b–b is $\pi x_2^2 R$, etc.

This may be proved as follows: Let dA, Fig. 60, represent an elementary part of the curved surface at a point where the surface makes

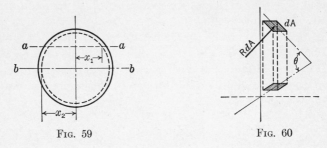

FIG. 59   FIG. 60

an angle θ with the horizontal. Then the force exerted by the pressure on this elementary surface is normal to the surface and equals $R\,dA$. The vertical component of this force equals $R\,dA \cos \theta$. But it is evident that $dA \cos \theta$ is the area of the projection of dA on the horizontal plane. Hence the vertical component equals R times the projection on the horizontal plane of the elementary area dA. By summing up the vertical components of the forces exerted on all the elementary areas that comprise the hemispherical surface, it becomes evident that the resultant upward force, F, equals R times the area of a diametral section through the hemisphere, i.e., equals R times the projection of the hemispherical surface on a plane at right angles to the direction of the force.

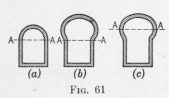

(a)   (b)   (c)

FIG. 61

The above reasoning applies to a vessel of any shape. Consequently for any vessel (such as those in Fig. 61) the resultant force exerted by the pressure on the part on one side of a plane a–a equals the unit pressure times the area of the part of the plane included within the inner surface of the vessel.

The relation between the resultant force exerted on part of a container and the stresses produced will be considered in the next article.

38. Unit Stresses in Pressure Vessels. *Bolted covers.* If the cover of a cylindrical pressure vessel is held on by bolts uniformly spaced, in a circle, the load is equally divided between the bolts. Therefore the internal pressure produces a load on each bolt of AR/n, where R is the unit internal pressure, A is the area of the projection on the plane of the bolt circle of the part of the cover exposed to the pressure, and n is the number of bolts.[1]

Thin spherical shell. As shown in the preceding article, the force tending to cause a spherical container to burst is greatest on a section cut from the shell by a diametral plane and equals the unit pressure times the internal diametral area. This force is resisted by tensile stress distributed over the surface which the diametral section cuts from the shell wall. If the thickness of the shell is small in relation to its internal diameter, the stress may be considered uniformly distributed over the cut section. Also the area of this section may be considered as equal (practically, and with error on the " safe " side), to the internal circumference of the shell times the wall thickness. Therefore the tensile unit stress equals

$$\frac{\frac{1}{4}\pi D^2 R}{\pi D t} = \frac{DR}{4 t}$$

Thin cylindrical shell. If a pressure container consists of a thin cylindrical shell with closed ends, there are two possibilities of rupture which need sometimes to be considered. The rupture may occur along a circumference of the shell or along one of its elements.

The stress which acts on a circumferential section *acts in a longitudinal direction* and is accordingly called *longitudinal stress.* The force tending to cause rupture along a circumferential section equals the unit pressure times the internal cross-sectional area of the container. The area resisting this force may, as in the thin-walled sphere, be considered to be uniformly distributed over the cross-section of the container wall, which may ordinarily be taken as the product of the internal circumference and the thickness. Therefore the longitudinal stress is $DR/4\,t$, as for the spherical container.

The stress which tends to cause rupture along an element of the cylinder acts in a direction tangent to the circumference and is called circumferential stress, or sometimes *hoop tension.* If the wall is thin in comparison with the diameter, this stress may be considered as uniformly distributed across the thickness of the wall.[2]

---

[1] In addition to the tension caused in the bolts by the internal pressure, there will generally be some tension due to the initial tightening of the bolts.

[2] The stress in the walls of such a container actually varies from point to point across the thickness. But if the thickness of the wall is small compared to the inner diameter, the maximum stress is only slightly above the average. If the thickness is $\frac{1}{50}$ of the inner diameter, the maximum stress is only about 2 per cent above the average. The walls of most boilers and tanks are sufficiently thin in comparison with their diameters to make negligible the error resulting from the assumption of uniform stress distribution. " Thick-walled " cylinders are considered in Chapter XXI.

The method of solving for circumferential stress is as follows. Imagine two transverse planes L in. apart. The part of the hollow cylinder between these planes is a body in equilibrium with normal forces on the inner surface. This is shown in Fig. 62a. Next imagine that this is cut into two equal parts by a plane. Each half is then also a body in equilibrium. One of these is shown in b. The resultant force, F, of the pressure on the inner surface of this half ring is equal to the product of the unit pressure and the area $L \times D$. If the unit pressure is R lb. per

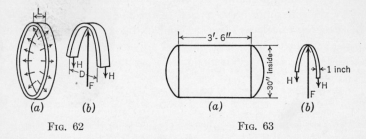

FIG. 62   FIG. 63

sq. in., $F = LDR$. This resultant, F, is balanced by the two tensile forces marked H, each of which is the product of the area $t \times L$ and the unit tensile stress in the metal, or tLS_t.

The unit circumferential stress is obtained by dividing the force $F/2$ by the area tL, or $S_t = \frac{1}{2} LDR/tL = DR/2\,t$. Comparison of this value with the longitudinal stress shows that, in a container having a uniform wall thickness throughout, the circumferential stress is twice the longitudinal stress.

Example. A small tank has dimensions as shown in Fig. 63. It is made of steel plate $\frac{3}{8}$ in. thick. What is the maximum allowable unit pressure in the tank if the tensile stress in its wall is not to exceed 12,000 lb. per sq. in.?

Solution: (a) Pressure as limited by longitudinal stress: Since, for a given unit pressure, the longitudinal unit stress is only one-half as great as the circumferential unit stress, the pressure will be limited by the circumferential unit stress.

(b) Pressure as limited by circumferential stress: Consider a portion of the tank included between parallel transverse planes 1 in. apart. Let the unit internal pressure as limited by circumferential stress be R lb. per sq. in. Then the resultant force F which causes the tensile forces H and H, Fig. 63b, is $R \times 30 \times 1 = 30\ R$, whence $H = 15\ R$.

But $H = 1 \times \frac{3}{8} \times 12,000.$

Therefore 15 $R = 1 \times \frac{3}{8} \times 12,000$, and $R = 300$ lb. per sq. in., which is the allowable unit pressure in the tank.

(NOTE. At points near the ends of the tank, the circumferential stress in the shell is somewhat less than the maximum, because of the supporting effect of the ends. A short distance away from the ends, however, the internal pressure of 300 lb. per sq. in. would cause the 12,000 lb. per sq. in. stress allowed.)

Since the plane dividing the ring into two half rings (Fig. 63b) may cut the ring at any two opposite points, it follows that the total tension is the same at all cross-sections of the ring. If for any reason the area of the ring is not the same for all cross-sections, the maximum unit stress will occur at the cross-sections where the area is least.

Tanks and pipes are sometimes made of wooden staves held together by hoops. The construction is somewhat like that of a wooden barrel. The total stress on these hoops may be found much as the force H is found. The maximum unit stress is then found by dividing the total stress by the minimum cross-section of the hoop. The distance L between the two transverse planes should be taken equal to the distance between the hoops. This same method applies to other types of fastenings which occur at intervals along a pipe or tank.

PROBLEMS

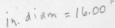

1. A " blind " flange is used to close the end of a 16-in. (outside diameter, see Table VIII) steam line which is subjected to a pressure of 600 lb. per sq. in. at a temperature of 750° F. The " American standard " for this service requires that the flange be held on with twenty $1\frac{1}{2}$-in. alloy steel bolts. (a) What is the maximum stress in each bolt? (b) On this same pipe and flange a hydraulic (non-shock) pressure of 1,000 lb. per sq. in. at ordinary temperature is permitted. What is the maximum bolt stress? *Ans.* (a) $S = 4,240$ lb. per sq. in.

2. Specifications of the American Water Works Association provide that a 36-in.-diameter Class A (wall thickness 0.99 in.) cast-iron pipe must withstand a hydrostatic pressure of 150 lb. per sq. in. What circumferential unit stress does this pressure cause?

3. The Outardes hydroelectric project in Canada includes what is believed to be the largest wooden-stave pipe so far constructed. (See *Civil Engineering*, December, 1937.) This pipe has an internal diameter of 17 ft. 6 in. and operates under a maximum head of 113.0 ft. The staves are held together by 1-in. steel bars, threaded. The minimum bar spacing is $2\frac{5}{32}$ in. What maximum tensile unit stress does the water pressure cause in these bars?

4. A welded steel water pipe used as a " siphon " in the Owyhee reclamation project in eastern Oregon has a diameter of 9 ft. and is made of $1\frac{3}{16}$-in. plate. After fabrication this pipe was tested under a water pressure of 200 lb. per sq. in. What circumferential stress was developed? *Ans.* $S = 13,300$ lb. per sq. in.

GENERAL PROBLEMS

(In all these problems except Problem 2, disregard the effect of stress concentration.)

1. A tension member or a short compression member, made of two materials (for example, a steel pipe filled with concrete), carries an axial load P. The cross-sectional area and modulus of elasticity for material 1 are respectively A_1 and E_1, and for material 2 they are respectively A_2 and E_2. Show that the part of the load carried by material number 1 is $P_1 = \dfrac{A_1E_1}{A_1E_1 + A_2E_2} P$.

2. Each block in Fig. 64 has the same minimum cross-section. The blocks are of soft steel, the proportional limit being 25,000 lb. per sq. in. and the yield point 30,000 lb. per sq. in. Using the curve of Fig. 48, find the ratio of maximum stress in A to maximum stress in B when P equals (a) 5,000 lb., (b) 20,000 lb., (c) 30,000 lb.

3. One of the 72-in.-by-48-in.-by-48-in. bronze shaft caps used in City Tunnel No. 2 of the New York City water supply is shown in Fig. 65. The cover of this cap is 7 ft. $2\frac{1}{2}$ in. in outside diameter and closes an opening 6 ft. $0\frac{1}{2}$ in. in diameter. The cover weighs 4,500 lb. and is bolted down with 44 nickel steel bolts 2 in. in diameter. The working pressure is 125 lb. per sq. in., and each shaft cap was tested at a pressure of 200 lb. per sq. in. Calculate the maximum stress in the bolts caused by the test pressure.

4. Lengths of the cylinders (Fig. 66) are exact as shown at 20° F. The dimension 17.002 in. remains fixed. What is the unit stress in the brass at 100° F.?

For brass: $C = 0.000010$, $E = 16,000,000$ lb. per sq. in.

For cast iron: $C = 0.0000062$, $E = 12,000,000$ lb. per sq. in.

(Assume uniform stress distribution throughout each cylinder.)

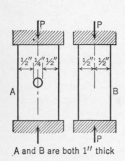

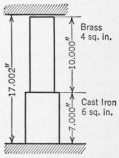

A and B are both 1″ thick

Courtesy, New York Board of Water Supply.

FIG. 64   FIG. 65   FIG. 66

5. A rectangular tank is 20 in. square by 40 in. long (interior dimensions). It is cast in two sections, as shown in Fig. 67. The two halves are bolted together with ten $1\frac{1}{2}$-in. bolts having an ultimate strength of 55,000 lb. per sq. in. Find the factor of safety for the bolts when the pressure in the tank is 200 lb. per sq. in. Is there any shearing stress on the bolt cross-sections? Slope of joint is 45°.

6. A welded cylindrical steel drum has an inside diameter of 40 in. and a plate thickness of $\frac{1}{4}$ in. Assuming no temperature change, how much will the diameter be increased by a gas pressure of 180 lb. per sq. in.: (a) if the effect of longitudinal stress is neglected? (b) if the effect of longitudinal stress is considered?

Ans. (a) $\Delta = 0.0193$ in.

7. A locomotive driving wheel without a steel tire has an outside diameter of 71.50 in. To what inside diameter should the tire be machined so that its unit stress will not exceed 15,000 lb. per sq. in. after being shrunk on? (Assume that the diameter of the inside of the tire after shrinking will be 71.48 in.)

Ans. $D = 71.44$ in.

8. A small gas holder (Fig. 68) consists of two cylindrical steel shells having the diameters and heights shown. The wall thickness of each shell is $\frac{3}{16}$ in. What is the maximum tensile stress that can come into the outer shell?

9. A bar consists of two strips of brass enclosing and soldered to a strip of zinc (Fig. 69). Each of the three strips has the same cross-sectional area. $E_b = 14,000,000$ lb. per sq. in., $E_z = 11,000,000$ lb. per sq. in., $C_b = 0.0000104$, $C_z = 0.0000173$. When not subjected to loads and at 60° F., the stress is zero in both materials. What stress is produced in each of the two materials if the temperature is raised to 150° F.?

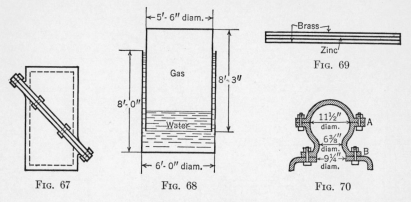

Fig. 69

Fig. 67 Fig. 68 Fig. 70

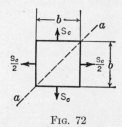

10. A steel rod 1 in. in diameter and threaded at both ends passes through an annealed copper tube which is $1\frac{1}{4}$ in. in inside diameter, $\frac{3}{8}$ in. thick, and 20 in. long. Nuts on the end of the rod are tightened until at 70° F. the stress in the rod at the root of the thread is 10,000 lb. per sq. in. If the temperature of rod and tube falls to 10° F., what do the stresses become in rod and tube, assuming that deformation of the nuts may be neglected? What must the temperature become for the stress to decrease to zero?

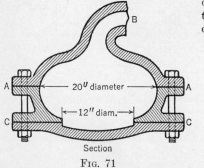

Section

Fig. 71 Fig. 72

11. An air chamber for a pump is shown in Fig. 70. For a pressure of 220 lb. per sq. in. calculate the number of $\frac{3}{4}$-in.-diameter bolts required at A and also at B. Stress not to exceed 6,000 lb. per sq. in.   *Ans.*   13 bolts at A.

12. A piece of apparatus is cast in three pieces and is fastened together with nine $\frac{7}{8}$-in. bolts, as shown (Fig. 71). A liquid is admitted at B with a pressure of 110 lb. per sq. in. What unit stress does this pressure cause in the bolts at planes $A–A$ and $C–C$?

13. As shown in Art. 38, the longitudinal stress in a thin-walled pipe subjected to internal pressure is only half the circumferential stress. Fig. 72 shows a small portion of the material included between two elements of the cylindrical surface and two transverse sections. If the circumferential unit stress is S_c lb. per sq. in., what are the shearing and normal unit stresses on section a–a? (*Hint:* Consider separately the effect of the longitudinal force and the effect of the circumferential force in causing stress on a–a, and then combine the effects.)

14. A water tank made of wood staves has an inside diameter of 11 ft., and is 16 ft. high. Hoops are flat steel bars 2 in. by $\frac{1}{4}$ in. spaced 10 in. center to center. (*a*) What is the unit stress in a hoop 20 in. above the bottom of the tank when the tank is full? (*b*) If instead of fresh water the tank is to hold brine (specific gravity = 1.20), to what should the hoop spacing be reduced for retention of the same factor of safety? *Ans.* (*a*) $S = 8,200$ lb. per sq. in.

15. Three wires, each 0.0400 sq. in. in cross-section, connect two rings as shown in Fig. 73. One wire is steel; it is 100.000 ft. long, unstressed. One wire is copper; it is 99.950 ft. long, unstressed. One wire is Duralumin; it is 99.900 ft. long, unstressed. Find the elongation of the steel wire and the unit stress in it when a load of 1,500 lb. is hung on the lower ring. (Given $E_s = 30,000,000$; $E_c = 17,000,000$; and $E_d = 10,000,000$ lb. per sq. in.)

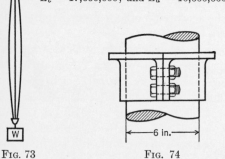

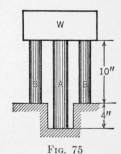

Fig. 73   Fig. 74   Fig. 75

16. A flanged collar is to be bolted onto a vertical steel post as shown in Fig. 74. This collar is to receive a load of 5,000 lb. acting along the axis of the post. The post diameter is 6 in. The coefficient of friction between post and collar may be assumed as 0.25, and the force exerted between the collar and post may be assumed to act normally to the surfaces before the load is applied, and to be uniformly distributed over them. If four bolts are used to hold the two halves of the collar together and if the unit stress in these bolts is not to exceed 10,000 lb. per sq. in., what diameter bolts should be used?

→ **17.** The rod A in Fig. 75 is of steel $2\frac{1}{4}$ in. in diameter; rods B are of cast brass $1\frac{3}{4}$ in. in diameter. What load W will cause a stress of 10,000 lb. per sq. in. in A if the supports are rigid?

Courtesy, Chicago Bridge and Iron Co.

Fig. 76

→ **18.** The "Hortonsphere" shown in Fig. 76 is used to store gas under a pressure of 60 lb. per sq. in. Its diameter is 46 ft. 9 in. It is made of 0.765-in. steel plate with butt-welded seams. What is the maximum tensile unit stress developed in the shell?

CHAPTER V

RIVETED AND WELDED JOINTS

39. Introduction. Steel tanks and boilers, the steel frames of buildings, etc., are ordinarily made of a number of separate pieces joined together. There are two principal methods of joining pieces of metal in this way. One method is by welding them together, the other by riveting them.

In this chapter joints of both types are described, the stresses resulting in them are discussed, and the accepted methods for calculating the allowable loads for such joints are illustrated.

40. Welded Joints. The common methods of welding in wide use at present are arc welding and oxyacetylene welding. In both these methods, fused metal is caused to flow between the parts to be welded, which, in turn, are themselves fused to an appreciable depth where in contact with the fused weld metal. When this fused metal has cooled, the parts are joined by the new metal. If properly made, such welds are as strong as the metal which has been melted to form them. If not properly made, the welds may have little strength.

In these methods of welding the new metal is melted from a slender rod. In arc welding the heat is supplied by an electric arc, generally formed between the metal to be joined and the rod. The arc heats the parts to be welded and fuses the tip of the rod. The weld metal is usually deposited in the form of a " bead " or " fillet." Oxyacetylene welding differs from arc welding in that the source of heat is a jet of burning oxygen and acetylene gas.

These types of welding are extensively used in repairing breaks in castings and forgings and in making tanks, machine frames, and numerous other products of rolled steel. When such welded machine frames are used in place of castings there may be considerable saving in weight, increase in strength, and reduction in cost.

Welding of structural steel for bridges and buildings is emerging from the experimental stage and offers great advantages and promises some economies. This use of welding is increasing rapidly at the present time.

41. Types of Welded Joints; Allowable Stresses. The two most frequently encountered types of welds are *fillet* welds and *butt* welds. These are illustrated in Fig. 77. Structural welds are generally of the fillet type (Fig. 78a). Often the fillet A is omitted, only the fillets B

61

being used. In both fillets A and B, shearing stress limits the allowable load. In B, the maximum shearing stress is evidently on the " throat " (Fig. 77a) of the fillet. In fillet A it can be shown that the shearing stress on the throat equals the shearing stress on the vertical face. Therefore, in all fillet welds, shearing stress on the fillet throat is the im-

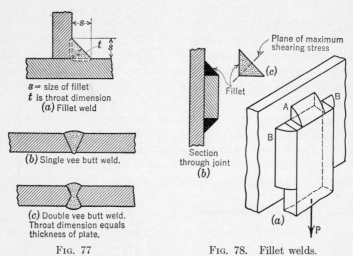

$s=$ size of fillet
t is throat dimension
(a) Fillet weld

(b) Single vee butt weld.

(c) Double vee butt weld.
Throat dimension equals
thickness of plate.

Fig. 77

Plane of maximum shearing stress

Fillet

Section
through joint
(b)

Fig. 78. Fillet welds.

portant stress. The Specifications of the American Welding Society permit this stress to be 11,300 lb. per sq. in.[1] Based on this unit stress, the following values are specified as the allowable load per linear inch of fillet for fillets of different sizes.[2]

SIZE OF FILLET (inch)	ALLOWABLE LOAD (lb. per linear inch)
$\frac{1}{2}$	4,000
$\frac{7}{16}$	3,500
$\frac{3}{8}$	3,000
$\frac{5}{16}$	2,500
$\frac{1}{4}$	2,000

[1] " Code for Fusion Welding and Gas Cutting in Building Construction." Supplement to *American Journal of Welding*, Vol. 14, No. 3, March, 1935.

[2] Use of these values implies that in a " side " fillet weld (Fig. 78, fillet B) n in. long, $1/n$ of the load is transmitted by each inch of the weld. This is known not to be strictly true. More load is transmitted by the ends of the fillet than by the middle portion of its length. This fact is generally disregarded in the design of fillet welds, in much the same way that non-uniform stress distribution over the cross-section of a tension member with a hole in it (Art. 31) is disregarded, and with the same justification. For a fuller and simple discussion of the actual stress distribution in welds see H. M. Priest, " The Practical Design of Welded Steel Structures," *Journal of the American Welding Society*, August, 1933.

As an example of the way in which the above allowable loads per inch are determined, consider a $\frac{1}{2}$-in. fillet. As shown in Fig. 78c, the minimum shear area is along the plane bisecting the right angle and for the $\frac{1}{2}$-in. fillet is $0.5 \times 0.707 = 0.3535$ sq. in. This area multiplied by the allowable shearing stress of 11,300 lb. per sq. in. gives 4,000 lb. per in. of fillet.

42. Design of Joints with Fillet Welds. In connections for members of symmetrical cross-section, the weld fillet should be symmetrically placed with respect to the axis of the member (Fig. 79). Connections for unsymmetrical members may be designed by methods equivalent to the following.

Assume that the stress in the member shown in Fig. 80 is uniformly distributed over the cross-section, as it must be if the member is to carry the maximum load consistent with a given allowable stress. Then the resultant of the stress is a force P which acts through the centroid of the

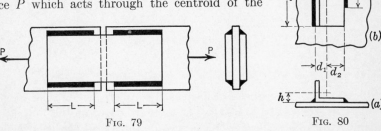

FIG. 79   FIG. 80

cross-section of the member. Obviously the resultant force exerted by the welds upon the member is collinear with the force P as required by the principles of equilibrium. In order to make this true and at the same time have the average load per linear inch of weld the same in both fillets, the following conditions must be met.

$L_1 + L_2 = P/F$, where F is the allowable load per inch of fillet; and $L_1 d_1 = L_2 d_2$. This second equation is based on the condition that the moment of any number of forces with respect to a point on the line of action of their resultant is zero.[1]

43. Design of Joints with Butt Welds. Butt welds are used principally in pressure containers such as boilers, tanks, and standpipes.

---

[1] This method makes no provision for the fact that the line of action of P is a distance h from the surface of the gusset plate as shown in Fig. 80a, while the stressed areas of the welds are a less distance from the surface of the gusset plate. This "eccentricity" induces some additional stresses which can be neglected if h is not too large and which are, in fact, commonly neglected. A more general discussion of eccentric connections is given in Art. 275.

However, the use of butt welds in structural work is increasing. Since the throat dimension of a butt weld is the thickness of the plates which the weld joins, the allowable pressure in a butt-welded container is affected by the weld only in so far as the metal of the weld, or the metal adjoining the weld, is weaker than the metal at other parts of the container. The Boiler Construction Code of the American Society of Mechanical Engineers[1] provides that a butt weld shall be assumed to have a certain percentage of the strength of the unwelded plate. The specified percentage varies from 90 for the highest-grade, most carefully inspected double-vee work, down to a minimum of about 60 per cent for single-vee welds subjected to a much less rigid type of inspection.

For structural butt welds the specifications of the American Welding Society previously referred to specify as allowable stresses the following:

Tension on section through weld throat, 13,000 lb. per sq. in.

Compression on section through weld throat, 18,000 lb. per sq. in.

The Building Code of the City of New York (1938) specifies: tension, 13,000 lb. per sq. in., and compression, 15,000 lb. per sq. in.

PROBLEMS

1. A tank is made of $\frac{5}{16}$-in. plates, butt-welded. The (internal) diameter is 33 in. If the ultimate tensile strength of the plate is 60,000 lb. per sq. in. and if the strength of the weld is 90 per cent of the strength of the plate, what pressure would burst the tank?   *Ans.* $R = 1,023$ lb. per sq. in.

2. A steel pipe 20 in. in diameter and with a wall thickness of $\frac{1}{4}$ in. has a welded spiral seam which intersects elements of the cylinder at 45° as shown in Fig. 81. There is no longitudinal stress in the pipe. Allowable tensile stress in the pipe wall away from the seam is 12,000 lb. per sq. in. Allowable tensile and shearing stresses in the seam are 9,000 and 6,600 lb. per sq. in., respectively. What is the allowable unit pressure in the pipe? Does the presence of the seam affect the allowable pressure?

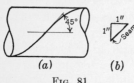

(a)   (b)

Fig. 81

(*Hint:* Consider the forces acting on the small triangular portion of the pipe wall shown in Fig. 81b.)

3. In Fig. 79 the length L is $6\frac{1}{2}$ in. (a) If $P = 80,000$ lb., what is the necessary size of fillet according to the specifications of the American Welding Society? (b) If L is 8 in. and the fillet size is $\frac{5}{16}$ in., what is the allowable value of P?

Ans. (b) $P = 80,000$ lb.

4. The angle in Fig. 80 is a 6-in. × 4-in. × $\frac{3}{8}$-in. angle. The fillets are applied to the 6-in. leg. What are the proper lengths L_1 and L_2 if the stress is to be uniform along the length of the fillets and is not to exceed 2,000 lb. per in. when $P = 20,000$ lb.?

---

[1] This very comprehensive set of specifications, commonly called the A.S.M.E. Boiler Code, has been adopted by law in many cities and states and is widely followed in the design and construction of boilers and other pressure containers.

44. Riveted Joints. To make a simple riveted joint, holes are drilled or punched in each of the plates to be joined. The plates are then lapped over one another, with the holes matched, and a red-hot steel rivet is inserted in each hole. A rivet has a head already formed on one end. Pressure is exerted on this head to hold the rivet in place, while the projecting shank of the rivet is hammered with a pneumatic hammer, or is pressed, to form a head on the other end. The rivet is cooling off during this process, but is still at a high temperature at its conclusion. Subsequent cooling of the rivet shortens it and thus sets up in it a tensile stress which draws the two plates very tightly together.[1]

45. Kinds of Stress in a Riveted Joint. As an introduction to the stresses which occur in riveted joints, consider the simple example of a steel plate (Fig. 82) to which a weight of P lb. is attached. The plate is supported as shown, by means of a round pin projecting from a vertical wall and fitting in a hole of the same diameter drilled in the plate. At any horizontal cross-section of the plate between the pin and the load there is evidently a tension due to the supported weight, and the unit stress due to this tension is evidently a maximum at the section which passes through the center of the hole. This tensile unit stress (considered uniformly distributed) is equal to the load P divided by the area at the net section.

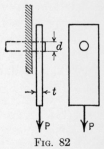

FIG. 82

On that part of the plate which is in contact with the upper half of the cylindrical surface of the pin, the pin exerts a compressive force. The variation in the compressive unit stress that results from this force is very uncertain, and in practice no attempt is made to determine how the stress varies. Instead an arbitrarily defined " bearing unit stress " is computed. This bearing unit stress is the quotient obtained when the compressive force exerted by the pin is divided by a rectangular area the dimensions of which are t and d, the plate thickness and the pin diameter, respectively.

This bearing stress is thus a fictitious stress in the sense that it is not known to be equal to the compressive stress at any particular point in the plate. The use of this bearing stress is quite legitimate, however, since allowable values for it are determined from a corresponding " ultimate bearing strength " of the plate material. This bearing strength is determined by testing to destruction joints which have been so proportioned that they fail by crushing of the plate where the compressive stress in it is highest. The ultimate bearing strength is defined

---

[1] In structural work rivets are sometimes driven cold.

as the quotient obtained when the load causing a compressive failure is divided by the area td. The allowable bearing stress is then obtained by dividing the ultimate bearing strength by a suitable factor of safety.

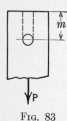

Fig. 83

The stresses which have been considered up to this point are those in the plate. However, the pin is also stressed by the force which is exerted on it by the plate, this being evidently equal and opposite to the force exerted on the plate by the pin. One effect of this force on the pin is to cause shear on every vertical section between the plane of the wall and the adjoining face of the plate. The total shearing force is, of course, equal to the weight of plate and supported load. On the assumption that this shearing force is equally distributed over the circular cross-section of the pin, the shearing unit stress in the pin is the load P divided by the cross-sectional area of the pin. The deformations of the rivet in specimen S5A (Fig. 84) indicate high shearing stresses on two planes.

Dimensions of plate and load at failure are given. Rivets, $\frac{7}{8}$-in. diameter. The joints were identical except that from center of hole to edge of plate was 2 in. in S5 and $2\frac{1}{2}$ in. in S5A.

Because of insufficient edge distance in S5 the plate failed in front of the rivet before the tensile strength was reached. Note the evidence of over-stress in bearing above the hole in the plate. Note also the effect on the rivet of over-stress in shear.

Courtesy, Bethlehem Steel Co.

Fig. 84.   Test specimens from two single riveted joints.

In addition to this shearing stress, the pin is subjected to a bending stress, which is a maximum at the surface of the wall. If the plate is hung close against the wall, this bending stress is not of great importance, and in the ordinary riveted joint, where the plates are actually in contact with one another, the effect of the bending is neglected.

In the plate, in addition to the bearing and tensile stresses discussed, shearing stresses exist on the two planes tangent to the sides of the pinhole (Fig. 83). These stresses can be kept as low as desired by making the edge distance m sufficiently large. The actual failure of a plate with insufficient edge distance in front of a rivet is the result of a complex state of stress and is more likely to be somewhat like that of specimen S5, Fig. 84. Specifications for riveted joints specify the minimum edge distance (usually $1\frac{1}{4}$ to 2 times the diameter of the rivet). It will be assumed that the edge distance of the joints considered hereafter is sufficient to prevent failure of the plate in front of the rivet.

Example. A mild steel pin with a diameter of 1 in. supports a mild steel plate of the dimensions shown in Fig. 85. What is the greatest load which the plate can support without causing failure of the joint? The ultimate strengths of the materials are as follows:

FIG. 85

Tension, 55,000 lb. per sq. in.
Bearing, 95,000 lb. per sq. in.
Shear, 44,000 lb. per sq. in.

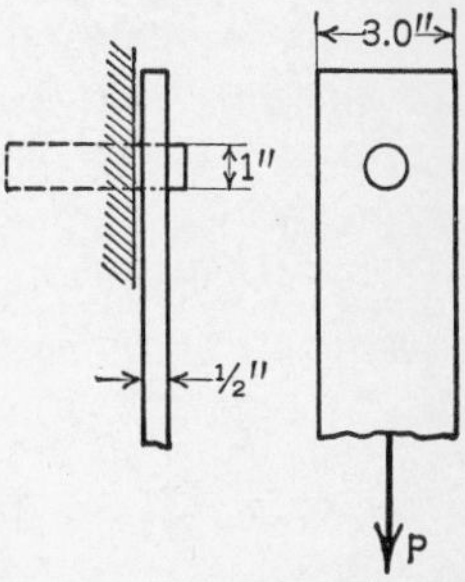

Solution: Shear strength of pin = 44,000 × 0.7854 = 34,600 lb.
Bearing strength of plate above pin = 95,000 × 1 × $\frac{1}{2}$ = 47,500 lb.
Tensile strength of plate at net section = 55,000 × $(3 - 1)$ × $\frac{1}{2}$ = 55,000 lb.
Therefore strength of joint = 34,600 lb., which is the maximum load that can be carried.

In the example just solved, the strength of the joint is limited by the shear strength of the pin. If the pin diameter were made $1\frac{1}{4}$ in., instead of 1 in., its cross-sectional area would be increased in the ratio of 1.25^2 to 1^2, or by 56 per cent, and the shear strength of the joint would be equally increased. At the same time, the bearing strength would be increased by 25 per cent. The tensile strength would be decreased, however, by 12.5 per cent, and would become the least strength of the joint.

But if, with a $1\frac{1}{4}$-in. pin as before, a plate of the same gross cross-sectional area were used, but with half the thickness and twice the width of the original plate, the effect of this difference in the plate dimensions would be to leave unchanged the shear strength of the pin, to increase the tensile strength of the plate, and to halve the bearing strength. With these dimensions, the bearing strength of the plate above the pin would become the limiting strength of the joint — failure would occur by crushing the plate above the pin before the pin itself sheared or the plate failed in tension at the net section.

From this discussion it is evident that the type of failure of a joint of this sort depends on the relative dimensions of pin and plate.

PROBLEMS

1. In Fig. 85 let the pin and pin hole diameters be $\frac{3}{4}$ in., and the plate dimensions 2 in. by $\frac{3}{8}$ in. What is the maximum weight which can be supported if the following unit stresses are not to be exceeded: tension, 16,000 lb. per sq. in.; bearing, 24,000 lb. per sq. in.; shear, 12,000 lb. per sq. in.?   *Ans.* $P = 5,300$ lb.

2. A $\frac{7}{8}$-in.-diameter pin fits closely in a hole in a plate of 4-in.-by-$\frac{1}{4}$-in. cross-section arranged as in Fig. 85. What are the unit tensile, bearing, and shearing stresses in plate and pin when a load of 10,000 lb. is supported by the plate?

3. If the two plates shown in Fig. 39 are each $\frac{5}{8}$ in. thick and the diameter of the pin is $2\frac{3}{8}$ in., calculate the bearing stress between the pin and plates.

46. Single-Riveted Lap Joint.   The simplest possible riveted joint is illustrated in Fig. 86; it consists merely of two narrow plates or bars joined by means of a single rivet. The stresses in this joint, when it is used to transmit tension from one plate to another, are similar to the stresses in the plate and pin which have been discussed.

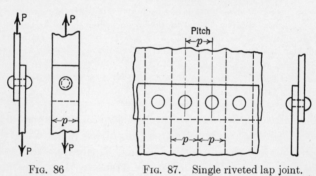

FIG. 86   FIG. 87.   Single riveted lap joint.

The ordinary *single-riveted lap joint* differs from the joint just discussed in that it has more than one rivet to hold the bars or plates together, the rivets being in a single row. The rivets are equally spaced and the distance between the rivets is called the " rivet pitch," generally represented by the symbol p. Such a joint may be considered as equivalent to several joints with one rivet each, placed side by side as in Fig. 87.

This same idea can be extended to apply to joints in boilers and tanks. Fig. 88 shows such a joint, which, as indicated by the dotted lines, can be thought of as consisting of a number of " unit joints," or " repeating sections," to employ the term ordinarily used. For a single-riveted lap joint the repeating section is equal to the rivet pitch.

In investigating a joint of this sort, it is not necessary to deal with more than one repeating section of joint, since the stresses are the same in each repeating section,[1] and the strength of all repeating sections is the same.

The problems which occur in investigation of boiler and tank joints may involve: (*a*) determination of the ultimate strength of joint (the total force which will cause failure of a repeating section); (*b*) determination of the safe load for a repeating section, based on given allowable unit stresses or on given ultimate strengths and a given factor of safety; (*c*) determination of the unit tensile, bearing, and shear stresses in a joint, due to a given load on a repeating section. For a single-riveted lap joint, these determinations are made just as was outlined in the preceding article.

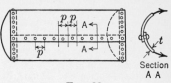

Fig. 88

Example. A single-riveted lap joint has the following dimensions: plate thickness, $\frac{1}{4}$ in.; rivet pitch, $1\frac{3}{4}$ in.; diameter of rivet holes, $\frac{11}{16}$ in. What is the allowable load on the repeating section of the joint if allowable stresses are: tension, 11,000 lb. per sq. in.; bearing, 19,000 lb. per sq. in.; shear, 8,800 lb. per sq. in.?
Solution: Length of repeating section $= 1\frac{3}{4}$ in.
Allowable load as limited by tension $= (1\frac{3}{4} - \frac{11}{16}) \times \frac{1}{4} \times 11,000 = 2,920$ lb.
Allowable load as limited by bearing $= \frac{11}{16} \times \frac{1}{4} \times 19,000 = 3,270$ lb.
Allowable load as limited by shear $= \pi/4 \times (\frac{11}{16})^2 \times 8,800 = 3,260$ lb.
Therefore the allowable load on a repeating section is 2,920 lb.

47. Efficiency of a Joint. By the efficiency of a joint is meant the ratio of the strength of a repeating section of the joint to the strength of the same length of the unpunched plate. This ratio is expressed as a percentage. Instead of using ultimate strengths, the efficiency of a joint can also be found by dividing the *allowable load* on a repeating section of the joint by the *allowable load* on an equal length of the unpunched plate and multiplying by 100 to express the ratio as a percentage.

Example. What is the efficiency of the joint considered in the preceding example?
Solution: Allowable load on joint $= 2,920$ lb.
Allowable load on $1\frac{3}{4}$-in. length of $\frac{1}{4}$-in. plate $= 1\frac{3}{4} \times \frac{1}{4} \times 11,000 = 4,810$ lb.
Efficiency $= 2,920/4,810 \times 100 = 60.7$ per cent.

It should be evident that the efficiency of a riveted joint can never be as great as 100 per cent, since the tensile strength of the repeating

[1] Except in the parts of the joint near the boiler heads where the stiffening effect of the head decreases the load on the joint somewhat.

section can never be as great as the tensile strength of the same length of the unpunched plate, and since the strength of the joint can never be more than the tensile strength of the joint. The higher the efficiency of a joint, the more nearly can the full strength of the plates at sections between the joints be developed. For instance, in the example above, when the joint is carrying its allowable load the tensile stress in the plate at any section away from and parallel to the joint is only 60.7 per cent of the allowable tensile stress. Hence it is important that the efficiency of joints be kept as high as is compatible with economy of fabrication. This results in the frequent use of more complicated joints than single-riveted lap joints, the efficiency of which is seldom higher than 60 per cent. Single-riveted lap joints are often used, however, for the circumferential joints of boilers and tanks, since the efficiency of such joints is unimportant provided it is at least half the efficiency of the longitudinal joint (Art. 38).

PROBLEMS

1. A single-riveted lap joint is used to join two plates $\frac{3}{8}$ in. thick. The rivet pitch is $1\frac{7}{8}$ in., diameter of rivet holes $\frac{13}{16}$ in. Find the allowable load per repeating length of joint if the ultimate strengths of plates and rivets are: tension, 55,000 lb. per sq. in.; bearing, 95,000 lb. per sq. in.; shear, 44,000 lb. per sq. in.; and if the joint is to have a factor of safety of 5. What is the efficiency of this joint?

Ans. Eff. = 56.7 per cent.

2. What are the stresses in this joint when it is subjected to a load of 2,000 lb. *per in. length of joint?*

3. A single-riveted lap joint is used to connect two plates $\frac{7}{16}$ in. thick. The rivet pitch is $2\frac{1}{8}$ in., and rivet holes are $\frac{15}{16}$ in. in diameter. What is the efficiency of the joint if the material is the same as in Problem 1?

48. Allowable Stresses in Riveted Boiler and Tank Joints. The A.S.M.E. Boiler Code states that steel acceptable for use in boilers must have strengths not less than the following:

> Tension: 55,000 lb. per sq. in.
> Bearing: 95,000 lb. per sq. in.
> Shear: 44,000 lb. per sq. in.

The Code also prescribes a factor of safety of 5. Consequently the allowable stresses become:

> Tension: 11,000 lb. per sq. in.
> Bearing: 19,000 lb. per sq. in.
> Shear: 8,800 lb. per sq. in.

For unfired pressure containers (tanks, water mains, standpipes, etc.) the Code specifies the above allowable stresses for shear and for bearing.

The allowable tensile stress is specified to be one-fifth of the ultimate tensile strength of the plates. Such plates are often made of steel having a specified minimum tensile strength considerably greater than 55,000 lb. per sq. in.

49. Investigation of Boiler and Tank Joints. The rupturing force which an internal unit pressure exerts on a given length of a boiler or tank shell, in either a longitudinal or a transverse direction, can be determined by principles derived in Chapter IV.   Preceding articles in the present chapter have shown how to determine the force which may be applied to a given length of a joint, without exceeding given allowable stresses, and also how to determine the unit stresses set up in a joint by the application of a given force to it.   These principles may be combined to determine the stresses caused in the joints of a given boiler shell by a given internal unit pressure, or to determine the maximum internal unit pressure which can be used in a given boiler shell without causing unit stresses greater than those allowed.   The following examples illustrate these investigations.

Example 1.   The single-riveted lap joint of the example of Art. 46 is a longitudinal joint in a pipe 24 in. in diameter.   What unit pressure is permissible if the stresses are not to exceed the allowable stresses in the example?

Solution: Consider a half hoop of the pipe with a length equal to the length of the repeating section. This is shown in Fig. 89.   The rupturing force on this caused by a pressure of R lb. per sq. in. is $1\frac{3}{4} \times 24 \times R$ lb.   This is resisted by the two tensions in the hoop which can each equal 2,920 lb. as calculated in Art. 46.   Therefore

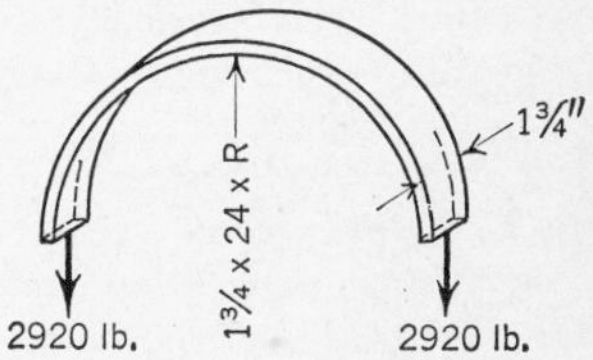

2920 lb.   2920 lb.

Fig. 89

$$1\tfrac{3}{4} \times 24 \times R = 2 \times 2,920$$
$$R = 139 \text{ lb. per sq. in.}$$

Example 2.   If this same single-riveted lap joint is a circumferential joint in a boiler 48 in. in diameter, to what steam pressure does it limit the boiler?

Solution: Imagine the boiler to be cut in two by a *transverse* plane and consider one of the two parts as a body in equilibrium.   Since the allowable load for the $1\frac{3}{4}$-in. repeating section of this joint is 2,920 lb., it is evident that 2,920 lb. can act on each $1\frac{3}{4}$-in. length of the circumference without causing excessive stresses in the circumferential joints.

Therefore the total longitudinal force on the entire circumference can equal $2,920 \times 48 \, \pi/1\frac{3}{4} = 252,000$ lb.

But the total force developed on the head of the boiler by the steam pressure of R lb. per sq. in. is $\pi \times 24^2 \times R$.   Hence

$$R = \frac{252,000}{\pi \times 24^2} = 139 \text{ lb. per sq. in.}$$

PROBLEMS

1. A water main 28 in. in diameter is made of $\frac{5}{16}$-in. plates. Longitudinal joints are single-riveted lap joints with a rivet pitch of 2 in. Rivet holes are $\frac{13}{16}$ in. Using A.S.M.E. stresses for this type of container, and assuming the pipe made of steel plate with a tensile strength of 60,000 lb. per sq. in., what head of water is allowable? What is the efficiency of this joint?

2. A steam boiler 50 in. in diameter is made of $\frac{1}{2}$-in. plates and has single-riveted circumferential joints. These have a rivet pitch of $2\frac{1}{8}$ in. and rivet holes $\frac{15}{16}$ in. in diameter. When the boiler pressure is 175 lb. per sq. in., what is the factor of safety of the circumferential joints?

3. What is the efficiency of the joint in Problem 2, using the Boiler Code stresses?

Ans. 52 per cent.

50. Double-Riveted Lap Joints.

To secure higher efficiencies and greater tightness than can be secured with single-riveted lap joints, double-riveted lap joints are often used. Such a joint is illustrated in Fig. 90. The repeating length of joint is again equal to the rivet pitch.

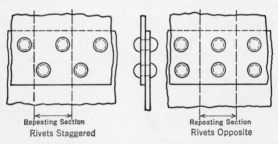

Repeating Section
Rivets Staggered

Repeating Section
Rivets Opposite

Fig. 90.   Double-riveted lap joints.

The distance between the two rows of rivets is made great enough so that if the plate fails in tension it will tear between the holes of one row and not along a zigzag line between rivets in both rows. Evidently for a double-riveted joint the tensile strength is the same as for a single-riveted joint with the same pitch, plate thickness, and rivet diameter. The shear and bearing strengths are twice as great as for the single-riveted joint.

PROBLEMS

1. A small compressed air tank has an inside diameter of 25 in. and a plate thickness of $\frac{3}{8}$ in. Its longitudinal joints are double-riveted lap joints with the rivets staggered. The pitch of the rivets in each row is 3 in., and the rivet holes are $\frac{13}{16}$ in. in diameter. What are the stresses in the longitudinal joints when the internal unit pressure in the tank is 200 lb. per sq. in.? *Ans.* $S_b = 10,700$ lb. per sq. in.

2. The ultimate strengths of the tank plates and rivets in Problem 1 are 95,000, 55,000, and 44,000 lb. per sq. in. for bearing, tension, and shear, respectively. What is the greatest internal unit pressure which can be developed in the tank, if its factor of safety is to be not less than 5?

R = 384 #/in²
work stem
a pw 2

3. For circumferential joints this tank has single-riveted lap joints with a rivet pitch of $2\frac{1}{4}$ in. and a rivet-hole diameter of $1\frac{5}{16}$ in. Which have the greater factor of safety, the longitudinal or the circumferential joints, for any given internal unit pressure?

J. refer

4. Calculate the efficiencies of the longitudinal and circumferential joints, respectively, of the tank referred to in the preceding problems.   *Long j² e = 686%*
Circ j² e = 583%

51. Bending Stresses in Plates of Lap Joints. In a lap joint, in addition to the stresses which have been spoken of, there is a bending stress in the plates which results from their natural tendency to assume such a position that the tensile forces become collinear. This is illustrated in Fig. 91. The stresses which result from this bending are not ordinarily taken into consideration in the design and investigation of lap joints. In large tanks and boilers, however, these stresses are often obviated by using butt joints in which the bending effect is not present. The A.S.M.E. Boiler Code provides, for instance, that butt joints must be used for the longitudinal joints of all power boilers having diameters greater than 36 in. In tanks, butt joints are recommended for joining plates of $\frac{1}{2}$-in. thickness and greater.

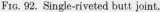

Fig. 91   Fig. 92. Single-riveted butt joint.

52. Single-Riveted Butt Joints. In a butt joint which transmits tension there occur tensile, compressive, and shear stresses. If a tensile force is applied to plate A (Fig. 92), it is transmitted from A to the rivets which pass through A, thence to the cover plates, thence to the rivets which pass through plate B, and thence to B.

It is readily seen that the tensile unit stress in the main plates is greatest along the lines of rivets, where the net section occurs. In the cover plates, the greatest tensile unit stress occurs along the same lines. If the thickness of each cover plate is one-half the thickness of each main plate, the area which supports this tension in the cover plates is equal to the area supporting it in the main plates. Under this condition, the tensile unit stress in the cover plates would be the same as in the main plates. Actually, to guard against any possible failure in the cover plates, they are always made more than one-half as thick as the main plates, and the tension in the cover plates need not be calculated. For the same reasons, the maximum bearing stress in the joint may be found by finding the bearing stress in the main plates.

In a lap joint a shear failure necessitates that each rivet be sheared through once, at the section where the faces of the two plates are in contact with one another. In the butt joint, however, if a shear failure occurs, it will involve pulling the main plate out from between the cover plates, and this cannot be done without shearing each rivet at two sections.

It is therefore evident that the tensile strength and the bearing strength of a single-riveted butt joint are the same as those of a single-riveted lap joint of the same plate thickness and rivet size and pitch, whereas the shear strength of the butt joint is twice that of the lap joint.

PROBLEMS

1. A single-riveted butt joint is used to connect two $\frac{1}{2}$-in. plates.   Cover plates are $\frac{7}{16}$ in. thick, rivet holes $1\frac{1}{16}$ in. in diameter, rivet pitch 3 in.   Determine the allowable load on a repeating length of the joint and its efficiency, using A.S.M.E. Boiler Code stresses.   *Ans.* Load = 10,100 lb.

2. Determine the diameter of the largest boiler in which the joint in Problem 1 could be used longitudinally if the steam pressure is to be 100 lb. per sq. in.

53. Double-Riveted Butt Joints. In butt joints, as in lap joints, the joint efficiency can be increased by the addition of another line of

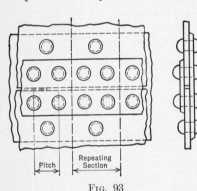

Pitch | Repeating Section

Fig. 93

rivets to each side of the joint, making a double-riveted butt joint. Most double-riveted butt joints have only half as many rivets in the outside rows as in the inside rows (see Fig. 93). A little thought will show that this increases the tensile strength of the joint. A butt joint is usually much stronger in bearing and in shear than it is in tension when the rivet spacing is the same in all rows of rivets. Hence the removal of alternate rivets in the outside rows, by increasing the tensile strength, increases the strength of the joint.

In double-riveted butt joints it is common practice to use one wide and one narrow cover plate. The rivets in the outer lines are therefore in single shear. A narrow cover plate ordinarily does not reduce the strength of the joint below what it would be with two wide plates.[1]

---

[1] The narrow cover plate is desirable from the standpoint of joint tightness. " Calking " is more effective if applied to the edges of the narrow plate since the rivets are closer together and consequently hold the edge of the cover plate more tightly against the shell plate.

Example. In the double-riveted butt joint shown in Fig. 93 the thickness of the main plate is $\frac{1}{2}$ in., thickness of splice plate is $\frac{7}{16}$ in., diameter of rivet holes is $\frac{15}{16}$ in., " short "-pitch is $2\frac{1}{2}$ in. (these are dimensions of a standard double-riveted boiler joint for $\frac{1}{2}$-in. plate). Calculate the allowable load on a repeating section and the efficiency of this joint, using A.S.M.E. Boiler Code allowable stresses.

Solution: Before proceeding with the calculations for allowable load on the joint, it is convenient to have available the following values:

Allowable load in single shear on one rivet $= \pi/4 \times (\frac{15}{16})^2 \times 8,800 = 6,080$ lb.
Allowable load in bearing on $\frac{1}{2}$-in. plate $= \frac{1}{2} \times \frac{15}{16} \times 19,000 = 8,910$ lb.
Allowable load in bearing on $\frac{7}{16}$-in. plate $= \frac{7}{16} \times \frac{15}{16} \times 19,000 = 7,790$ lb.

The allowable load on the repeating section may be limited by any one of several combinations of the above values.

1. The two rivets in the inner row are each stressed in shear on two planes and the rivet in the outer row is stressed in shear on one plane, making a total of five cross-sections.

Allowable load as limited by shearing $= 5 \times 6,080 = 30,400$ lb.

2. Three rivets bear against the $\frac{1}{2}$-in. plate, but it will be observed that the least value of the outer rivet is determined by shear rather than by bearing against either the main plate or the cover plate.

Allowable load on repeating section, as determined by bearing of two inner rivets and shearing of outer rivet, is

$$2 \times 8,910 + 6,080 = 23,900 \text{ lb.}$$

3. Allowable load as determined by tension in plate at outer row (one hole in 5-in. width) $= (5 - \frac{15}{16}) \times \frac{1}{2} \times 11,000 = 22,350$ lb.

4. The tensile strength of the plate is less at the inner row where two holes occur in the 5-in. width, but it will be observed that this failure cannot occur without simultaneous failure of the rivet in the outer row. The allowable load for this combination is

$$(5 - \tfrac{15}{8}) \times \tfrac{1}{2} \times 11,000 + 6,080 = 23,280 \text{ lb.}$$

The allowable load[1] for the joint is 22,350 lb.

The efficiency of the joint is $\dfrac{22,350}{5 \times \frac{1}{2} \times 11,000} \times 100 = 81.3$ per cent.

[1] Although it is customary to calculate allowable loads for double-, triple-, and quadruple-riveted butt joints by considering various combinations, as was done here, there is no positive assurance that some greater stress than the allowable may not be caused by the " allowable load " so determined. For instance, if it is assumed that each plane of shear carries an equal part of the load (and this assumption was made in calculating the allowable load in shearing), then, when the load on the repeating section is 22,350 lb., the outer rivet carries $\frac{1}{5}$ of 22,350 or 4,470 lb., and each inner rivet carries 8,940 lb., which exceeds the allowable load for a rivet in bearing.
The only certain conclusion that can be drawn is that, if the load on the repeating section exceeds the calculated allowable load, stresses will result that do exceed the allowable stresses.
It was previously stated that " inaccuracy in the calculation of stress " is one of the conditions for which the " margin of safety " provided by a low allowable stress must provide. Riveted joints furnish examples of stresses which cannot be accurately calculated.

PROBLEMS

1. The double-riveted butt joint in the above example is used as a vertical joint in a standpipe 20 ft. in diameter, and made of plate with a tensile strength of 60,000 lb. per sq. in. If allowable stresses are 12,000, 8,800, and 19,000 lb. per sq. in., for tension, shear, and bearing, respectively, to what height above the joint may the standpipe be filled?

2. What change in the efficiency of the joint of the preceding example and problem results from changing the allowable tensile stress from 11,000 to 12,000 lb. per sq. in.?

3. Standard dimensions for a double-riveted butt joint joining plates $\frac{3}{8}$ in. in thickness are: splice plate thickness, $\frac{5}{16}$ in.; diameter of rivet holes, $\frac{13}{16}$ in.; "short" pitch, $2\frac{1}{4}$ in.; "long" pitch, $4\frac{1}{2}$ in. Find the allowable load on a repeating length, and the joint efficiency, using A.S.M.E. stresses for boilers. 82% $15,200$

54. Triple-Riveted and Quadruple-Riveted Butt Joints.

In boilers, tanks, or pipe which are subject to very heavy pressures, and which therefore require heavy plates, the saving in material which results from increased efficiency in the joints justifies the use of triple- and even quadruple-riveted butt joints. In every case, determination of the strength of the joint, or the stresses caused in the joint by a given pressure, involves determination of the repeating length of the joint, and then determination of the areas of metal which resist each possible method of failure of the joint, as was done in the preceding example.

55. The Design of Joints in Pressure Containers.

In designing joints it would seem economical to make the strengths of the joint in tension, bearing, and shear as nearly equal as possible. The design must be influenced, however, not only by this ideal consideration, but also by others of a practical nature, such as the necessity of using plates of standard thicknesses and rivets of standard diameters. Simplicity results, moreover, from using rivet pitches which do not involve very small fractions of an inch — such as thirty-seconds or even sixteenths. These and other considerations have led to a rather complete standardization of joints on the part of boiler and tank makers. Handbooks of mechanical engineering contain many standard designs for lap and butt joints, with single, double, triple, and quadruple riveting. The efficiencies of these joints range from about 50 per cent for single-riveted lap joints in light plates, to about 94 per cent for the elaborate joints of large boilers and pipes carrying very heavy pressures.

PROBLEMS

1. To design a single-riveted lap joint which will have the greatest efficiency in joining two plates of thickness t, the allowable load as limited by shear ($P_s = \frac{1}{4} \pi d^2 S_s$) is equated to the allowable load as limited by bearing. This fixes the rivet hole diameter, d, in terms of t, S_s, and S_b. The proper rivet pitch is then established by equating the load as limited by tension to the load as limited by bearing. Following this procedure, derive expressions for (a) rivet-hole diameter, d, in terms of t, S_s, and S_b; (b) pitch, p, in terms of d, S_t, and S_b.

$$Ans. \quad (a) \quad d = \frac{4}{\pi} \times \frac{S_b}{S_s} \times t.$$

2. Using the expressions called for in Problem 1, determine values of d and p for a single-riveted lap joint for joining plates $\frac{1}{2}$ in. thick, using 11,000, 19,000, and 8,800 for S_t, S_b and S_s, respectively. Compare the dimensions of this joint with those of the joint given in Problem 2, Art. 49. What is the ratio of the efficiency of this joint to that of the joint in Problem 2, Art. 49?

3. Following the procedure outlined in Problem 1, derive expressions for d and p in a double-riveted lap joint that has maximum efficiency in joining two plates of thickness t.

56. Riveted Joints in Structural Work. All the joints which have been discussed so far have been used to transmit tensile stress from one plate to another. In a building frame, the typical joint is one used to connect floor beams to one another or to the columns which support them. This joint, or *connection* as it is frequently called, is made by riveting short lengths of steel angles to both sides of the web of the beam as shown in Fig. 94, and riveting the outstanding legs of the angles

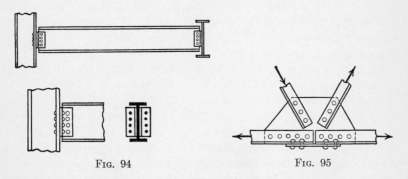

FIG. 94   FIG. 95

to the column. The angles are usually riveted to the beam in the fabricating shop, and to the column in the field as the building is erected.

Another important type of structural joint is that used to connect the different members of a truss. Fig. 95 shows such a joint. In a truss joint usually there are both tension and compression members connected to the " gusset plate."

Important differences exist between the fabrication of structures such as buildings and the fabrication of boilers and other pressure containers. In boiler work the rivet holes are *drilled*, with the plates bolted in position so that a perfect matching of holes is secured. Drilling does not injure the plate metal adjoining the rivet holes, and the matching of the holes result in the driven rivet being a cylinder every cross-section of which equals the area of the rivet hole. Therefore the diameter of the rivet hole is used in computing tensile, bearing, and shearing stresses. In ordinary structural work, however, most rivet holes are *punched* (the punch being 1/16 in. larger than the diameter of the rivet), and the punching of each part is done separately. Consequently, when the various parts are assembled, the matching of the rivet holes is usually somewhat imperfect. Since this is so, the driven rivet is likely not to be a single cylinder, but to consist of two or more cylindrical portions with axes not collinear. Hence, at the planes separating poorly matched rivet holes, the cross-section of the rivet is likely to be less than the cross-section of the rivet holes. For this reason, it is customary to use the diameter of the *undriven* rivet in figuring the shearing stresses in structural joints. The same diameter is used in computing bearing stress, which in structural work is therefore definable as the load on a rivet divided by the area, td, where d now represents the diameter of the rivet before driving. In figuring tensile stress in a structural member transmitting tension, however, the practice is to deduct for a rivet hole having a diameter 1/8 in. greater than that of the undriven rivet. This allows not only for the fact that the hole is 1/16 in. larger than the rivet, but also for damage done to the plate in the punching operation.

In calculating the load that can be transmitted safely through a riveted structural connection, it is customary to assume that each rivet in a group of n rivets (as, for example, the 8 field rivets that connect the beam to the column in Fig. 94) carries $1/n$ of the load transmitted by the rivet group. This assumption is not rigidly true at low stress values, but becomes more nearly true (due to yielding) as ultimate loads are approached, and it is a satisfactory working assumption.

57. Allowable Stresses in Structural Joints. Various specifications covering the allowable stresses in riveted structural joints have been prepared at different times and by different authorities. Specifications for steel highway bridges adopted by the American Association of State Highway Officials (1935) permit the following unit stresses (pounds per square inch):

	SHEAR	BEARING
Pins and shop-driven rivets	13,500	27,000
Power-driven field rivets and turned bolts	11,000	22,500
Unfinished bolts	9,000	18,000

These specifications permit a tensile stress of 18,000 lb. per sq. in. in structural steel.

The specifications (1936) of the American Institute of Steel Construction for structural steel for buildings, referred to in Chapter III, permit the following stresses in structural joints (pounds per square inch):

| | Shear | Bearing | |
		Rivets in Double Shear	Rivets in Single Shear
Power-driven rivets, turned bolts.	15,000	40,000	32,000
Pins......................	15,000	32,000	.....
Unfinished bolts..............	10,000	25,000	20,000

These specifications allow a tensile stress of 20,000 lb. per sq. in. in structural steel.

In the highway bridge specifications a distinction is made between shop and field rivets, on the assumption that rivets can be better driven under shop conditions and can safely carry higher stresses. This distinction is disregarded in the A.I.S.C. Specifications. Both specifications make a distinction between " turned bolts " and " unfinished bolts," however. Turned bolts are bolts machined to an exact size. They are used in holes drilled to a close fit. Unfinished bolts are ordinarily used in punched holes in which the bolts fit imperfectly. Consequently, much less even bearing is secured on unfinished bolts, and allowable stresses are reduced accordingly.

The A.I.S.C. Specifications make a further distinction, as regards bearing stress, between rivets in single shear and those in double shear. Experiment has indicated that, with rivets in double shear, a bearing failure does not occur until substantially higher bearing stresses have been reached than those which cause a bearing failure of parts joined by rivets in single shear.

In general, the A.I.S.C. Specifications represent a less conservative practice than those of the American Association of State Highway Officials. This is due, in part, to the fact that conditions of service in buildings are less severe than in bridges, and in part to a feeling that former specifications were unnecessarily conservative. This difference of opinion has been referred to in Chapter III in the general discussion of allowable stresses. The greatest difference in the allowable stresses permitted by the two sets of specifications is in bearing stresses. The A.I.S.C. Specifications allow higher bearing stresses than have formerly been permitted in American practice. The increase is based in part on a study of European practice and in part on recent tests of riveted connections.

PROBLEMS

1. Two structural-steel bars are connected to one another as shown in Fig. 96. The rivets are power-driven field rivets. Find the maximum axial tension which

the connection can transmit in accordance with the A.I.S.C. stresses given in this article. (Note that *tensile* stress must be investigated at more than one section through the connection.) $\frac{7}{8}$ in. rivets. *Ans.* $P = 45,000$ lb.

2. What is the maximum axial tension permitted on the joint of Fig. 96 by the A.A.S.H.O. specifications referred to in this article?

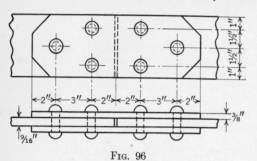

FIG. 96

58. Allowable Loads on Beam Connections. Owing to the loads on a beam, the beam pushes down on the shop rivets. This causes shearing stresses in the rivets, and bearing stresses in the rivets and in the web of the beam and in the connection angles. The field rivets, in turn, transmit the load from the connection angles to the column or other supporting member. This develops shearing stresses in the field rivets, and bearing stresses in the rivets and in the connection angles and in the supporting member. The design or investigation of a beam connection includes consideration of these various shearing and bearing stresses. There are no tensile stresses which require consideration.

Example. Calculate the allowable end reaction for a 15-in., 42.9-lb. I-beam connected to the web of a 20-in., 65.4-lb. I-beam by two 4-in.-by-3$\frac{1}{2}$-in.-by-$\frac{3}{8}$-in. angles, as shown in Fig. 97. The rivets are all $\frac{3}{4}$ in. Rivet stresses are those in the specification for steel highway bridges given in the preceding article. The rivets attaching the connection angle to the 15-in. beam are shop rivets; the others are field rivets. Web thickness of the 20-in. beam is 0.50 in.; of the 15-in. beam, 0.410 in.

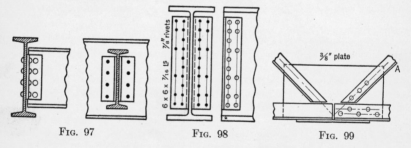

FIG. 97   FIG. 98   FIG. 99

Solution: Consider first the eight field rivets connecting the angle to the web of the deeper beam and assume the reaction to be divided equally among the eight rivets. The load which these rivets can carry will be limited by either shearing of the rivets, bearing of the rivets against the $\frac{3}{8}$-in.-thick angles, or bearing of the rivets against the 0.500-in.-thick web. It is obvious, however, that the last of these need not be computed.

The allowable loads, as limited by the first two considerations, are as follows: Shearing of 8 field rivets

$$P = 8 \times \pi/4 \times (\tfrac{3}{4})^2 \times 11,000 = 8 \times 4,860 = 38,800 \text{ lb.}$$

Bearing of 8 field rivets against $\tfrac{3}{8}$-in. angles.

$$P = 8 \times \tfrac{3}{8} \times \tfrac{3}{4} \times 22,500 = 50,640 \text{ lb.}$$

Consider next the four shop rivets connecting the angles to the web of the 15-in. beam. Assume these four rivets to be equally loaded. Each rivet bears against two angles (total thickness of $\tfrac{3}{4}$ in.) and against the web of the beam (thickness of 0.410 in.). Obviously bearing against the angles will not limit the allowable load for the connection.

The allowable load, as limited by bearing on the web of the 15-in. beam, is

$$P = 4 \times \tfrac{3}{4} \times 0.410 \times 27,000 = 33,240 \text{ lb.}$$

Each rivet is in double shear, making eight cross-sections in shear, which is the same number of shears as for the field rivets. But the unit stress allowed on the shop rivets is 13,500 lb. per sq. in., which is much more than allowed on the field rivets, and consequently the shearing value of the shop rivets will not limit the allowable load.

It is evident from the above considerations that the allowable load for the joint is limited by bearing of the shop rivets against the web of the 15-in. beam. The allowable load is therefore 33,240 lb.

PROBLEMS

1. Using the A.I.S.C. (1936) stresses, find the allowable end reaction on the beam connection of the foregoing example.

2. In the beam connection just discussed, replace the $\tfrac{3}{4}$-in. rivets with $\tfrac{7}{8}$-in. rivets and find the allowable reaction (*a*) using A.A.S.H.O. stresses, and (*b*) using A.I.S.C. stresses.

3. Where very heavy end reactions are to be resisted, the connection shown in Fig. 98 is specified by the handbook of the A.I.S.C. for wide-flanged beams 36 in. deep. A 36-in., 150-lb. beam has a web thickness of 0.625 in. If this connection is used to attach it to a column flange $1\tfrac{1}{4}$ in. thick, what is the allowable reaction in accordance with A.I.S.C. stresses?   *Ans. R = 288,000 lb.*

GENERAL PROBLEMS

1. A boiler is 80 in. in diameter and has longitudinal joints in which the repeating section is $6\tfrac{1}{4}$ in. long. The safe load (factor of safety = 5) for the repeating section is computed and found to be 26,000 lb. (*a*) What steam pressure is safe for this boiler? (*b*) If the plate of which the boiler is made is $\tfrac{7}{16}$ in. thick, what is the efficiency of the joint? (A.S.M.E. Boiler Code stresses.) *104 #/□ = 86.5%*

2. Member *A*, made of two 5-in.-by-$3\tfrac{1}{2}$-in.-by-$\tfrac{7}{16}$-in. angles as shown in Fig. 99, carries a load of 90,000 lb. How many $\tfrac{7}{8}$-in. rivets are required to connect it to the gusset plate? (A.I.S.C. stresses. Assume all rivets equally loaded.)

Ans. 5 rivets required.

3. In the foregoing problem, if the member is welded to the gusset plate, to what thickness may the angle be reduced below $\tfrac{7}{16}$ in.? What saving in weight of the member (per foot of length) results? Using the stresses of Art. 41, determine how many inches of $\tfrac{5}{16}$-in. weld should be used along each edge of each of the two angles which compose *A*.

4. Using the A.I.S.C. stresses given in Art. 57, find the allowable load P if 14-in., 78-lb. wide-flanged beams are connected to 21-in., 63-lb. wide-flanged beams through the standard connections shown in Fig. 100.   *Ans.* $P = 86,100$ lb.

5. Suppose that in the pipe of Problem 2, Art. 43, there is a longitudinal stress equal to one-half the circumferential stress. Does this change the allowable pressure in the pipe?

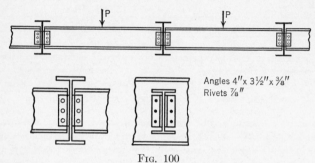

Angles 4″x 3½″x ⅜″
Rivets ⅞″

Fig. 100

6. The boom of a crane is made of two 10-in., 30-lb. channels, latticed together. It is supported on a steel pin 3 in. in diameter. The maximum load exerted on the pin by the boom is 87 tons. To reduce the bearing stress set up in the webs of the channels, each channel has a " pin plate " riveted to it as shown in Fig. 101. After riveting, the pin hole is bored through the plate and web, so as to get an even bearing on both. (*a*) If bearing in the web and plates is limited to 27,000 lb. per sq. in., what is the required thickness of each pin plate? (*b*) Available plates have thicknesses varying by sixteenths of an inch ($\frac{1}{4}$, $\frac{5}{16}$, etc.) What plate should be selected for use? (*c*). Using this plate and assuming that the same load comes on each rivet, are the six rivets shown adequate to transfer to the column the load that comes on the pin plate? Allowable stresses are 13,500 lb. per sq. in. and 27,000 lb. per sq. in. in shear and bearing, respectively.

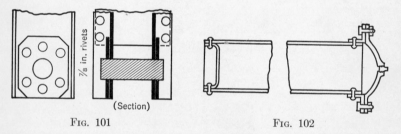

⅞ in. rivets

(Section)

Fig. 101   Fig. 102

7. A piece of standard 16-in. pipe (inside diameter 15.25 in. and outside diameter 16.00 in.) 12 ft. long is to be made into a gas container by riveting a head into one end and a flange $\frac{3}{4}$ in. thick onto the other end, to which a cast cover is bolted, as shown in Fig. 102. Allowable stresses are: tension, 10,000 lb. per sq. in.; shearing 8,000 lb. per sq. in.; bearing, 14,000 lb. per sq. in. What gas pressure is allowable for the pipe (assuming that the ends are made strong enough)? With this pressure, how many $\frac{15}{16}$-in. rivets should be used to attach the flange to the pipe? How many $1\frac{1}{4}$-in. bolts to attach the cover to the flange?   *Ans.* 21 rivets required.

8. A tensile load of 105,000 lb. is applied along the centroidal axis of an 8-in. $\times$ 6-in. $\times \frac{7}{16}$-in. angle, which is welded to a plate as shown in Fig. 103. To minimize the lengths L_1 and L_2, a fillet is applied along the 8-in. end of the angle. What lengths of L_1 and L_2 will result in a load of 4,000 lb. per in. along the fillet?

$L_1 = 14.2 \qquad L_2 = 4.05$

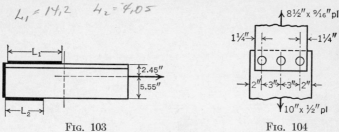

FIG. 103   FIG. 104

9. Two plates are connected by three rivets as shown in Fig. 104. Rivet holes are $\frac{7}{8}$ in. in diameter. What load, P, is allowable? The factor of safety is to be 5, and the ultimate strengths are: tensile, 55,000 lb. per sq. in.; shearing, 44,000 lb. per sq. in.; bearing, 95,000 lb. per sq. in.

CHAPTER VI

TORSIONAL STRESS, SHAFTS AND HELICAL SPRINGS

59. Introduction. In all the stressed bodies considered up to this point, the equation

$$\text{Unit stress} = \frac{\text{Force}}{\text{Area}}$$

has been used to give the stress intensity. In some of the situations considered, this equation gives very nearly the true stress at any point of the stressed area; that is, the stress is very nearly uniform. It holds for an eyebar, at a section well away from the "heads." In other situations the assumed relationship is not true, but in connection with appropriate allowable stresses it forms a practical basis for satisfactory design. "Bearing" stresses in riveted joints illustrate this. There are, however, many important situations where the stress is known to vary from nothing at all at some point or points of the cross-section of a member, to a maximum value at some other point or points. As applied to situations of this sort, the above equation has no useful meaning and some other relationship must be developed.

Fig. 105

The torsional stress that occurs on the cross-section of a round bar subjected to twisting moments or torques is an example of this non-uniform stress distribution.

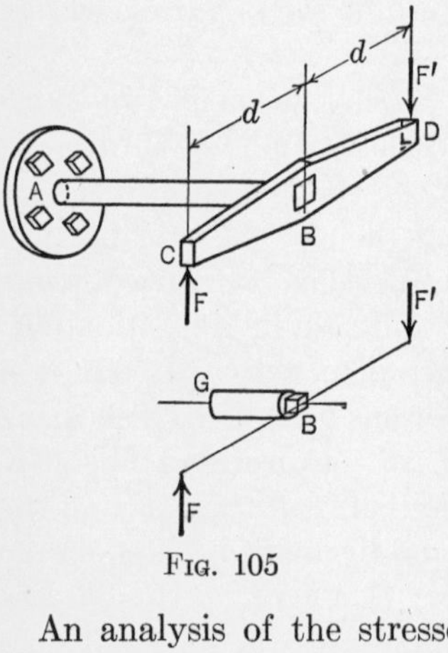

60. Torsion. Let AB in Fig. 105 represent a round bar of steel rigidly fastened to a fixed support at A so that it cannot turn and with a square end at B on which is fitted a bar CD. If the two forces, F and F', are equal and opposite, they do not bend AB.

An analysis of the stresses resulting from this torque can be made by the free-body method. Imagine a plane perpendicular to the axis of AB cutting AB at any point, G, between A and B. Consider the part of the bar from B to this plane as a free body in equilibrium. The body is evidently subjected to a moment of $2 Fd$ with respect to its geometrical axis. Since the body is in equilibrium, evidently an opposite moment must be exerted on the body. This moment must be exerted

84

by forces which act on the cut surface of the bar and which act *in the plane* of the cut surface. Therefore these forces result from shearing stresses. The name *torsional stress* is given to shearing stress caused in this way. The moment of the torsional stresses is called a *resisting torque*. From the equilibrium of the free body it is evident that

Resisting torque = External torque

This relation holds true whether the shaft to which the torque is applied is stationary as shown in Fig. 105, or whether it is rotating at uniform speed under equal and opposite torques applied to it by driving and driven pulleys or equivalent mechanisms.[1]

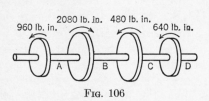

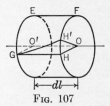

Fig. 106   Fig. 107

61. Distribution of Torsional Stress. It has been stated that the stress distribution in torsion is not uniform over the cross-section; that is, the unit stress in pounds per square inch is not the same at all points. That this is true, and the way in which the unit stress varies, will be evident from the discussion which follows.

Let the cylinder shown in Fig. 107 be part of a shaft between two transverse planes E and F. GH is an element of the cylindrical surface extending from plane E to plane F. Now if the shaft is subjected to a torque, stresses and deformations result and each of these planes will rotate relative to the other. If plane E is regarded as being fixed, plane F will rotate slightly so that the radius OH will assume a position OH' and the element GH will become GH', part of a helix. If GH is a " fiber " of the material in the shaft, this fiber has been given a shearing distortion and the unit deformation is HH'/dl. Consider a fiber JK (not shown) parallel to the axis and half way between the axis and the surface. It has been shown by experiment and by analysis based on the theory of elasticity that any radius such as OH *remains a straight line* as the shaft is twisted, provided the maximum stress in the shaft does not exceed the proportional limit. Therefore, the distortion of this

---

[1] The amount of torque, or torsional moment, existing on any cross-section of a shaft equals the algebraic sum of the torques applied to that part of the shaft on either side of the cross-section in question. For example, for the shaft shown in Fig. 106, the torques on the cross-sections A, B, C, and D are 960 lb-in., 1,120 lb-in., 640 lb-in., and 0 lb-in., respectively.

fiber, JK, is half as much and the unit deformation half as great as that of GH'. If the material obeys Hooke's law, and if all the stresses are below the proportional limit, the shearing unit stress in the fiber JK is half as great as the shearing unit stress in the fiber GH. By this reasoning the conclusion is reached that the shearing unit stress is proportional to the distance from the geometrical axis of the cylinder. Therefore the law of distribution of stress caused by torsion may be stated thus:

The shearing stress is zero at the geometrical axis of the shaft and increases in direct proportion to the distance from the geometric axis. It is, therefore, a maximum in the fibers at the outer surface of the cylinder.

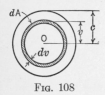

FIG. 108

Starting with this law of stress variation it is possible to establish a relation between the shearing unit stress in the outermost fibers, the torque, and the size of the cross-section. With such a relation, it will be possible to compute any one of the three quantities if the other two are given.

Consider a short length of a shaft as a free body. Fig. 108 shows the circular cross-section at one end of this part. The resisting torque of the stresses on this cross-section is equal to the torque T exerted by the external forces twisting the shaft. Let the unit stress in any fiber at the surface of the shaft $= S_s$. Let dA be a differential area in the form of a narrow ring of radius v. Applying the above law of stress variation, the unit stress at $dA = \dfrac{v}{c} S_s$. The force exerted by the stress over the

area $dA = \dfrac{v}{c} S_s dA$. The moment of this force with respect to the axis of

the shaft $= v \times$ the force, $= \dfrac{v^2}{c} S_s dA$. The sum of the moments of all

the stresses on the entire cross-section is

$$\int_0^c \frac{v^2}{c} S_s dA = \frac{S_s}{c} \int_0^c v^2 dA = \frac{S_s}{c} J$$

where J is the polar moment of inertia[1] of the circle with respect to a

perpendicular axis through the center. $\dfrac{S_s}{c} J$ is the resisting torque and

equals the external torque, T. We therefore have the relation

$$T = \frac{S_s}{c} J \quad \text{or} \quad S_s = \frac{Tc}{J}$$

[1] See Appendix B for discussion of moments of inertia.

in which S_s is the shearing unit stress in the outside fibers (pounds per square inch); T is the torque on the shaft (pound-inches); c is the outside radius of the shaft (inches); J is the polar moment of inertia of the cross-section (inches^4). These formulas apply to solid or hollow circular shafts. J for the cross-section of a hollow shaft is found by subtracting J for a circle of the inside diameter from J for a circle of the outside diameter. The polar moment of inertia for a circle with respect to an axis through the center is $\pi r^4/2$ or $\pi d^4/32$ in.^{4}

If the torque and stress in extreme fibers are given and the size of shaft is to be determined, the value of J/c is calculated. J/c is a function of the dimensions of the cross-sections, and the size of a solid or hollow shaft having the required J/c may be computed.[1]

It should be kept in mind that the stress given by the above formula is that due to torsion alone. Shafting is usually subject to other forces besides axial torque at the ends. Transverse loads (such as weight of shaft itself and of pulleys, and tensions in belts) cause bending stresses which may be serious. Sometimes axial stresses are also present. In such cases as these the torsional stress must be computed and combined with other stresses. The combination of these stresses is treated in Chapter XV.

Example. What torque will cause a stress of 10,000 lb. per sq. in. in the extreme fibers of a shaft 5 in. in diameter?

Solution: The polar moment of inertia of a circle is $\pi r^4/2$.

$$T = \frac{S_s J}{c} = \frac{10{,}000 \times \dfrac{\pi \times 2.5^4}{2}}{2.5} = 245{,}500 \text{ lb-in.}$$

PROBLEMS

1. Solve the example above if the shaft is hollow, with an inside diameter of 2 in. What is the stress at the inner surface of the shaft?

2. Calculate the diameter of a solid steel shaft to transmit a torque of 30,000 lb-ft., with a unit stress of 10,000 lb. per sq. in.

$5.68''$

[1] The external torque is applied to torsion members in many different ways. Couplings or pulleys may be shrunk onto the shaft or attached by set screws or made in two parts which are bolted together and which grip the shaft firmly when the nuts are tightened. A " key " fitting in a slot in the shaft and in the pulley or coupling (Fig. 115) is one of the most widely used fastenings. The keyway in a shaft causes increased stresses on cross-sections through the keyway. The Code for the Design of Transmission Shafting of the A.S.M.E. specifies that the allowable torque on a shaft with a keyway shall be 25 per cent below that on the same shaft if there is no keyway. Forged shafting is sometimes " upset " at the ends so that slots or keyways cut in the enlarged section do not weaken the shaft.

3. A heavy monitor window is to be opened by a rack-and-pinion device. The maximum force which the pinion must exert is 150 lb. applied at a distance of 3 in. from the axis of the shaft, as shown in Fig. 109. The pinion and the hand wheel at the lower end of the shaft will be " shrunk " onto the shaft, there being no keyways or other devices to weaken the shaft. What should the shaft diameter be if the torsional stress is not to exceed 8,000 lb. per sq. in.?

4. What should be the diameter of the stem of the wrench shown in Fig. 110 if the maximum torsional stress in it is not to exceed 10,000 lb. per sq. in., each of the forces P being 50 lb.?

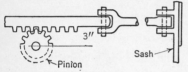
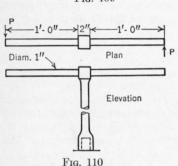

Fig. 109

$Ans.$ $d = 0.872$ in.

5. In Fig. 111, AB is a shaft carrying pulleys C and D. The bearings which support the shaft are not shown. The shaft is driven by pulley D and turns pulley C. $T_1 = 400$ lb.; $T_2 = 80$ lb.; $T_4 = 70$ lb. What is the tension T_3? The

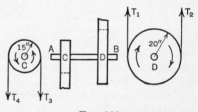

Fig. 110

Fig. 111

diameter of the shaft is 3 in. What is the unit stress at the surface of the shaft?

6. Show that the weight of a hollow shaft having an internal diameter equal to half the external diameter is only 78.1 per cent of the weight of a solid shaft which will transmit the same torque with the same maximum stress.

62. Angle of Twist.

In the design of certain types of machinery it is important to be able to calculate the angle of twist that is caused in a shaft of given length by the torque.

The cylinder shown in Fig. 112 is part of a shaft subject to a torque which is the same for all sections. AB represents an element of the cylindrical surface of the untwisted shaft, and AB' the curve (part of a helix) which this same element assumes after the torque is applied. A horizontal radius OB on the end which rotates assumes a position OB' after the torque is applied. The angle BOB' is the angle of twist for which a value will be found.

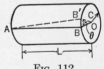

Fig. 112

Let this angle of twist, expressed in *radians*, be θ.

The deformation of a " fiber " at the surface of the shaft is shearing deformation. For the fiber represented by AB the total deformation in the length L inches is BB'. The unit deformation ϕ, is BB'/L. But $BB' = c\theta$ if θ is expressed in radians. Also $\phi = S_s/E_s$. Hence

$$\frac{c\theta}{L} = \frac{S_s}{E_s} \quad \text{or} \quad \theta = \frac{S_sL}{E_sc}$$

which gives the angle of twist in terms of the stress in the extreme fibers.

But $S_s = \dfrac{Tc}{J}$. Then $\theta = \dfrac{TcL}{E_sJc} = \dfrac{TL}{E_sJ}$, which gives the angle of twist in terms of the torque.

As would be expected, the longer the shaft and the greater the torque, the greater will be the angle of twist. On the contrary, the stiffer the material and the larger the cross-section, the smaller will be the angle of twist. For steel, E_s is 12,000,000 lb. per sq. in., as stated in Art. 7.

PROBLEMS

1. Compute the length of a $\frac{1}{4}$-in. steel wire that can be twisted through one revolution without exceeding a torsional stress of 20,000 lb. per sq. in. *p72*

2. A hollow shaft has a length of 40 in., an inside diameter of 2 in., and an outside diameter of 3 in. A force of 520 lb. with a moment arm of 5 ft. twists the shaft through 1°. (a) Find S_s and E_s. (b) What torque would be required to stress a solid shaft with 3-in. diameter to the unit stress found in (a), and through what angle would this torque twist the solid shaft if 40 in. long?

$S_s = 7,330$ *Ans.* (a) $E_s = 11,200,000$ lb. per sq. in.

3. A bar of hot-rolled steel $\frac{3}{4}$ in. in diameter was tested in a torsion testing machine. When the applied torque was 2,920 lb-in. the angle of twist in a length of 6 in. was 2.7°. Find the shearing modulus of elasticity of the material.

4. If a $\frac{3}{4}$-in.-diameter rod is used for the shaft in Problem 3, Art. 61, through what angle will the shaft be twisted when the 150-lb. force acts on the pinion, if the length of the shaft is 60 ft., 0 in.?

63. Torsional Stress on Axial Planes.

In Art. 35 it was shown that, if a shearing unit stress of any intensity exists on a plane through some point of a stressed body, a shearing unit stress of equal intensity must exist on a perpendicular plane. Therefore, since there is shearing stress on the cross-section of a shaft subjected to torsion, there must also be shearing stresses on all planes that contain the axis of the shaft.

FIG. 113

Fig. 113 makes this clear. It shows an enlarged view of a small particle of material taken from the surface of a twisted shaft. On the horizontal faces of this particle, there are shearing forces acting in the directions shown. For equilibrium of the particle, it is therefore necessary that there be shearing forces on the vertical faces. These forces will constitute an opposing couple.

Suppose that a shaft is thought of as being composed of a " bundle " of elements or fibers side by side. Then, if the shaft is acted on by a torque and undergoes a shearing deformation, these elements *tend* to slide past one another. This tendency is resisted by the longitudinal shearing stress.[1]

PROBLEM

In an agitator where chemical action on metal parts would be injurious, a round shaft which must resist a torque of 600 lb-in. is to be made of wood. For material of select grade, it may be assumed that the allowable stresses for shear parallel to the grain (horizontal shear) as given in Table XI may be increased 25 per cent. What will be the necessary diameter if the shaft is made of (a) spruce; (b) hickory?

64. Horsepower, Torque, and Speed of Rotation.

If a torque turns a shaft, work is done by the torque. A torque of T' lb-ft. is equivalent to the torque exerted by a force of T' lb. at a radius of 1 ft. The work done in one revolution is

$$\text{Force} \times \text{Distance} = T' \times 2\,\pi \text{ lb-ft.}$$

If the shaft turns N r.p.m., the work done per minute equals $2\,\pi T'N$ lb-ft., and the horsepower equals $2\,\pi T'N/33,000$. Note that in this expression T' is the torque in *pound-feet*. If the torque T is found in pound-inches by the formulas previously given, it must be changed to pound-feet to get T' for use in the horsepower formula.

Example. A torque of 18,000 lb-in. is transmitted by a shaft turning 220 r.p.m. What horsepower is being transmitted by the shaft?
Solution: T', the torque in pound-feet, $= 18,000/12 = 1,500$.

$$\text{Hp.} = \frac{2\,\pi \times 1,500 \times 220}{33,000} = 62.8$$

PROBLEMS

1. A hollow steel shaft has an outside diameter of 4 in. and an inside diameter of 2 in. What horsepower does it transmit if when turning at 80 r.p.m. it is twisted through an angle of $1\frac{8}{10}°$ in a length of 9 ft.? $1\ 05$

2. What is the diameter of a solid shaft which transmits the same horsepower at the same speed and with the same angle of twist as the shaft in Problem 1?

3. Derive an expression giving the horsepower, H, transmitted by a solid round shaft of diameter, d, when turning at N r.p.m. with a maximum shearing stress of S_s lb. per sq. in.

$$\textit{Ans.} \quad H = NS_s d^3/321,000.$$

[1] This tendency can be made very apparent if a number of small, slender, flexible rods are bound together side by side, to form a round bundle and the ends are then grasped by the hands and twisted oppositely.

4. Plot a curve having as abscissas rotational speeds of shafting in revolutions per minute and as ordinates the required diameter of a solid shaft to transmit 50 hp. without exceeding a torsional stress of 8,000 lb. per sq. in. Let the speed vary from 16 to 16,000 r.p.m. (Scales: 1 in. = 2 in.; 1 in. = 4,000 r.p.m.)

5. The hollow steel shafts for the 82,500-kva. generators at Boulder Dam have a minimum external diameter of 38 in. and an internal diameter of $7\frac{1}{2}$ in. They transmit 115,000 hp. when turning at a speed of 150 r.p.m. What is the maximum torsional stress developed in the shafts? *4,485*

65. Shaft Couplings. It is often necessary to connect two pieces of shafting end to end so that they act as a single shaft. A common type of connection is known as a " flange coupling." Large-diameter shafting is sometimes forged with flanges at the ends. The flanges at the ends of two lengths of shafting are bolted together by a number of bolts arranged in a circle as shown in Fig. 114.

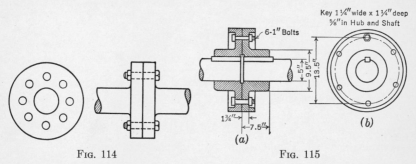

Fig. 114   Fig. 115

A more common type of coupling is not forged as part of the shaft but may be attached to the ends of two pieces of plain shafting which are to be joined. Each half of the coupling consists of a casting or forging combining a " flange " and a " hub." The hub is bored to fit the shaft. The shaft is " keyed " to the hub to prevent either one turning independently of the other. This is effected by a steel " key " (a rectangular prism of steel) which is inserted in keyways in the hub and shaft. For large shafting more than one key is generally used. Fig. 115 illustrates a flange coupling for 5-in. shafting. The two flanges are bolted together with six bolts. Each hub is keyed to its shaft with one key.

If the left-hand piece of shafting is assumed to be held from turning and a torque is assumed to be applied to the right-hand piece it is obvious that the coupling is called upon to transmit this torque from the right-hand piece to the left-hand piece of shafting. Let it be assumed that the torque is increased until failure occurs. It will be seen that failure might occur in any one of seven different ways, and each of these possible ways of failure should be considered if the joint is to be investigated. These possible ways of failure are:

1. Shearing of the six bolts on the plane between two flanges.
2. Compression (or bearing) on the surface of contact between the bolts and either flange.
3. Shearing of the metal along the area where the flange meets the hub. (The area is a cylindrical surface the thickness of the flange and the circumference of the hub.)
4. Bearing between the key and the hub.
5. Shearing of the key on the surface between the shaft and the hub.
6. Bearing between the key and the shaft.
7. Shearing of the shaft at a cross-section through the keyway.

An exact analysis of most of the unit stresses occurring in the various parts of a coupling of this sort is impossible. Common practice is to calculate stresses (except for item 7) as though they were uniformly distributed, using the methods shown in the following example. The results so obtained are satisfactory if used in connection with suitable allowable stresses.

Example. The flange coupling for 5-in.-diameter shafting (shown in Fig. 115) is subject to a torque of 245,500 lb-in. Calculate the stresses which result in the coupling.

Solution: Shearing unit stress in bolts: The torque of 245,500 lb-in. must be transmitted by the bolts. Since the radius of the bolt circle is 6.75 in., the total force exerted by the bolts is 245,500/6.75 = 36,400 lb. Each bolt exerts a force of 36,400/6 = 6,070 lb., and the unit shearing stress is 6070/0.785 = 7,730 lb. per sq. in.

Bearing unit stress between bolts and flange equals the force on each bolt divided by the product of the thickness of the flange and the diameter of the bolt.

$$S_c = \frac{6070}{1.75} = 3,470 \text{ lb. per sq. in.}$$

Shearing stress between flange and hub: The total shearing force is the torque divided by the external radius of the hub, or $F = 245,500/4.75 = 51,500$ lb. The area resisting this shearing force is the cylindrical surface 9.5 in. in diameter and 1.75 in. long. The shearing stress,

$$S_s = \frac{51,500}{1.75 \times 29.84} = 990 \text{ lb. per sq. in.}$$

Shearing stress in key: The total force exerted by the shearing resistance of the key is $F = 245,500/2.5 = 98,200$ lb. This, divided by the shear area of the key, gives the shearing unit stress

$$S_s = \frac{98,200}{1.25 \times 7.5} = 10,470 \text{ lb. per sq. in.}$$

Bearing stress between key and hub: The force which the shaft exerts against the key and the force which the key exerts against the hub of the coupling are equal to the shearing force in the key calculated above.[1] The bearing area between the key and hub is the product of the length of the hub and the depth of the keyway in the hub. Therefore,

$$S_c = \frac{98,200}{7.5 \times 0.625} = 21,000 \text{ lb. per sq. in.}$$

The bearing stress between the key and the shaft is the same as that calculated above between the key and the hub. This is true because the areas in contact are the same and the forces are the same.

Shearing of shaft at reduced section: Determination of stress in a shaft on a cross-section through a keyway has only been made experimentally.[2]

[1] This must be true since the key is in equilibrium and the sum of the horizontal forces on it is zero.

It may seem that the force which the key exerts against the shaft must be greater than the force which the key exerts against the hub since the distance from the axis of the shaft to the force against the shaft is less than the distance to the force against the hub and the torque transmitted is, of course, the same. This apparent inconsistency disappears when it is realized that there must be other forces acting on the key to prevent it from turning. These may be as shown in Fig. 116a. The torque

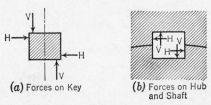

(a) Forces on Key   (b) Forces on Hub and Shaft

Fig. 116

which the key exerts on the shaft is the *sum* of the torques exerted by the forces H and V shown in (b) of Fig. 116. The torque exerted by the key on the hub is the *difference* between the torque exerted by the forces H and V on the hub. Hence the two horizontal forces may be equal and at different distances from the axis of the shaft and still the torques may be equal.

This analysis assumes that the key is a close fit in the keyway, so that forces can act normally on the top and bottom as well as on the sides. This is very often not the case, a small clearance existing between the top of the key and the hub. In this situation the forces on the key are more complex, but the reasoning is basically the same.

[2] Professor H. F. Moore has derived (see Bulletin 42, Eng'g. Exp't. Sta., Univ. of Illinois) the following relationship between the strengths at elastic limit of a shaft with a keyway and a shaft without: $e = 1.0 - 0.2\,w - 1.1\,h$. In this expression w and h are the width and depth, respectively, of the keyway, divided by the shaft diameter. The quantity e is a factor by which the allowable shearing stress in a shaft without a keyway should be multiplied to give the allowable shearing stress in a shaft of the same material which has a keyway. This formula indicates that the strength of the shaft in the above example is reduced 19 per cent by the keyway cut in it.

PROBLEMS

1. The allowable shearing unit stress in a solid steel shaft 10 in. in diameter is 8,000 lb. per sq. in. (*a*) What horsepower can it transmit at 120 r.p.m.? The flange couplings of this shaft have ten $1\frac{5}{8}$-in.-diameter bolts whose centers lie on a circle $26\frac{3}{4}$ in. in diameter. (*b*) What is the average shearing stress in the bolts?

2. The coupling in Problem 1 is keyed to the shaft with two keys, each 2 in. by 2 in. in cross-section and 15 in. long. The keys are sunk 1 in. in the shaft. Find the shearing and bearing unit stresses in the keys.

66. Helical Springs. Helical springs are widely used for two purposes: for exerting forces in certain mechanisms and for their " cushioning " effect.

The stress on any cross-section of a helical spring is a shearing stress, and of this shearing stress the greater part is torsional stress. The load on such springs is nearly always axial (the resultant coinciding with the axis of the spring as a whole) as shown in Fig. 117.

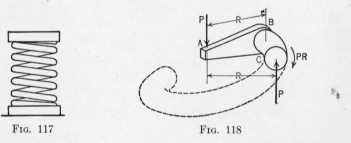

FIG. 117   FIG. 118

Fig. 118 shows a small length of a helical spring and the axial load P on the spring. The load is here shown attached to this small length of spring by means of a lever arm AB, although generally the end of the spring itself is bent into a hook or a plate rests against the end of the spring as in Fig. 117. In any case the remainder of the spring must exert on any small length, such as the one here shown, a vertical force P and a torque or couple PR. Both the force and the torque cause shearing stress.

The torsional shearing stress is Tc/J. The shearing stress due to the force P on the cross-section is P/A. The maximum shearing stress on the cross-section is therefore $S_s = \dfrac{P}{A} + \dfrac{Tc}{J}$. For springs made of wire of solid circular cross-section $J = \pi r^4/2$ and $c = r$. Since $T = PR$, the equation just above reduces to

$$S = \frac{P}{A}\left(1 + \frac{2R}{r}\right)$$

Example. A helical spring is made of $\frac{1}{2}$-in.-diameter steel wire bent into coils with a diameter of 2 in., center to center of wire. What load applied axially to the spring will cause a maximum shearing stress of 10,000 lb. per sq. in.? How much will the torsional shearing stress be? The " direct " shearing stress?

Solution: For this spring $A = \pi(\frac{1}{4})^2 = \pi/16$ sq. in.

$$P = \frac{AS_s}{1 + (2\,R/r)} = \frac{10,000\,\pi/16}{1 + (2 \times 1/0.25)} = 218\,\text{lb.}$$

Of the 10,000 lb. per sq. in. stress, $\frac{8}{9}$ or 8,890 lb. per sq. in., is due to torsion and the remaining 1,110 lb. per sq. in. is due to the direct shearing effect of the load.

In *this* example a considerable part of the stress is due directly to the load rather than to its torsional effect. In springs where the ratio R/r is larger, however, the direct shearing stress is often negligible in comparison with the torsional shearing stress and is disregarded.

PROBLEM

What maximum shearing stress is caused in the steel spring (Fig. 119) by the loads of 1,000 lb. each? What percentage of this stress is due to torsion? *16,543 p.s.i.* *92.2%*

67. Deflection of Helical Springs. If in Fig. 118 the cut cross-section shown at C is assumed to be fixed so that it neither rotates nor moves vertically, the motion of point A will be due to the shearing deformation of the rod between B and C. Practically all this motion will be due to the *twist* of the rod, and little to the direct effect of P. Therefore disregarding the movement due to direct shear, if the length BC of the rod is twisted through an angle θ, the vertical movement of A will be $R\theta$.

For a circular shaft

$$\theta = \frac{TL}{E_s J}$$

If BC is dL,

$$d\theta = \frac{PR\,dL}{E_s J}$$

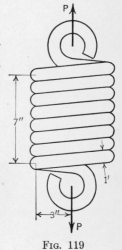

FIG. 119

and for a spring made of a number of coils in which the total length of wire is L

$$\theta = \frac{PRL}{E_s J}$$

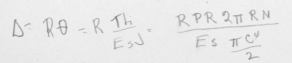

$\Delta = R\theta = R\dfrac{TL}{E_s J} = \dfrac{R \cdot PR \cdot 2\pi R N}{E_s \cdot \dfrac{\pi c^4}{2}}$

and the axial shortening or extension is

$$\Delta = R\theta = \frac{PR^2L}{E_sJ}$$

It is customary to neglect the slope of the wire in calculating the length of a spring of N complete turns. If this is done,

$$L = 2\pi NR \quad \text{and} \quad \Delta = \frac{2\pi PR^3N}{E_sJ}$$

PROBLEMS

1. Using the equations given above, find the increase in the length of the steel spring (Fig. 119) which includes seven turns, when the 1,000-lb. loads are applied. What is the value of θ for this part of the spring? $\Delta=1.01\ m$ $3.36\ rad.$

2. Show that the lengthening (or compression) of a helical spring due to direct as well as torsional shear is given by the equation

$$\Delta = \frac{2\pi PRN}{E_sA}\left[1 + 2\left(\frac{R}{r}\right)^2\right]$$

3. Using the equation of Problem 2, show what error results from disregard of the effect of direct shear in stretching the spring of Problem 1.

68. Torsion in Bars of Non-Circular Cross-Section.

When a bar of non-circular cross-section is acted on by torsional forces, the section cut by a plane perpendicular to the axis of the untwisted bar does not

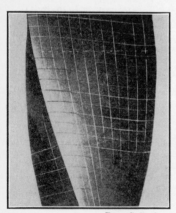

From C. Bach

Fig. 120

remain a plane when the bar is subjected to torsion, but becomes a warped surface. This may easily be demonstrated by scribing a straight line on the surface of a square bar and perpendicular to its length. When the bar is twisted, the straight line assumes a reversed curvature (Fig. 120). The transverse plane section of the untwisted bar which contained this line has evidently become a warped surface.

The torsional (shearing) stress is not uniformly distributed over this warped surface. This is easily demonstrated experimentally by scribing a series of small squares on the side of a bar of square cross-section and then twisting the bar. Fig. 120 shows how the various squares are deformed by the twisting. Those adjacent to the edges of the bar are least deformed; those midway between the edges of the face of the bar are most deformed. Since the shearing unit stress is proportional to the shearing deformation, it is evidently greatest along the median line of the face. At the edges of the bar, it is zero. If the cross-section of the bar is rectangular but not square, the unit shearing stress at the middle of the wide face is greater than at the middle of the narrow face. That is, the greatest shearing stress occurs at that point of the surface which is nearest the axis of the bar. (See Fig. 121.)

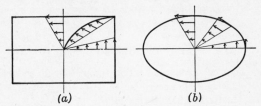

(a)   *(b)*

Fɪɢ. 121. Shearing stress on non-circular shafts.

The equation giving the maximum torsional stress in a bar of rectangular cross-section is very cumbersome. An empirical equation proposed by Saint Venant is $S_s = \dfrac{(15\,h + 9\,b)T}{5\,h^2 b^2}$, where h and b are the lengths of the long and short sides of the rectangle, respectively.[1] This equation gives values which are correct within 4 per cent. For a square shaft, it reduces to $S_s = \dfrac{24\,T}{5\,b^3}$.

Analysis of the stress distribution over the cross-section of a bar of elliptical cross-section that is subjected to torsion shows that the maximum stress (which is at the ends of the short axis) is $S_s = \left(\dfrac{a^2 + b^2}{2\,b^2}\right)\dfrac{Tb}{J}$, where a and b are the long and short semi-axes, respectively, and J is the polar moment of inertia of the cross-section of the bar with respect to a centroidal axis.

PROBLEM

A valve stem with a diameter of $\frac{1}{2}$ in. has its end machined down as shown in Fig. 122 to receive the hand wheel. Disregarding local stresses due to the change in

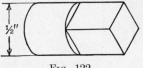

$\frac{1}{2}''$

Fɪɢ. 122

section, what is the maximum torsional stress on the square cross-section when the maximum stress on the round cross-section is 5,000 lb. per sq. in.? What is the ratio of the two stresses?

[1] A. Morley, " Strength of Materials."

GENERAL PROBLEMS

1. The hollow vertical shaft connecting the turbine and electric generator in a hydroelectric plant is 16 in. in outside diameter and 9 in. in inside diameter. The speed is 120 r.p.m. When it transmits 10,000 hp., what is the unit stress? Calculate the diameter required for a solid shaft to transmit the same horsepower at the same speed and with the same unit stress. If the solid shaft costs 11 cents per pound and the hollow shaft costs 14 cents per pound, compare the cost per linear foot of the two shafts.   *7,250 #/in   D=15.45 in   s are $4.50*

2. Find the ratio of the weight of a hollow shaft with an internal diameter equal to three-fourths the external diameter to that of a solid shaft that transmits the same torque with the same maximum stress.   *Ans.* ratio = 0.564 : 1.

3. The 4-in.-diameter shaft shown in Fig. 123 carries a flywheel which has an I of 270 ft.^{2}-slugs and which rotates at 300 r.p.m. The brake is suddenly applied, stopping the flywheel in 20 revolutions, the machine having been thrown out of gear before the brake is applied. Friction in the bearings may be neglected. What is the maximum torsional stress in the shaft, and where is it found?

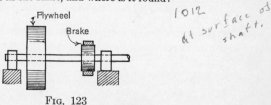

1012 at surface of shaft.

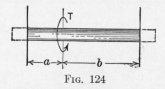

Fig. 123

4. A torque T is applied to a round bar, both ends of which are fixed as shown in Fig. 124. Find, in terms of T, a, b, and the diameter d of the bar, the maximum torsional stress produced. In which length of the bar (a or b) is it found? (*Hint:* Evidently the two parts of the bar undergo the same twist.)

Fig. 124

5. In Problem 4, derive an expression for the angle of twist, θ, in terms of T, E_s, a, b, and d.

6. Compare the weights of solid shafts of steel and aluminum alloy designed so that both will have the same angle of twist in a given length when transmitting the same torque. (For aluminum alloy $E_s = 3,700,000$ lb. per sq. in.)

7. The clutch pedal assembly of the 1936 Plymouth automobile includes a small, close-coiled steel spring made of 40 turns of wire with a diameter of 0.083 in. The outside diameter of the coil is $\frac{5}{8}$ in. The length of the unstretched coil is $3\frac{1}{2}$ in. In use, the length of the coil varies from $4\frac{3}{4}$ in. to 6 in. (*a*) What is the maximum torsional stress in the coil? (*b*) If $E_s = 12,000,000$ lb. per sq. in., what are the maximum and minimum forces exerted on the spring when in use?   *67,700*   *n 8, 14*

8. A handbook formula which has been very widely used for determining the proper diameter of line shafting well supported in bearings is: $d = \sqrt[3]{40\ H/N}$, in which d = shaft diameter in inches, H = horsepower transmitted, and N = r.p.m.

of shaft. (*a*) Show whether or not this equation is rational. (*b*) On what value for torsional stress is it based? *Ans.* (*b*) S_s = 8,025 lb. per sq. in.

9. In the mechanism shown in Fig. 125, the pull, *P*, must overcome a resistance of 500 lb. The pins at *A* and *B* have a diameter of $\frac{1}{4}$ in. and are made of steel which may be assumed to have 80 per cent of the shearing strength of the shaft steel. The arms are shrunk onto the shaft. What should be the diameter of the shaft in order that it may have a factor of safety against shear 25 per cent greater than that of the pins? (The shaft is supported in bearings not shown.)

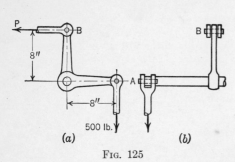

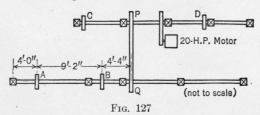

FIG. 125   FIG. 126

10. A steel pipe is to be used as a standard to support a signboard with the dimensions shown in Fig. 126. Maximum wind pressure against the board is assumed to be 45 lb. per sq. ft. Twisting of the pipe must not allow the lower support of the sign to rotate through more than 6°, and the torsional stress in the standard is not to exceed 5,000 lb. per sq. in. What size pipe should be used?

11. Fig. 127 shows two lines of shafting which are driven at 260 r.p.m. by a motor that delivers 20 hp. This power is taken from the shafts as follows: At *A* and at *C*, 6 hp.; at *B* and at *D*, 4 hp. Each shaft is 2 in. in diameter. (*a*) What is the maximum torsional stress in either shaft, and where does it occur? (*b*) What is the maximum torsional stress between *C* and *P*? (*c*) What is the maximum torsional stress between *A* and *B*? (*d*) What is the maximum torsional stress to the right of *Q*? (*e*) Through what angle is the shaft twisted between *Q* and the left end of the longer shaft when running at full load?

FIG. 127

12. A steam turbine is to deliver 5 hp. at 20,000 r.p.m. The allowable shearing stress in the shaft is 5,000 lb. per sq. in. What is the required shaft diameter?
Ans. *d* = 0.252 in.

13. If the maximum allowable angle of twist in a shaft is 1° in a length equal to 15 times the diameter, what is the diameter of a steel shaft that will transmit 18 hp. at 120 r.p.m.? What is the maximum shearing unit stress in the shaft?

14. Two 1-in. shafts, approximately in line, are joined by a Hooke's joint with dimensions as shown in Fig. 128. The maximum allowable shearing unit stress in the shafts is 6,000 lb. per sq. in. What is the average shearing unit stress in each connection bolt?

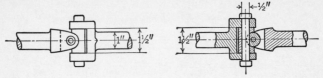

FIG. 128

15. As noted in Art. 61 (footnote), the allowable stress in a shaft with a keyway is sometimes specified to be 25 per cent less than that in a shaft without one. According to the formula given in Art. 65 (footnote), what values of w and h will weaken a shaft 25 per cent, if $w = 2 h$?

CHAPTER VII

BEAMS — SHEAR AND BENDING MOMENT

69. Introduction. A beam is a structural member or machine part which carries transverse loads. Most beams are prisms with the loads perpendicular to the axis, and such beams will be considered in this chapter. A diagrammatic representation of a beam is shown in Fig. 129. The supporting forces of the beams are called " reactions " (indicated by R_L and R_R in the diagram). The amounts of these reactions are such as to satisfy the conditions of static equilibrium $\Sigma H = 0$, $\Sigma V = 0$, and $\Sigma M = 0$. If the load P is shifted to another position the reactions will change in amount, as required for equilibrium.

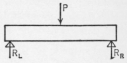

FIG. 129.   Simple beam.

70. Types of Beams. A *simple* beam is one which rests on two supports and carries any system of loads *between* the supports. The beam in Fig. 129 is a simple beam carrying a single concentrated load.

A *cantilever* beam is one which projects beyond the supports and carries loads which are not between the supports. Cantilever beams are generally represented as being built into a wall or mass of masonry at one end (Fig. 130a). When built into a wall, the wall exerts two

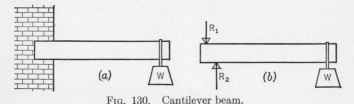

FIG. 130.   Cantilever beam.

reactions which are distributed, but the resultants of which act like R_1 and R_2 in Fig. 130b. Although this is the conventional method of representing a cantilever beam, it should be noted that the definition does not limit this type of beam to one built in a wall in this manner. The reactions may be provided by a wide variety of means. The essential feature is that a cantilever beam projects beyond its support and is loaded on the projecting part.

Beams may be combinations of simple beams and cantilevers, as shown in Fig. 131. In this figure the part BC is a cantilever and the beam is

101

said to " overhang the reaction." Such beams are called *overhanging beams.* Beams may overhang at one or at both ends. The stresses

in the part BC are the same as if it were fixed in a wall at B, but the stresses in the part AB are quite different from what they would be were there no part BC of the beam.

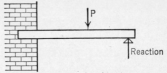

Beam fixed at one end and having a support

All the beams just described are called *statically determinate beams* because the conditions of static equilibrium determine the external forces on the beams sufficiently to allow the internal

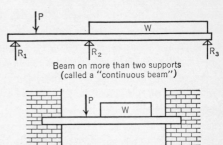

Beam on more than two supports
(called a "continuous beam")

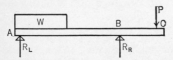

FIG. 131.   Overhanging beam.

Beam fixed at both ends.

FIG. 132.   Statically indeterminate beams.

forces or stresses to be calculated. There are also several classes of beams which are said to be " statically indeterminate." because the reactions cannot be determined by the conditions of equilibrium alone. Among these are beams fixed at one end and supported at the other, beams on more than two supports (called *continuous beams*), and beams fixed at both ends (Fig. 132). Certain relations in addition to the conditions of equilibrium are required for the determination of the reactions on such beams.

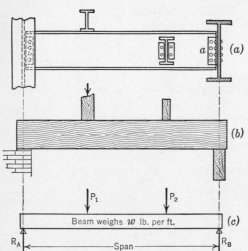

FIG. 133.   Distributed and concentrated loads.

Determination of the bending stresses in statically determinate beams will be considered in this chapter and Chapter VIII. Indeterminate beams will be considered in Chapters XI and XVIII.

Fig. 133 illustrates several common ways of supporting beams. At (*a*) the connection angles are so much less stiff than the beam itself that they fix the ends very slightly, and such a beam is ordinarily treated as a simply supported beam, with the reaction at the end of the beam.

71. Distributed and Concentrated Loads. Loads on beams are classed as *distributed* and *concentrated*. A distributed load extends over a considerable length of the beam. It is *uniformly distributed* if the load on each unit of the loaded length is the same as on every other unit. Most distributed loads are uniformly distributed, or at least sufficiently nearly so to be so considered. The weight of the beam itself is evidently one of the uniformly distributed loads which the beam carries (Fig. 133).

A concentrated load is a load which extends over so small a part of the length of the beam that, without appreciable error in the calculated bending and shearing effects of the load, it may be assumed to act at one point on the beam. Many " concentrated " loads are actually loads distributed over a short length of the beam, as when one beam rests on another, or when a post is supported on a beam (Fig. 133). In determining *bearing* stresses in a beam, the actual mode of application of the loads must of course be considered.

72. Determination of Reactions. Before the stresses in a beam on two supports can be figured, the reactions must be known. These are found by applying the conditions of statics $\Sigma V = 0$, $\Sigma H = 0$, and $\Sigma M = 0$. If the loads and reactions are all vertical, $\Sigma H = 0$ is not used.

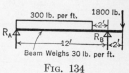

Fig. 134

Example. Calculate the reactions on the beam shown in Fig. 134.

Solution: Use $\Sigma M_A = 0$ (*A* as moment center):
$$- (300 \times 10) \times 5 - (30 \times 14) \times 7 - 1{,}800 \times 14 + 12\,R_B = 0$$
$$12\,R_B = 15{,}000 + 2{,}940 + 25{,}200 = 43{,}140$$
$$R_B = 3{,}595 \text{ lb.}$$

Use $\Sigma M_B = 0$ (*B* as moment center):
$$(300 \times 10) \times 7 + (30 \times 14) \times 5 - 1{,}800 \times 2 - 12\,R_A = 0$$
$$12\,R_A = 21{,}000 + 2{,}100 - 3{,}600 = 19{,}500$$
$$R_A = 1{,}625 \text{ lb.}$$

Using $\Sigma V = 0$ as a check (the sum of the reactions should equal the sum of the loads):
$$1{,}625 + 3{,}595 = 5{,}220 \text{ lb.} \qquad 3{,}000 + 420 + 1{,}800 = 5{,}220 \text{ lb.}$$

It is possible to calculate one reaction by using $\Sigma M = 0$ once, using the other reaction as a moment center, and then to determine the other reaction by using $\Sigma V = 0$. If a mistake is made in the amount of the reaction first determined, the second one will also be wrong. It is better to proceed as in the example above and calculate each reaction

by means of a moment equation.   The calculation may then be checked
by seeing that the sum of the reactions equals the sum of the loads.

PROBLEM

Calculate the reactions on the beam shown in Fig. 143.

73. Bending Moment and Shear.   Consider a simple beam carrying
a load of P lb. in addition to its own weight (Fig. 135a).   This beam will
be bent somewhat as shown in Fig. 135b.   If the beam is slender, the
bending may be noticeable.   If it is short compared with the depth,
the bending may not be visible but could be detected by accurate
measurements.

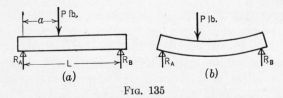

(a)   (b)

FIG. 135

The bending of the beam involves lengthening of the lower, convex
surface and shortening of the upper, concave surface.   The bottom
fibers are lengthened and are stressed in tension; the top fibers are
shortened and are stressed in compression.   There is a surface somewhere between the top surface and the bottom surface which remains
the original length, and the fibers in this surface are unstressed.   This
surface is called the " neutral surface " of the beam.   The line of intersection of the neutral surface and any vertical cross-section is called the
" neutral axis " of the cross-section.   It will be shown later that this
axis passes through the centroid of the cross-section.

Since the whole beam is in equilibrium any part of it is.   Consider
a segment of the beam to the left of any imaginary vertical plane between

FIG. 136   FIG. 137

the load and the right reaction (Fig. 136). W is the weight of the segment.   The forces holding this segment in equilibrium are P, W, R_A,
and the forces (not shown in Fig. 136) exerted by the right segment of

the beam on the left segment. These forces are exerted by the stresses in the beam at the cross-section separating the two segments. For all the forces on the left segment $\Sigma H = 0, \Sigma V = 0$, and $\Sigma M = 0$.

Since the top fibers of the beam are shortened, they are subjected to compression, or compressive forces are exerted by the top fibers in the right segment of the beam on the top fibers of the left segment of the beam, which is shown as a free body. Similarly tensile forces are exerted by the bottom fibers in the right segment of the beam on the bottom fibers of the left segment. In Fig. 137 let the resultant of these compressive forces or stresses be C, and the resultant of the tensile stresses be T. Applying $\Sigma H = 0$, it is evident that $C = T$, or the resultant of the compressive stresses equals the resultant of the tensile stresses.

Applying $\Sigma V = 0$ (Fig. 137), it becomes apparent that the rest of the beam must be exerting on the left segment a vertical force such that $R_A - P - W + V = 0$, or $V = P + W - R_A$ (that is, $V =$ the algebraic sum of all the external forces on the left segment). The algebraic sum of the external forces on the segment is called the " external shear " or simply the " shear " at the section. The force V exerted by one segment on the other is called the *resisting shear* and is the resultant of all the *shearing stresses* on the section.

Applying $\Sigma M = 0$, with a horizontal line on the cut face of the beam as a moment axis (this line is perpendicular to the paper), it is evident that the sum of the moments of C and T must be equal in magnitude and opposite in sense to the algebraic sum of the moments of the external forces R_A, P, and W. The algebraic sum of the moments of all the external forces on the segment is called the *bending moment* at the section. The sum of the moments of all the tensile and compressive *stresses* is called the *resisting moment* at the section. At any section in the beam, the resisting moment and the bending moment are numerically equal.

74. Shear Diagrams. Art. 73 stated that, if a beam is cut into two segments by an imaginary transverse plane, the resultant of the external forces on either segment equals the amount of shear at the cross-section cut by the plane. That is,

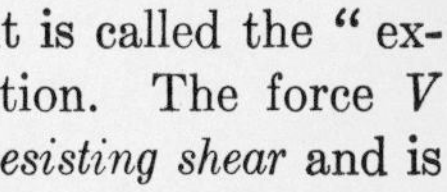

+Shear   −Shear

Fig. 138

The shear at any section of a beam is the algebraic sum of all the external forces on either side of the section.

The shear is considered positive if the segment of the beam on the left of the cross-section tends to move up with respect to the segment on the right, and vice versa (Fig. 138).

As will be shown later in this chapter, the maximum bending stress in a beam occurs on the cross-section where the shear is zero. Also the maximum shearing unit stress in a beam occurs at the section where the shear is a maximum. These and other considerations frequently make it desirable to know in what way the shear varies at successive cross-sections along the length of a beam. The most convenient means of determining and representing this variation is through a *shear diagram* (Fig. 139).

In a shear diagram, the abscissas of successive points on the shear line represent the locations of successive cross-sections of the beam. The ordinate of each point represents the shear at that particular cross-section. It is customary to draw the shear diagram directly below a sketch of the loaded beam, and to the same horizontal scale, so that the relationship of the shearing forces to the loads is immediately apparent.

75. Construction of a Shear Diagram. As an illustration of the construction of a simple shear diagram, Fig. 139 may be considered. The reactions due to this load are first computed and recorded. At any cross-section between the left-hand reaction and the load, the resultant of the forces on the left-hand segment is seen to be simply the reaction, and the left-hand segment tends to move up with respect to the right-hand segment. Therefore, for the length of the beam from the left reaction to the load, there is a positive shear equal in amount to the left reaction. But if a section is taken immediately to the right of the load and the part of the beam to the left of this section is considered, it is seen that the resultant of the forces on it is the left reaction minus

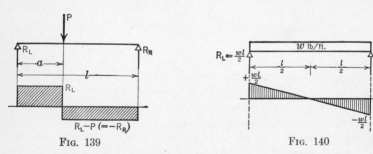

Fig. 139   Fig. 140

the load. This continues to be the amount of the shear at every section until the right-hand reaction is reached. Since the load is necessarily larger than the left-hand reaction, the segment on the left of the section tends to move *down* with respect to the segment on the right, or the shear is *negative*. Obviously the amount and nature of this shear can also be figured from the segment of the beam that lies to the right of any cross-section, and the same results will be secured.

The shear diagram for a uniformly distributed load on the beam is shown in Fig. 140. If a section is taken any distance x ft. from the left reaction, the resultant of the forces on the left-hand segment is $R_1 - wx$. Since $R_1 = wL/2$, the shear at any section is $wL/2 - wx$. The amount of shear evidently decreases uniformly with increase in x, becoming zero at the midpoint of the beam, and having its maximum negative value just to the left of the right-hand reaction, where it is $-wL/2$.

For any kind of loading on any statically determinate beam, the shear diagram is constructed by the methods that have been illustrated. Values of the shear are figured for every cross-section at which there is any change in the amount of distributed load, and at cross-sections just to the left and just to the right of all concentrated loads (including reactions), and the values are plotted above or below the axis of zero shear according to the convention already given. These statements can be verified by study of Figs. 141 and 142. It should be noted that for the cantilever beam, it is necessary to consider successive lengths measured *from the free end of the beam*, since the forces acting (within

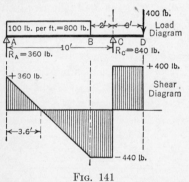

FIG. 141

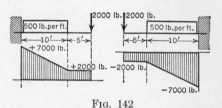

FIG. 142

the wall) on the fixed end of the beam are unknown. It is also useful to note that (1) for all lengths of the beam where there is no distributed load, the shear line is a straight, horizontal line; (2) for all lengths of the beam where there is a distributed load of uniform intensity the shear line is a straight inclined line, the slope of the line being proportional to the intensity of the load, and downward to the right if the load is a downward load; (3) at each concentrated load (including reactions) the shear line drops (or rises) by an amount equal to the load (or reaction).[1]

[1] If there is a non-uniform distributed load on the beam, the shear line will be a curved line, the ordinates of which are found, as in any other problem, by determining the resultant of the forces on either side of the section corresponding to the abscissa.

PROBLEMS

1. Draw the shear diagram for the beam shown in Fig. 143.

2. Draw the shear diagram for the beam shown in Fig. 144.

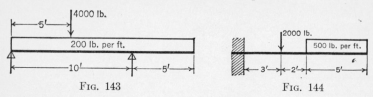

FIG. 143   FIG. 144

76. Bending Moment and Bending-Moment Diagrams. A more complete definition of bending moment than was given in Art. 73 is the following.

> The bending moment at any section of a beam is the algebraic sum of the moments of all the external forces on either side of the section.

The sign commonly given to bending moment is plus if the beam is concave up (or the top fibers are in compression) at the section. It may be diagrammatically shown as in Fig. 145. It is frequently stated that the bending moment is positive if the resultant moment of the forces on the left-hand segment is clockwise.

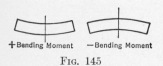

+Bending Moment   —Bending Moment

FIG. 145

A simple way of arriving at the correct sign in calculating bending moment is to give the moments of upward forces + signs and the moments of downward forces — signs. The algebraic sum of the moments will then have the correct sign whether the right or left segment is used.

In calculating bending moment use the segment for which the arithmetic will be simplest. (For a cantilever beam this is *always* the segment between the free end of the beam and the section under consideration.)

For determining the deflections of beams, for determining the maximum bending stresses in fixed and continuous beams, and for other purposes, it is necessary to know how the bending moment varies throughout the length of a beam. Just as a shear diagram is used to show the amount of shear at any cross-section of a beam, a *bending-moment* diagram is used to show the amount of bending moment. Fig. 146 shows such a diagram for the same beam and loading that are pictured in Fig. 139. In Fig. 146 the moment " curve " is placed just below the beam. The abscissa of any point on this curve indicates the location of a cross-section of the beam, and the ordinate of the point is the bending moment at that cross-section of the beam.

77. Construction of a Bending-Moment Diagram. The bending-moment diagram of Fig. 146 is constructed as follows: At any distance

x from the left-hand reaction, and between the reaction and the load, the beam is cut into two segments by an imaginary transverse plane. The only force which the load P causes to act on the segment to the left of the section is the reaction R_L, and the moment of this force with respect to the section in question is R_Lx. This moment evidently increases as x increases. That is, the moment " curve " for this case is a straight line, increasing to a maximum value at the load. If a section is now taken to the right of the load, and if the segment of the beam on the left of this section is considered, it is seen that the moment at this section is $R_Lx - P(x - a)$. This is necessarily a smaller moment than that corresponding to the value $x = a$. At successive sections between the

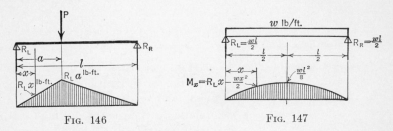

Fig. 146   Fig. 147

load and the right support, the amount of moment is constantly less until at the right-hand support it becomes zero. It is also obvious that the bending moment at any section between the load and the right-hand reaction is given either by the equation $M = R_Lx - P(x - a)$, or by the equation $M = R_Rx'$, where x' is the distance of the section from the right-hand reaction.

At any section throughout the length of this beam, the moment is shown as a *positive* moment. This is in accordance with the usual convention (Fig. 145).

Fig. 147 shows the bending moment diagram for a beam carrying a uniformly distributed load of w lb. per ft. For this case the bending moment at any section distant x from the left-hand reaction is evidently $R_Lx - wx \cdot x/2$, or $M = R_Lx - wx^2/2$. This is evidently the equation of a parabola with its axis vertical and its apex at the midlength of the beam.

To construct a moment diagram for a more complex loading, the same procedure is followed. Compute the external reactions. Imagine the beam to be cut into two segments by a transverse plane, and compute the moments (with respect to the plane) of the forces on either segment, the moment of every upward force being considered positive, and vice versa. Plot the resultant of these moments (in pound-feet or pound-inches) as the ordinate of a point (the abscissa is the distance of the cross-section from the end of the beam).   Repeat this procedure for as many points as may be necessary to permit the drawing of the curve.

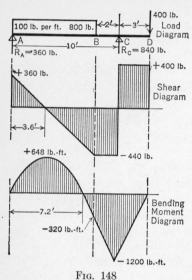

FIG. 148

The procedure for a beam carrying both concentrated and distributed loads is outlined below:

Example.   Draw shear and bending-moment diagrams for the beam shown in Fig. 148.

Solution: This is the same beam and loading that was shown in Fig. 141. The shear diagram is drawn in accordance with the procedure outlined in Art. 75. After this has been done, values of the bending moments at selected cross-sections of the beam are computed. In the computations as given below, the subscript after M shows the distance from the left-hand end of the beam to the section. Each value of M is calculated by considering the forces either on the left-hand segment or the right-hand segment of the beam, as may be most convenient.

$$M_0 \;\; = 0 \;\; \text{evidently}$$
$$M_2 \;\; = +360 \times 2 - 200 \times 1 = +520 \text{ lb-ft.}$$
$$M_{3.6} = +360 \times 3.6 - 360 \times 1.8 = +648 \text{ lb-ft.}$$
$$M_8 \;\; = +360 \times 8 - 800 \times 4 = -320 \text{ lb-ft.}$$
$$(\text{or } M_8 \;\; = +840 \times 2 - 400 \times 5 = -320 \text{ lb-ft.})$$
$$M_{10} = -400 \times 3 = -1,200 \text{ lb-ft.}$$
$$M_{13} = 0$$

PROBLEMS

For each of the following beams, Figs. 149 to 154, draw shear and bending-moment diagrams.   (These should be drawn below a diagram of the beam showing the

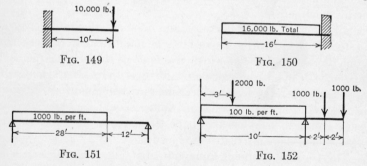

FIG. 149   FIG. 150

FIG. 151   FIG. 152

loading.)   Use a scale of 1 in. = 4 ft. for lengths up to 20 ft., and 1 in. = 10 ft. for lengths from 20 to 40 ft.   All necessary computations should appear on the sheet beside the diagrams. Scales for shears and moments should be such as to give diagrams which will go on a single sheet with the diagram of beam. Values should be

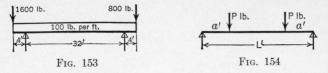

FIG. 153   FIG. 154

written on diagrams at important points as in the example, and dimensions should be given to points of zero shear.

1. Fig. 149.   3. Fig. 151.   5. Fig. 153.
2. Fig. 150.   4. Fig. 152.   6. Fig. 154.

78. Relations Between Loads, Shears, and Bending Moments.

The following relations can be derived from the equations which express the shears and bending moments at successive points on the length of a beam. Reference to the foregoing examples illustrates the application of these relations to specific cases.

(*a*) For any part of a beam where there are no loads, the shear line is a straight horizontal line and the moment line a straight sloping line.

(*b*) For any part of a beam where there is a uniformly distributed downward load the shear line is a straight line sloping downward to the right and the moment line is a parabolic curve which is concave downward.

(*c*) The numerical change in bending moment between two points equals the area of the shear diagram between those points, taking into account the sign of the shear. This will be proved in the following article.

(*d*) It follows from (*c*) that at any point where the shear line crosses the zero line there is a maximum ordinate of the moment diagram. (By maximum is meant that the ordinate is numerically greater than ordinates on either side of it.)

The drawing of shear diagrams and moment diagrams is greatly facilitated by keeping the above facts in mind, and by an intelligent selection of cross-sections at which the value of the bending moment is calculated. It should be calculated for every cross-section at which there is a concentrated load, or a change in the amount of distributed load. In addition, the maximum value should be computed and sufficient values to establish the shape of the curve along any length of the beam where there is a distributed load.

79. The General Moment Equation.

Let Fig. 155 represent a portion of a beam between two sections x ft. apart. Let the bending moments be M_0 and M_x on the left and right ends respectively, and let the shear at the left end be V_0. Let the resultant of any system of concentrated loads on the segment be a force P acting at a distance a ft. from the left end.   Let there be a uniformly distributed load of

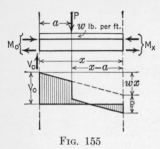

FIG. 155

w lb. per ft. extending throughout the segment.   Then, since the segment is a body in equilibrium, the sum of all the moments about any point on the right-hand end of the segment is equal to zero, or

$$M_0 + V_0 x - P(x - a) - wx \cdot x/2 - M_x = 0$$

This may be written

$$M_x = M_0 + V_0 x - P(x - a) - wx \cdot x/2$$

This is the equation for the bending moment at the right end of the segment shown.   Stated in a general way, for any loading on the segment, the equation becomes

$$M_x = M_0 + V_0 x - \text{Moments of any forces on the segment}^{1}$$

This is called the *general moment equation*.   It is applicable to any segment of any beam.   When the loads on a beam or segment and the shear and moment at one end are known, the moment at the other end can be found by this equation.

The relations between shear and bending moment which are stated in Art. 78 can be derived from the general moment equation.   The relations stated under (a) and (b) are too simple to require further discussion.

It is stated under (c) that " the numerical change in bending moment between two points equals the area of the shear diagram between those points, taking into account the sign of the shear."   The truth of this will now be shown.   Referring to Fig. 155, the general moment equation for the segment shown may be written

$$M_x - M_0 = V_0 x - P(x - a) - wx \cdot x/2$$

The left-hand side of this equation is the difference in bending moment between the two ends of the segment.   The right-hand side of the equation is evidently the net area under the shear curve; that is, the rectangle $V_0 x$ minus the parallelogram $P(x - a)$ and the triangle $wx \cdot x/2$.   Consequently the proposition is proved for this particular loading.   It can be similarly proved for any loading.

[1] The negative sign is used for the moments of any forces on the segment on the supposition that the forces act downward. The moments of any upward forces (such as reactions) should be *added*.

It follows directly from this proposition that the maximum (numerical) value of the bending moment occurs where the shear passes through zero, as stated in Art. 78 (d). In the figure just discussed, it is evident that the positive shear area is increasing until the shear curve crosses the zero line; after that point, the net area decreases. Consequently the bending moment increases numerically until the shear passes through zero, after which it decreases.

80. Application to Shear and Bending-Moment Diagrams. Often the principle that the change in bending moment between two points along the length of a beam is equal to the area of the shear diagram between those points can be advantageously used in drawing moment diagrams. Applying this principle to the beam shown in Fig. 156, the reactions are calculated and the shear diagram is drawn.

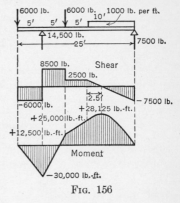

Fig. 156

Significant values of the bending moment at the successive points are then found by cumulatively totaling up the areas under the shear line, from left to right. Since the first three shear areas are rectangles, it is evident that the moment curve consists of straight lines until the left end of the distributed load is reached. The calculations are shown below:

$$
\begin{aligned}
M_5 &= -6{,}000 \times 5 && = -30{,}000 \\
&\quad +8{,}500 \times 5 && = +42{,}500 \\
M_{10} &= && \quad\;\; +12{,}500 \\[4pt]
&\quad +2{,}500 \times 5 && = +12{,}500 \\
M_{15} &= && \quad\;\; +25{,}000 \\[4pt]
&\quad +2{,}500 \times 1.25 && = +\;\;3{,}125 \\
M_{17.5} &= && \quad\;\; +28{,}125 \\[4pt]
&\quad -7{,}500 \times 3.75 && = -28{,}125 \\
M_{25} &= && \quad\;\; 00{,}000
\end{aligned}
$$

Since, in the method used, each moment value was based on the preceding moment value, the correct value secured at the right end of the beam checks the accuracy of all the intermediate computed values.

In drawing a moment diagram by summing up the areas under the shear curve, it is to be noted that, following the convention as to the algebraic signs of shears and bending moments, the shear areas should be summed up *from left to right*. The bending-moment diagram can be started at the right and carried through to the left end of the beam, but then the sign of each shear area must be reversed.

PROBLEMS

1. Fig. 157 shows a shear diagram for a beam on two supports. Draw the bending-moment diagram.

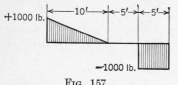

FIG. 157

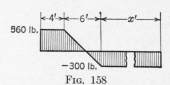

FIG. 158

2. The shear diagram shown in Fig. 158 is that of a beam on two supports without overhang. Determine the length x and draw the beam with its load, and the bending-moment diagram.

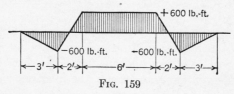

FIG. 159

3. A beam AB is 16 ft. long. The bending-moment diagram is shown in Fig. 159. Draw the shear diagram and make a sketch of the beam showing the loads.

81. Dangerous Section. In most beams the bending stress is the most serious stress, and since this is a maximum at the cross-section of the beam where the shear is (or passes through) zero, sections of zero shear are called *dangerous sections*. Frequently in the design or investigation of a beam it is not necessary to determine any stresses except the maximum bending stress. This requires the determination of the moment at the dangerous section, and this necessitates finding where the dangerous section occurs. Where a beam carries large concentrated loads, the shear will generally change sign under one of these loads, and to find the dangerous section in such a case merely requires that the shear on both sides of each load be determined to ascertain at which load the shear changes sign. Where a beam carries both concentrated and distributed loads, it is possible that the dangerous section will occur at some point where there is no concentrated load. The approximate location of such a point may be observed from the shear diagram. Its exact location should not be scaled, but should be calculated from the forces on the beam.

82. Inflection Points. An overhanging beam may be concave down throughout part or parts of its length, and concave up throughout the remainder, as in Fig. 148. In such a beam the points where the curvature reverses are called *inflection points*. They are evidently points of zero bending moment, since they are points where the beam is not bent. They can be located by setting up an expression for the bending moment and equating it to zero.

Example. In the beam of Fig. 148, find the distance from the left reaction to point of zero bending moment.

Solution: The bending moment x ft. from R_A (if x is not more than 8) may be expressed by this equation

$$M = 360\,x - \frac{100\,x^2}{2}$$

Equating this to zero we have

$$\frac{-100\,x^2}{2} + 360\,x = 0$$

Dividing by $-50\,x$ $\qquad\qquad x - 7.2 = 0$

or $\qquad\qquad\qquad\qquad\qquad x = 7.2\text{ ft.}$

If the value of x found by solving this equation had been more than 8 it would not have been the correct distance to the point of zero moment, as the equation written is true only for values of x from zero to 8.

If the shear diagram has been drawn, the inflection point may often be very easily found simply by noting the point for which the positive and negative shear areas on the segment on either side balance. Thus, in Fig. 148, the shear diagram shows immediately that the inflection point is at $2 \times 3.6 = 7.2$ ft. from the left end of the beam. Both these methods of finding inflection points should be understood.

83. Relation Between Shear and Bending Moment. Consider a segment of a beam between two planes, the distance between which is dx as shown in Fig. 160. This segment is a body in equilibrium, the forces acting on it being the tensile and compressive forces on the two faces (which constitute the two resisting moments M and M'), the two shearing forces V and V', and a small part of the distributed load which also includes the weight of the segment. If the distributed load is w lb. per unit of length, the load on this segment is $w\,dx$. Taking the moments of these forces with respect to the neutral axis of the right-hand face of the segment and placing the sum equal to zero

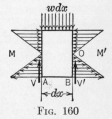

FIG. 160

$$M' - M - V\,dx + w\,dx \times \frac{dx}{2} = 0$$

Neglecting the term containing the square of dx and noting that $M' - M = dM$,

$$dM = Vdx \quad \text{or} \quad \frac{dM}{dx} = V$$

This relationship will be used in deriving the equation for shearing unit stress in beams.

PROBLEM

Derive the above relationship between M and V by differentiation of the general moment equation $M_x = M_0 + V_0x - P(x - a) - wx^2/2$ given in Art. 79.

GENERAL PROBLEMS

1. Calculate the maximum bending moment in a simple beam L ft. long carrying a load of P lb. at the center.

2. Calculate the maximum bending moment in a simple beam L ft. long carrying a uniformly distributed load of w lb. per ft. What does this M equal if the total weight of the distributed load is W lb.?

3. Draw, approximately to scale, shear and bending-moment diagrams for each of the beams shown in Fig. 161. Write shear and moment values on diagrams at significant points.

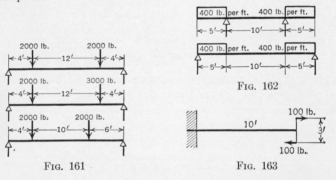

FIG. 161   FIG. 162

FIG. 163

4. Draw, approximately to scale, shear and bending-moment diagrams for each of the beams shown in Fig. 162. Write shear and moment values on diagrams at significant points.

5. Draw shear and bending-moment diagrams for the beam shown in Fig. 163.

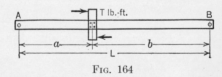

FIG. 164

6. At a point in a beam a distance of a ft. from one end a moment of T lb-ft. is applied as shown in Fig. 164. Draw the shear and bending-moment diagrams.

7. The beam AB (Fig. 165) is supported at A and B by supports which may exert reactions in any direction required for equilibrium.   Draw shear and bending-moment diagrams for the load as shown.

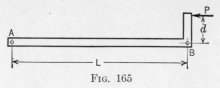

FIG. 165

8. The shear and bending moment at the left-hand end of a 10-ft. segment of a beam are $+1,600$ lb. and $+5,200$ lb-ft., respectively.   A uniform load of 1,000 lb. per ft. extends for 4 ft. from the left end of the segment, and 8 ft. from the left end there is an upward reaction of 3,600 lb.   Calculate the shear and moment at the right end of the segment.

9. Draw shear and bending-moment diagrams for the beam shown in Fig. 134.

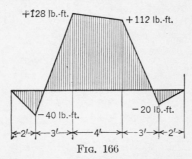

FIG. 166

10. Fig. 166 shows the bending-moment diagram for a beam on two supports. Draw the shear diagram and a diagram showing the beam and loads.

CHAPTER VIII

STRESSES IN BEAMS

84. Introduction. For the design or investigation of a beam it is necessary to calculate the actual unit stresses (tensile, compressive, and shearing) which occur at certain cross-sections. The greatest unit stress that occurs must not exceed the allowable stress for the material used. For this reason a formula expressing a relation between the bending moment at a given section of a beam, the size and shape of the cross-section, and the maximum tensile or compressive stress is used and will now be derived.[1] Afterwards a formula relating shearing unit stress to the shear on a cross-section will be derived.

85. Bending Unit Stress: The Flexure Formula. In determining the unit stresses due to bending it is ordinarily assumed that a plane cross-section of an unbent beam remains a plane after the beam is bent. This assumption is not always exactly true, but only in very unusual cases does it lead to errors of any seriousness. Making the assumption, two parallel plane cross-sections AB and CD of an unbent beam will be planes after the beam is bent but will no longer be parallel (Fig. 167b).

(a) Part of Unbent Beam (b) Part of Bent Beam

FIG. 167

If a third plane $C'D'$, parallel to AB, is now passed through the intersection of CD and the neutral surface, the distance between AB and $C'D'$ will be the original length of all fibers of the beam between the planes AB and CD in the unbent beam. It will be seen that the change in length of any fiber is proportional to the distance of the fiber from the neutral surface. *If the unit stress in no fiber exceeds the proportional*

[1] In 1638 Galileo published a treatise which contained a number of propositions relating to the behavior and strength of beams. His conclusions were erroneous, but his investigations interested others. The problem of the distribution of stress in beams was attacked by many investigators and completely solved for all ordinary cases by the French engineer Navier, about 1820. See H. F. Moore, " The History of the Flexure Formula," *Journal of Engineering Education*, Vol. XXI, No. 2 (October, 1930), page 156.

limit, it follows from Hooke's law that the unit stress in any fiber at a given section of the bent beam is proportional to the distance from the neutral axis to that fiber.

Let *ABCD* (Fig. 168) be any cross-section of a prismatic beam. One segment of the beam is shown in isometric. The shaded strip *dA* is an elementary part of the cross-section, its distance from the neutral axis being *y*. This strip represents any elementary area either above or below the neutral axis (y may have any value from $-c'$ to $+c$).

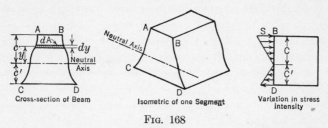

Cross-section of Beam   Isometric of one Segment   Variation in stress intensity

FIG. 168

Let S be the unit stress in the fibers farthest from the neutral axis (this will be the maximum unit stress), and let c be the distance to these fibers. Since the unit stress on any fiber is proportional to the distance of that fiber from the neutral axis, the unit stress on dA is Sy/c.

The force exerted on dA equals the unit stress multiplied by the area, or force on $dA = \dfrac{y}{c} SdA$. The moment of this force on dA about the neutral axis as the axis of moments equals

$$y \times \frac{y}{c} SdA = \frac{S}{c} y^2 dA$$

The sum of the moments of all the forces on all the elementary areas composing the cross-section is found by integrating and is, of course, the resisting moment M_R at this cross-section.

$$M_R = \frac{S}{c} \int_{-c'}^{+c} y^2 dA$$

The expression $\int_{-c'}^{+c} y^2 dA$ is the "moment of inertia" of the cross-section and is represented by the symbol I. The resisting moment M_R equals the bending moment M. The formula may therefore be written:

$$M = \frac{SI}{c}$$

It may also be written:
$$S = \frac{Mc}{I}$$

or
$$\frac{I}{c} = \frac{M}{S}$$

In this formula I is commonly expressed in inches[4], S in pounds per square inch, c in inches, and M in pound-inches.

The formula is given in three forms. With the dimensions of a beam given and the maximum allowable stress for the material known, the first form is used to solve for the greatest bending moment allowable. With the loading given (from which M can be computed) and the dimensions of the beam known (from which I and c are found), the second form is used to determine the maximum unit stress which results at the cross-section for which M is computed. With the loads given which the beam must carry (from which M can be computed) and the material of which the beam is to be made being known (so that a suitable allowable stress, S, is chosen), the third form is used to determine I/c for the cross-section. I/c is a function of the size and shape of the cross-section. Its value being known, a beam having a sufficient cross-section may be chosen. The quantity I/c is called the " section modulus " of the cross-section.

The tensile stresses and compressive stresses which occur in a beam as a result of the bending moment are often spoken of as " bending stresses," or " flexural stresses." They are sometimes called " fiber stresses," a reflection of the fact that the first beams discussed were wooden beams. The term is now applied also to non-fibrous materials such as concrete and steel.

86. Position of Neutral Axis. It was stated in Art. 73 that the neutral axis of any cross-section of a beam passes through the centroid of the cross-section. Its location is fixed by the fact that the sum or resultant of the tensile stresses equals the sum of the compressive stresses. In other words, the total horizontal force on one side of any cross-section of a bent beam equals zero. The unit stress on any differential area of a cross-section y in. from the neutral axis of the cross-section is $\dfrac{S}{c}y$,

and the force exerted by the stress on this differential area is $\dfrac{S}{c}ydA$.

The total horizontal force on the cross-section is then $\dfrac{S}{c}\displaystyle\int_{-c'}^{+c} ydA = 0.$

But in a bent beam S/c does not equal zero, hence $\displaystyle\int_{-c'}^{+c} ydA = 0.$

But $\displaystyle\int_{-c'}^{+c} y\,dA = \bar{y}A$, where $\bar{y}$ is the distance from the neutral axis to the centroid of the cross-section. Since $\bar{y}A = 0$, and since A does not equal zero, $\bar{y} = 0$, which shows that the neutral axis is a centroidal axis of the cross-section.

PROBLEMS

1. What bending moment is permissible for a wooden beam 3 in. wide and 12 in. deep, if the allowable stress for this wood is 1,400 lb. per sq. in.?

2. At a certain point on a beam the bending moment is 12,000 lb-in. The cross-section of the beam is 3 in. by 4 in. (4-in. sides vertical). What is the maximum bending stress? What is the stress 1 in. below the top surface?

3. What stress will result if the beam in Problem 2 is " laid flat " (3-in. dimension vertical)?

4. Compute the necessary dimensions for a wooden beam of square cross-section to carry a maximum bending moment of 82,000 lb-in., the allowable stress being 1,200 lb. per sq. in. What would be a suitable commercial size beam? *Ans.* $b = 7.43$ in.

5. Compute the size required for a steel beam of square cross-section to carry the same bending moment as in Problem 4, the allowable stress being 16,000 lb. per sq. in.

6. Solve Problem 4, making the depth of the beam twice the width.

7. The cross-section of a simple beam is a triangle. The base is 4 in. and altitude 6 in. The beam rests on supports at the ends with the apex up. The maximum bending moment is 60,000 lb-in. What is the maximum compressive stress? Tensile stress? *Ans.* $S_c = 10,000$ lb. per sq. in.

8. A T-shaped steel beam 5 in. deep is subjected to bending. Measurements of deformations are made with two extensometers. In a gage length of 8 in. the top fibers shorten 0.0028 in. and the fibers $\frac{1}{2}$ in. above the bottom lengthen 0.0034 in. (*a*) Calculate the distance from the top of the beam to the neutral axis. (*b*) Calculate the stresses at the top and bottom of the beam.

87. The Flexure Formula: Assumptions and Limitations.

In deriving the flexure formula, $S = Mc/I$, it was assumed that the unit stresses were proportional to the unit deformations. Because of this assumption the flexure formula applies without error only to materials which obey Hooke's law, and only so long as the maximum stress is within the proportional limit of the material, as has already been pointed out.[1]

There are also other restrictions upon the use of the flexure formula, the reasons for which and the limits of which are less obvious. The most important of these restrictions are mentioned below.

The common flexure formula will not give exact values of the bending stresses unless the beam and the loading conform to the following conditions:

(*a*) The beam is straight before loading. Curved beams are considered in Chapter XX.

---

[1] Without *serious* error the formula can be (and commonly is) applied to beams of cast iron and other materials which do not follow Hooke's law exactly.

(b) The cross-section of the beam has an axis of symmetry, and the resultant of each load lies in the plane containing the axes of symmetry of all cross-sections and is perpendicular to the geometrical axis of the beam. Beams not conforming to these conditions are discussed in Chapters XII and XX.

(c) The beam has sufficient lateral or transverse width relative to its length to prevent " buckling " (or is supported transversely so that it does not buckle). No part of the beam is so thin that local wrinkling or buckling occurs as the result of the forces developed. Beams not conforming to these conditions are discussed in Chapter XX.

(d) The longitudinal or " fiber " strains are not affected by the shearing strains which are also present. They will not be affected by shearing strains in any length of the beam where the shear is constant. They may be materially affected in a length of beam where the shear is rapidly changing.[1] This situation exists in short beams subjected to heavy distributed loads, and under certain other conditions.

(e) The loads are static or gradually applied. Stresses resulting from loads not gradually applied are discussed in Chapter XVII.

(f) The material of which the beam is made has the same modulus of elasticity in tension and compression. Exceptions to this condition are discussed in Chapter XX.

The majority of beams are straight, and do have cross-sections with an axis of symmetry, and have the loads applied substantially in the plane of these axes; most beams have loadings or dimensions such that shear strains do not greatly affect " fiber " strains, and have cross-sections such that local buckling cannot occur. Moreover, most loadings are either static, or can be converted into equivalent static loadings. Therefore the flexure formula applies quite satisfactorily to the determination of bending stresses in most beams. Bending stresses are usually the most important stresses in a beam, although under some conditions shearing stresses or normal stresses on other sections than cross-sections must be considered and may be more significant than bending stresses. Such stresses will be discussed in later chapters.

88. Modulus of Rupture. If a beam is loaded until failure occurs and the maximum bending moment M to which the beam was subjected is inserted in the formula $S = Mc/I$, the resulting value of S is called the *modulus of rupture* of the beam. It cannot be considered as the unit stress in the outermost fibers of the beam at the moment of failure, because the equation $S = Mc/I$ holds true only when no unit fiber stress in the beam exceeds the proportional limit. When a beam is stressed to failure, the deformations of the fibers continue throughout

[1] See Maurer and Withy, " Strength of Materials," Second Edition, page 146.

the test to be proportional to their distance from the neutral axis (in the ordinary beam the cross-sections of which are symmetrical with respect to the neutral axis). But since the proportional limit is exceeded in the outer fibers, Hooke's law no longer holds true for them, and the stresses in the fibers of the beam are not proportional to their distances from the neutral axis. The modulus of rupture is greater than the stress in the outer fibers, and bears no fixed relation to that stress. The more brittle the material, the more closely the modulus of rupture approaches the true stress.

The modulus of rupture, as determined from beams of similar cross-section, is used in comparing the bending strength of different materials, such as different species of wood. It is also sometimes used to determine the *probable* breaking load on a beam, and the term is one which is fairly frequently encountered in engineering literature. The stress distribution that occurs in beams at cross-sections where stresses exceed the proportional limit is discussed in Chapter XX.[1]

89. Shearing Unit Stresses in Beams. Articles in Chapter VII dealt with the determination of the total shearing force on any cross-section of a loaded beam. The natural assumption might be that this shearing force is uniformly distributed over the cross-section, with a resulting shearing unit stress at any point of the cross-section equal to V/A. This is not the case, however, as will now be shown. The shearing unit stress is zero at those points on the cross-section where the bending stress is a maximum, and increases to a maximum value which nearly always occurs at the neutral axis. For example, in a beam of rectangular cross-section, the maximum shearing unit stress, at the neutral axis, is $1\frac{1}{2}$ times the average stress V/A.

Derivation of the formula for shearing unit stress on a cross-section of a beam involves use of the principle proved in Art. 35: that, if a shearing unit stress of any intensity exists on any plane through a point in a stressed body, there is also a shearing unit stress of equal intensity at the same point on a plane at right angles to the first. The intensity of the vertical shearing unit stress at any point in a beam is most easily determined by finding the shearing unit stress on a horizontal plane through the point in question. Then, by the principle just stated, this horizontal shearing unit stress equals the desired vertical shearing unit stress.[2]

---

[1] That topic can be considered at this point in the course, if desired. (Art. 256.)

[2] The horizontal shearing unit stress is practically always as important as the vertical shearing unit stress, since the two are of equal intensity. And in wooden beams, which offer less resistance to shearing forces parallel to the grain, the horizontal (longitudinal) shear is much more important.

90. Horizontal Shear in Beams. The existence of *horizontal or longitudinal* shear in beams is well demonstrated by the following illustration. If planks are piled up as shown in Fig. 169 (*a*), placed on supports at the ends, and loaded with weights between the supports, they will bend as shown in (*b*). Consider the upper two planks. In each of these the top " fibers " are shortened and the bottom fibers lengthened. This evidently results in a sliding of the top plank over the one beneath it, shown by the fact that the originally straight line representing the ends of the planks has become broken. Now consider a beam made of a solid piece of wood (*c*) whose dimensions are the same as the four planks together in (*a*). This beam will deflect under the load (though the deflection will be much less than that of the four separate planks). The sliding that occurred between the lower surface of the top plank and the upper surface of the next plank is prevented by longitudinal shearing stresses in the wooden beam.

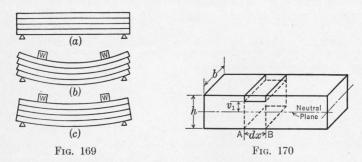

FIG. 169   FIG. 170

91. Formula for Shearing Stress in a Beam. Fig. 170 represents part of a loaded beam. At A and B planes are passed, between which is a slice of the beam having a short length dx, exaggerated in the figure.

Consider a part of this slice between the top surface of the beam and a parallel horizontal plane v_1 in. from the neutral axis. Fig. 171 is an end view of this block. On the face of this block which lies in plane A there is a set of forces (shown as compressive forces) which are the stresses exerted on the block by the part of the beam adjoining it. These compressive stresses increase in intensity as the distance from the neutral axis increases. On the face of the block which lies in plane B there is also a set of forces which vary in a like manner with the distance from the neutral axis.

If the bending moment M_B at plane B of the beam is greater than the bending moment M_A at the plane A, the forces on face B of the block will be greater than those on face A. Since this block is in equilibrium the sum of the horizontal forces acting on it equals zero. Consequently there must be a force acting on the block to the right in addition to these compressive forces. This force is the shearing force on the under surface of the block and is equal to the horizontal shearing unit stress multiplied by the area of the lower surface of the block. It is this shearing unit stress that is to be determined.

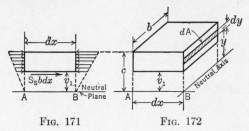

FIG. 171   FIG. 172

Fig. 172 is a perspective view of this block. Consider a rectangular area, dA, parallel to the neutral axis in the face B of this block, and having dimensions of b and dy. The compressive unit stress on this area $= M_B y/I$ and the force on the area is $\dfrac{M_B y}{I}\, dA$. The total force on the face B of the block then is

$$F_B = \int_{v_1}^{c} \frac{M_B}{I} y\, dA = \frac{M_B}{I} \int_{v_1}^{c} y\, dA$$

The quantity $\displaystyle\int_{v_1}^{c} y\, dA$ is called the " statical moment " of the face of the block with respect to the neutral axis. (The calculation of the statical moment of an area will be discussed later.) Let the statical moment be designated[1] as Q. Then $F_B = M_B Q/I$.

In the same way the resultant force F_A on the face A of the block is $M_A Q/I$. The difference between the two forces therefore is $F_B - F_A = (M_B - M_A)Q/I$. This is equal to the force exerted by the shearing stress S_s on the lower surface of the block. This equals $S_s b dx$. Hence

$$S_s b dx = (M_B - M_A)\frac{Q}{I} \quad \text{or} \quad S_s = \frac{(M_B - M_A)Q}{dx \cdot I \cdot b}$$

but $M_B - M_A = dM$, and it was shown in Art. 83 that

$$\frac{dM}{dx} = V$$

[1] The representation of the integral $\displaystyle\int_{v_1}^{c} y\, dA$ by Q is analogous to the representation of the integral $\displaystyle\int_{-c'}^{c} y^2 dA$ by I. See Appendix B.

Therefore

$$S_s = \frac{VQ}{Ib}$$

in which S_s = the horizontal (and vertical) shearing unit stress at a
given point of a given cross-section of the beam.

V = the total shear at the cross-section (may be obtained
from a shear diagram for a given loading).

Q = the statical moment of the part of the cross-section
between the point where the shearing stress is wanted
and the outside of the beam.

I = the moment of inertia of the whole cross-section with
respect to the neutral axis (same I as in Mc/I).

b = the width of the cross-section at the point where S_s is
being computed.

92. Application of the Formula for Shearing Stress. In the formula
$S_s = VQ/Ib$, all the terms are familiar through previous use in this book
with the exception of Q, which represents $\int_{v_1}^{c} ydA$. In the computation
of the statical moment Q, for beams of ordinary cross-section, the
indicated integration need not be performed. If the area for which Q
is wanted is a rectangle or triangle, Q equals the area times the distance
from the neutral axis to the centroid of the area. If the area for which
Q is wanted is a more complicated shape, it is divided into rectangles or
triangles and Q equals the sum of the statical moments of these rectangles and triangles. For example, let it be required to find the shearing
unit stress at a point 2 in. from the top surface of a beam 12 in. by 12 in.
in cross-section. The quantity Q would be the area 12 in. by 2 in.,
times 5 in., the distance from the neutral axis of the beam to the centroid of the area above the point where the stress is being found.

Example. Find the shearing unit stress at the neutral axis of a beam having the
cross-section shown in Fig. 173, if the total shear at the cross-section is 2,000 lb.

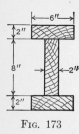

FIG. 173

Solution:

$$I = \frac{6 \times 12^3}{12} - \frac{4 \times 8^3}{12} = 693 \text{ in.}^4$$

$V = 2,000 \text{ lb.}$

$Q = 6 \times 2 \times 5 + 4 \times 2 \times 2 = 76 \text{ in.}^3$

$b = 2 \text{ in.}$

Therefore

$$S_s = \frac{2,000 \times 76}{693 \times 2} = 109.6 \text{ lb. per sq. in.}$$

The five diagrams shown in Fig. 174 represent the cross-sections of beams. Suppose that the unit shearing stress is to be determined at a distance v_1 from the neutral axis in each case. The quantity Q is the statical moment of the shaded area. For the first and fourth cases, Q is found by multiplying the shaded area by the distance from its centroid

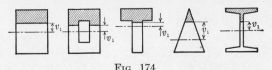

FIG. 174

to the neutral axis of the cross-section. For the other cases the shaded area should be divided into rectangles or triangles. Its statical moment is then the sum of the products of each partial area by the distance from its centroid to the neutral axis.

In Fig. 174, for each section shown, b is the length of the boundary line between the shaded and unshaded parts of the cross-section and I is the moment of inertia of the entire cross-section with respect to the neutral axis shown.

Considering the rectangular cross-section shown in Fig. 174, it is evident that, whatever the value of v_1, there will be no change in any quantity of the expression VQ/Ib except Q, which will increase as v_1 decreases. Q will have a maximum value when $v_1 = 0$, or the maximum shearing stress in the rectangular beam occurs at the neutral axis of the beam. The same line of reasoning shows that the maximum shearing stress will occur at the neutral axis in all beams except those in which the width, b, is greater at the neutral axis than at some other part of the cross-section. In such beams the maximum shearing stress may not occur at the neutral axis, but at some point where the width is narrower, as is true in a beam of triangular cross-section. For instance, in a beam of triangular cross-section, the maximum shearing stress occurs at a distance of one-half the altitude from the base.

PROBLEMS

1. A wooden beam is 10 in. wide and 12 in. deep. At a cross-section where the total shear is 10,000 lb. calculate the shearing unit stress at 1-in. intervals from top to bottom of the cross-section. Plot these unit stresses as abscissas showing the distribution of the shearing stress. *Ans.* S_s = 38.2 lb. per sq. in. 1 in. from top.

2. A wooden beam has a triangular cross-section, 6-in. base, and 6-in. height. (Apex is turned up.) The total shear on a cross-section is 1,800 lb. Solve for shearing unit stresses, and plot these as directed in Problem 1.

3. Prove that for a solid rectangular cross-section the maximum shearing unit stress is 1.5 times the average shearing stress. (This is a convenient relation which simplifies the computation of maximum shearing stress in solid rectangular beams.)

4. Fig. 175 shows the cross-section of a beam made of three planks securely fastened together. Calculate the total vertical shear which will cause a maximum shearing unit stress of 120 lb. per sq. in.   Calculate shearing unit stresses at intervals of 1 in. from top to bottom, and plot as directed in Problem 1.

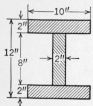

FIG. 175

GENERAL PROBLEMS

1. Find the maximum fiber stress in the beam of Fig. 148 if it is a piece of 3-in. standard pipe.

$Ans.$ $S = 8,350$ lb. per sq. in.

2. Four planks 2 in. by 8 in. (actual dimensions) are spiked together to make a box beam the cross-section of which is a rectangle with outside dimensions 8 in. by 12 in. (12 in. vertical). Calculate the maximum allowable bending moment and maximum allowable shear. Allowable stresses are: bending, 1,500 lb. per sq. in.; shearing, 110 lb. per sq. in.

3. When a dock was being constructed, 4-in.-by-12-in. (nominal size) wooden sheet piling 26 ft. long was used. The resident engineer was asked if one of these planks could be used as a temporary footwalk to enable workmen to reach an isolated part of the work. The span would be 22 ft. The wood appeared to be fir or hemlock free from defects of any sort. Would you permit its use (laid flat)? If so would you restrict its use to one man at a time?

4. A steel reinforcing bar has a diameter of 1 in. and is 25 ft. long. If it is picked up at the midpoint of its length, it may be considered to be two cantilever beams, each 12.5 ft. long. What is the maximum bending stress in the bar when it is so held?

5. Two men are to carry a square steel reinforcing bar $1\frac{1}{8}$ in. on a side and 40 ft. long. (a) If they pick it up at the ends, what will be the maximum bending stress in the bar? (b) Assuming that each man takes hold of the bar at the same distance from the end, between what points can this be in order that the bending stress in the bar may not exceed 20,000 lb. per sq. in.? $Ans.$ (a) $S = 43,500$ lb. per sq. in.

6. A floor and the ceiling below it together have a weight of 16 lb. per sq. ft. and the floor is to be designed to carry a live load of 75 lb. per sq. ft. The span of the 2-in.-by-10-in. (nominal size) joists supporting the floor is 15 ft. If the joists are spaced 16 in. on centers, will the resulting stresses be satisfactory? The joists are of southern pine, dense select grade.

7. A 5-in., 10-lb. American standard beam rests on supports 10 ft. center to center and carries a load of 3,000 lb. 3 ft. from one end. Calculate the maximum bending stress (a) if the weight of the beam is neglected; (b) if the weight of the beam is considered. $Ans.$ (a) $S = 15,720$ lb. per. sq. in.

8. What is the longest 1-in.-square bar of steel that can be supported at its midpoint without being stressed above 30,000 lb. per sq. in.?

9. A beam of T-shaped cross-section is made of a 2-in.-by-8-in. plank with the 8-in. dimension horizontal, adequately spiked to the top edge of another 2-in.-by-8-in. plank (8-in. dimension vertical). Calculate the allowable total shear if the wood is dense southern yellow pine, select grade, using the Forest Products Laboratory stress.

CHAPTER IX

DESIGN OF BEAMS

93. Introduction. The two preceding chapters have enumerated the kinds of beams and loads. They have discussed the shears and bending moments caused by the loads on a beam. They have derived the relationship between the bending moment and the bending unit stress in the extreme fiber of the cross-section and the relationship between the total shear on a cross-section and the shearing unit stresses.

In the present chapter the principles developed in the preceding chapter will be applied to the *design* of beams.

94. Design of Beams. Beams resist both bending stresses and shearing stresses. In the very large majority of cases, the bending stress is the stress which limits the allowable load on the beam. That is, when the load is such as to stress the beam to the full value of the allowable bending stress, it will usually be found that the allowable shearing stress has not been developed. For this reason, in designing a beam to carry given loads on a given span it is customary to select a beam which will support the required loads with safe *bending* stresses. If it then appears possible that the shearing stresses in the selected beam may be excessive, they are investigated. If it is found that they are excessive, a new beam is selected which combines the requisite shearing strength with the requisite bending strength.

This article will be limited to the design of beams from the standpoint of bending stresses.

In designing a beam, the following steps are usually necessary:[1]

(*a*) Preparation of a sketch giving locations of loads and reactions and amounts of loads.

(*b*) Calculation of reactions. This is not necessary for a cantilever beam.

(*c*) Drawing of a shear diagram. (For simple cases this may not be necessary.)

(*d*) Calculation of bending moments at cross-sections where shear changes sign or is equal to zero.

---

[1] For the simplest cases (for example, a beam with a single concentrated load at the midpoint), the maximum bending moment may be computed in terms of the load and length and the necessary section modulus found without other steps.

129

(e) Calculation of required section modulus, I/c, from $I/c = M/S$. (The greatest numerical value of M should be used, regardless of sign.)

(f) Selection of a beam the section modulus of which is slightly larger than that computed as necessary to carry the required load. (This excess is to provide for the additional moment caused by the weight of the beam itself.)

(g) Calculation of the moment caused by the weight of the beam itself *at the point where the bending moment caused by the given loads is a maximum.*

(h) Addition of this moment to the moment previously computed for the given loads, and calculation of the I/c required for the total bending moment.[1] This should not be more than the actual value of I/c for the beam which was selected. If it is more, it will be necessary to select a larger beam and repeat steps (g) and (h).

95. Effect of Weight of Beam. In some cases the weight of the beam is so small compared with the given loads that it may be entirely neglected. Until experience and good judgment have been acquired, however, it is safer to go through steps (g) and (h).

In general it is true that, for a beam of a given cross-section loaded so as to cause a given unit stress, the longer the span the greater is the proportion of the total load which is due to the weight of the beam. As an example take a 12-in., 53-lb. wide-flange beam with a uniformly distributed load such as to cause a stress of 18,000 lb. per sq. in. For a span of 9 ft. this load is 94,300 lb. The beam weighs 477 lb., which is about $\frac{1}{2}$ of 1 per cent of the total load. If the span is 18 ft., the total load can be 47,100 lb. This beam weighs 954 lb., which is about 2 per cent of the total load. If the span is 27 ft. the load can be 31,400 lb. This beam weighs 1,431 lb., which is $4\frac{1}{2}$ per cent of the total load.

If the weight of the beam does not add more than 2 or 3 per cent to the stresses, it can generally be neglected. For example, in selecting a steel beam to carry 90,000 lb. (distributed) on a span of 9 ft., the weight of the beam is negligible, but in selecting a beam to carry 30,000 lb. (distributed) on a span of 27 ft., the weight of the beam adds more than 4 per cent to the required section modulus, and this is not negligible.

96. Section Modulus. I/c is a function of the dimensions of the cross-section of the beam and is evidently independent of the material. For structural steel " shapes " (beams, channels, angles, etc.), values

---

[1] The maximum bending moment with the weight of the beam included may not occur at exactly the section at which the maximum bending moment neglecting the weight of the beam occurs. In some cases when the weight of the beam is large compared with the loads upon it, the true maximum bending moment should be computed after the weight of the beam is known.

of I/c are given in the steel makers' handbooks, in the tables usually designated " Elements of Sections." (See Appendix C.)

It sometimes happens that more than one size of steel beam has a suitable value of I/c. The lightest of these should be used unless there is some reason for using a heavier one.

For shapes not found in tables (such as beams of rectangular cross-section) it is necessary to compute I/c. It should be kept in mind that I is the moment of inertia of the cross-section with respect to the neutral axis (through the centroid of the cross-section). If the neutral axis is not midway between the top and bottom surfaces of the beam, there are two values of I/c corresponding to the stresses at the two " extreme fibers."

Wooden beams are generally rectangular in cross-section. For a rectangle I is $bh^3/12$ and c is $h/2$. Hence $\dfrac{I}{c} = \dfrac{bh^3/12}{h/2} = \dfrac{bh^2}{6}$. This simplified expression for I/c is convenient to use in solving for the dimensions of beams with solid rectangular cross-sections.

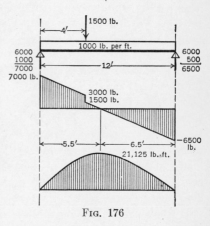

Example 1. A beam is to rest on two supports 12 ft. center to center and is required to carry a uniformly distributed load of 1,000 lb. per ft. and a concentrated load of 1,500 lb. 4 ft. from the left support. Select a satisfactory southern pine beam, using 1,600 lb. per sq. in. as the allowable bending stress and 125 lb. per sq. in. as the allowable shearing stress.

Solution: The reactions are computed

Fig. 176

and the shear and bending moments are drawn and are shown in Fig. 176. This covers steps (a) to (e) inclusive as outlined in Art. 94.

Step (f). Calculation of required section modulus:

$$\frac{I}{c} = \frac{M}{S} = \frac{21{,}125 \times 12}{1{,}600} = 158.5 \text{ in.}^3$$

For a rectangular cross-section $I/c = bh^2/6$. Hence

$$\frac{bh^2}{6} = 158.5$$

$$bh^2 = 951 \text{ in.}^3$$

Obviously there are numberless values of b and h which would make $bh^2 = 951$. It is economical to make the depth greater than the width, and a cross-section with a depth of about twice the width would probably be satisfactory. In that case

$bh^2 = h^3/2$.   Hence

$$h^3 = 1{,}902 \quad \text{and} \quad h = 12.4 \text{ in.}$$

Inasmuch as nominal sizes[1] of large timbers are multiples of 2 in. it will be necessary to have a nominal depth of 14 in. The actual depth of such a timber is 13.5 in. The necessary width can be calculated from $bh^2 = 951$,

$$b = \frac{951}{13.5^2} = 5.22 \text{ in.}$$

A beam nominally 6 in. wide has an actual width of 5.5 in. Hence a beam with nominal dimensions of 6 in. by 14 in. is large enough to resist bending stresses satisfactorily.

The weight of the beam should be considered. There are 7 board ft. per linear foot in a 6-in.-by-14-in. beam. The weight of the beam (at 4 lb. per board ft.) is 28 lb. per ft., which is provided for by the slight excess width of the beam. (The suitability of this beam from the standpoint of shear will be discussed in Art. 98.)

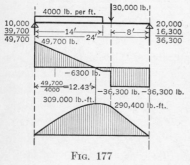

Fig. 177

Example 2. A steel beam is required to rest on supports 24 ft. center to center and to carry a distributed load of 4,000 lb. per ft. extending over 14 ft. at one end and a concentrated load of 30,000 lb. 8 ft. from the other end. Select a suitable beam if the bending stress is not to exceed 18,000 lb. per sq. in.

Solution: The sketch showing dimensions and loading is drawn in Fig. 177. Below are the shear and bending-moment diagrams. The maximum bending moment occurs 12.43 ft. from the left end and is 309,000 lb-ft.

The required section modulus is $\dfrac{I}{c} = \dfrac{309{,}000 \times 12}{18{,}000} = 206$ in.[3] Turning to the

tables, it will be noticed that the 18-in., 114-lb. wide-flange beam has a section modulus of 220.1 in.[3], which is ample. But the 21-in., 103-lb. beam, and the 24-in., 94-lb. beams also have adequate section moduli, and would therefore be better beams to use, in the absence of any condition making a shallow beam desirable. The table contains no beam lighter than the 24-in., 94-lb. with a sufficient section modulus.[2]

PROBLEMS

1. It is desired to support the loads shown in Fig. 178 with a piece of steel pipe. What size of standard steel pipe is necessary if the allowable stress is 18,000 lb. per sq. in.?   *Ans.* $1\frac{1}{2}$ in. pipe.

2. A wooden beam is to rest on supports 16.0 ft. center to center and to carry a load of 1,200 lb. 5 ft. from the left end and 1,600 lb. 6 ft. from the right end. Select

---

[1] Actual sizes of lumber corresponding to nominal sizes are given in Table X.

[2] A complete table, however, would include a 27-in., 91-lb. beam with a section modulus of 233 in.[3], which is the lightest standard beam that would carry the loads.

a suitable Douglas fir (dense, select grade) or southern yellow pine (dense, select grade), assuming continuously dry conditions. Make depth about three times the width.

3. A steel beam is to rest on supports 32 ft. center to center and to support a uniform load of 1,000 lb. per ft., and three loads of 8,000 lb., one at the midpoint and one at each quarter-point. Select the lightest steel beam to carry these loads if the allowable stress is 18,000 lb. per sq. in.

4. What percentage of the allowable bending moment for a beam 6 in. wide and 10 in. deep is the allowable bending moment for a commercial 6-in.-by-10-in. beam? What percentage is the allowable shear?

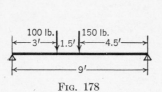

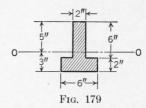

Fig. 178   Fig. 179

97. Design of Beams with Unsymmetrical Cross-Sections. For various reasons it is sometimes desirable or necessary to use a beam having a cross-section not symmetrical with respect to the neutral axis. Cast-iron beams, for instance, are always designed with the tension side wider than the compression side in order to reduce the tensile stress, since cast iron is weak in tension. The design consists in assuming a cross-section which seems suitable and then investigating this cross-section to determine whether it is large enough but not excessive.

Example. A cast-iron beam is required in the frame of a machine, the loads and lengths being such that the maximum bending moment is $+130,000$ lb.-in. and the maximum shear is 30,000 lb. Allowable stresses are tension, 3,000 lb. per sq. in.; compression, 12,000 lb. per sq. in.; shearing, 3,000 lb. per sq. in.

Solution: Assume the section shown in Fig. 179, and investigate it. The first steps are to calculate $\bar{y}$ and I_0. The neutral axis is found to be 5 in. from the top. I with respect to this axis is 136 in.[4]. Since the neutral axis is not midway between the top and bottom of the beam there are different values for c corresponding to the extreme fibers in tension and compression. Allowable bending moment as limited by compressive stress is

$$M = \frac{SI}{c} = \frac{12,000 \times 136}{5} = 326,000 \text{ lb.-in.}$$

As limited by tensile stress

$$M = \frac{SI}{c} = \frac{3,000 \times 136}{3} = 136,000 \text{ lb.-in.}$$

The formula for shearing stress $S = VQ/Ib$ may be written

$$V = \frac{SIb}{Q}$$

The allowable shear is

$$V = \frac{3,000 \times 136 \times 2}{5 \times 2 \times 2.5} = 32,600 \text{ lb.}$$

A beam of this cross-section will therefore carry the given loads with stresses below the allowable stresses.

It might be possible to save some material without exceeding the allowable stresses by slightly narrowing the web of the beam.

PROBLEMS

1. The maximum cross-section of a cast-iron beam has the dimensions shown in Fig. 180. Calculate the allowable bending moment if allowable stresses are: tension, 3,500 lb. per sq. in.; compression, 20,000 lb. per sq. in.

Ans. $M = 539,000$ lb-in.

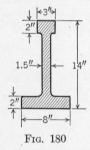

Fig. 180

Fig. 181

2. A beam is built up of a 12-in., 40.8-lb. American Standard I-beam and a 10-in., 20-lb. channel (Fig. 181). Calculate the allowable bending moment if the allowable stress is 20,000 lb. per sq. in. Compare with the allowable bending moment for the I-beam alone.

98. Investigation for Shearing Stress. In the beam that was selected in Example 1, Art. 96, the maximum shearing unit stress resulting from the given loads is found, from the equation $S_s = VQ/Ib$, to be 141 lb. per sq. in. The specified allowable stress, however, is only 125 lb. per sq. in. Therefore the selected beam, though satisfactory from the standpoint of bending stress, is not satisfactory from the standpoint of shear, and a beam of larger section must be used.

For a rectangular section, the value of Q/Ib is $1.5/A$, where A is the area of the cross-section. The maximum shearing stress in a beam of rectangular section therefore is $S_s = 1.5\ V/A$. This shows that, as far as shearing unit stress is concerned, the shape of the rectangle is of no importance. The necessary strength can be obtained by increasing either the depth or the width of the section. The area of the cross-section must be made equal to $1.5\ V/S_s$, which in this case is $10,500/125$ or 84 sq. in. If the nominal 14-in. depth is retained, this necessitates a width of $84/13.5$ or 6.22 in. To secure this width, a nominal 8-in.

dimension must be used. This results in a one-third increase in nominal cross-section over what was required for bending. If the nominal 6-in. width is retained, the depth must be at least 84/5.5 or 15.3 in. This requires a nominal 16-in. depth. It will evidently be more economical to increase the depth than to increase the width, and a 6-by-16 timber would be used, unless it were desirable to conserve headroom through the use of the shallower beam.

99. Shearing Stresses in Steel Beams. For steel I- and wide-flange beams, it is standard practice to use a slightly approximate method in connection with shearing unit stresses. Specifications ordinarily provide that the total shear, V, on any cross-section must not exceed the area of the *web* of the beam (which is considered to extend through the flanges) multiplied by a constant which is somewhat analogous to an average shearing unit stress acting *on the web only*. The 1929 Specification of the A.I.S.C., for example, requires that no beam shall be called on to withstand a shearing force greater than 12,000 times the web area. For the 24-in., 94-lb. wide-flange beam of Example 2, Art. 96, this would permit a maximum shear of 150,000 lb. Since the maximum shear caused by the load in that example is only 49,700 lb., it is evident that the beam selected in accordance with the requirements of bending stress will be entirely satisfactory from the standpoint of shear also.

This method of dealing with shears is purely empirical. Its justification rests on the fact that the shearing unit stress in the web of a steel beam is much more nearly uniform than in a beam of rectangular cross-section. Fig. 182 illustrates this fact for the 21-in., 112-lb. wide-flange section. For a rectangular beam, the intensity of horizontal and vertical shearing unit stresses varies in a parabolic arc from the top surface to the neutral axis, and thence to the bottom surface. But for the wide-flange steel beam, the shearing stress is very small at any point

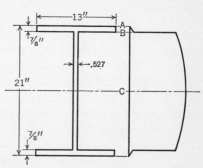

FIG. 182. Variation of shearing stress in wide-flange beam.

between A and B. At B, however, because of the sudden decrease in width, there is a large increase in unit stress. For successive points between B and C, the value of Q increases very slowly, so that the stress at C is not materially greater than that at B. As noted above, the A.I.S.C. Specification allows a maximum shearing force of 133,000 lb.

on this section, obtained by multiplying the web area by 12,000. With this shear on the beam, the maximum shearing unit stress as given by $S_s = VQ/Ib$ is 13,200 lb. per sq. in., which is a reasonable value. The empirical procedure gives satisfactory results.

100. When Shearing Stresses Are Important. The bending moment in a beam is usually a function jointly of the length of the beam and the loads on it. The shear, V, however, depends only on the loads, and is independent of the length. It is obvious that, from the standpoint of bending stresses, as the length of the beam decreases the amount of load can increase correspondingly without causing any increase in bending moment, and therefore in bending unit stress. But as the load increases, the maximum shear, V, increases proportionately. In a long beam, therefore, bending stresses are likely to be more serious; but in a short beam, shearing stresses may be more serious than bending stresses.

As a numerical example, consider two wooden beams each 6 in. by 10 in. in cross-section and with lengths of 15 ft. and 5 ft. respectively. Let the allowable bending stress be 1,600 lb. per sq. in., and the allowable shearing stress be 90 lb. per sq. in. Then the uniformly distributed load which each of the beams can carry without exceeding the shearing stress will be $\frac{4}{3} S_s A$ or 7,200 lb.

The flexure formula shows that a maximum bending stress of 1,600 lb. per sq. in. in the longer beam would be caused by a load of 7,100 lb. Therefore a load which would develop the allowable bending stress in the beam would be permissible from the standpoint of shear. On the other hand, the uniformly distributed load to produce the allowable bending stress of 1,600 lb. per sq. in. in the short beam is 21,300 lb. But this load would cause a shearing unit stress of 266 lb. per sq. in., which is almost three times what is permissible. Shearing stress is important in short beams carrying heavy, uniformly distributed loads. It is also important in beams of any length that carry heavy concentrated loads near the supports, since the effect of such loads is to cause shearing stresses disproportionately large in comparison with the bending stresses produced.

Obviously, also, shear is more likely to be of importance in wooden than in steel beams because of the low strength which wood possesses for resisting shearing stresses parallel to the grain.

PROBLEMS

1. With the cross-section and unit stresses used in the example above, find the minimum length of beam in which the allowable uniformly distributed load is determined by bending stress.   *Ans.* $L = 14.8$ ft.

2. In Fig. 183, what is the greatest allowable load P?   The members are Douglas fir.   Allowable stresses are: shearing, 90 lb. per sq. in.; bending, 1,600 lb. per sq. in.; bearing on side of grain, 347 lb. per sq. in.   Neglect weight of the beam.

3. The beam shown in Fig. 184 is a 4-in., 7.7-lb. I-beam.   Find safe loads P: (*a*) as limited by bending stress of 18,000 lb. per sq. in.; (*b*) as limited by allowable average shear on web of 12,000 lb. per sq. in.

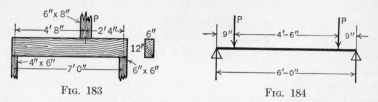

FIG. 183   FIG. 184

101. " Buckling " of Beam Flanges and Webs.   The factors that have so far been considered in the design of a beam are the maximum flexural stress and the maximum vertical and horizontal shearing stresses caused by the load.   There are two other conditions that may limit the allowable load.   The first of these is the possibility of lateral deflection or " buckling " of the compression flange.   The second is the possibility of buckling of the web of the beam under a heavy concentrated load (or reaction).

Tensile stress in the flange of a beam tends to *straighten* the flange; compressive stress, however, tends to cause the flange to " bow " out of line.   Where conditions are such that this sidewise deflection can occur, the beam may fail under a load much less than that which the beam could carry in the absence of any lateral deflection of the compression flange.   Most beams with cross-sections of such form as to make this lateral deflection a possibility are used in ways that restrain the compression flange against sidewise motion.   But when this is not the case, proper allowance for lateral deflection is an essential part of the beam design.

In the case of beams with deep and thin webs, danger exists that where large concentrated loads (or reactions) are applied to the beam, the web may buckle under the load, this part of the web acting like an overloaded column.

Methods of dealing with the possibility of buckling of either the web or the flange are discussed in Chapter XX.   They can be understood better after columns have been studied.

Consideration of the way in which a load is applied to a beam is not essentially a part of the design of the *beam*.   It may well be noted at this point, however, that all concentrated loads and reactions should be applied to beams in ways that will not cause excessive local compressive or bearing stresses.   For steel beams with loads applied through riveted connections, this matter was discussed in Chapter V. With wooden beams, which are much weaker in resisting compression perpendicular to the grain than compression parallel to the grain, the area over which a concentrated load is applied must often be increased by use of a *bearing plate*. The necessary area of this plate is determined by the relationship $A = P/S_c$, where P is the load and S_c is the allowable compressive unit stress perpendicular to the grain. The minimum length of bearing that a beam must have on the support on which it rests is also sometimes determined by the sidewise compressive stress.

102. Economical Sections of Beams. Where the necessary size of a beam is determined by *bending* stresses, depth is of special importance, since I/c increases much more rapidly with increase in the depth of a cross-section than with increase in its width. Example 2, Art. 96, illustrated this fact by showing that an 18-in., 114-lb. wide-flange beam, a 20-in., 112-lb. beam, a 24-in., 94-lb. beam, and a 27-in., 91-lb. beam all have section moduli of about the same amount. If there is no limitation on the depth of beam that may be used, the deeper sections will be more economical where bending stresses are the important stresses.

Where shearing stresses, rather than bending stresses, determine the size of a beam, the total *web area* is the only consideration, and a heavy shallow web usually has some advantages over a deep, thin web, which may " buckle."

In a beam made of a material such as steel, which is equally strong in tension and in compression, it is logical to make the cross-section

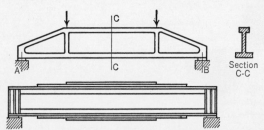

FIG. 185. Cast beam and built-up beam (plate girder) of variable cross-section.

symmetrical with respect to the neutral axis. Steel beams usually have cross-sections of this sort. On the other hand, with a material such as cast iron which is much stronger in compression than in tension, economy is gained by making the compression flange smaller than the tension flange (Fig. 180).

It is obvious that, if bending stresses determine the necessary cross-section of a beam, any beam which has the same cross-section throughout its length will have an excess of strength at sections other than the dangerous section. In certain beams, such as rolled steel beams, to vary the cross-section of the beam would cost more than any resulting economy of material would warrant. There are situations, however, in which it is practicable to vary the cross-section of the beam approximately in accordance with variation in the bending moment (Fig. 185). If this could be done perfectly, a beam of uniform flexural strength throughout its length would result. Beams of uniform strength are considered briefly in Chapter XVII.

GENERAL PROBLEMS

1. Select an I-beam to carry a load of 4,000 lb. per ft. over a span of 20 ft. with a maximum bending stress of 17,000 lb. per sq. in.

2. Three planks the dimensions of which are 2 in. by 6 in. are spiked together to form a beam of the type shown in Fig. 175. The span is 6 ft. center to center of supports. What uniformly distributed load will cause a maximum shearing stress of 120 lb. per sq. in.?   *Ans.* Total load = 3,610 lb.

3. A southern pine beam $11\frac{1}{2}$ in. deep and $7\frac{1}{2}$ in. wide rests on supports 16 ft. apart. What concentrated load at the midpoint will bring the stress up to 1,300 lb. per sq. in.? What percentage of this stress is caused by the weight of the beam itself? What is the maximum longitudinal shearing stress?

$$\textit{Ans.} \quad S_s = 40.9 \text{ lb. per sq. in.}$$

4. Solve Problem 3 if the beam is $11\frac{1}{2}$ in. wide and $7\frac{1}{2}$ in. deep.

5. Select the lightest steel beam to serve as a cantilever 20 ft. long with 5,000 lb. at the end. ($S = 16,000$ lb. per sq. in.)

6. Select the lightest steel beam to carry the loads shown in Fig. 186. ($S = 16,000$ lb. per sq. in.)

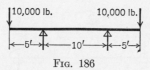

FIG. 186

7. Select a Douglas fir beam with span of 30 ft. (make $h = 2 b$, approximately) to carry 20,000 lb. uniformly distributed. (If depth exceeds 16 in. for one beam use more than one. Do not neglect weight of beam.)

8. Design a lintel to support the brickwork over a door opening 12 ft. wide in a brick wall 13 in. thick. Take the span of the lintel as 12 ft. 6 in. Consider that the load on the lintel is the weight of a triangular segment of the wall 12 ft. 6 in. long and with its sides making angles of 45° with the horizontal. The wall may be assumed to weigh 120 lb. per cu. ft. The lintel should be composed of two equal angles of the same weight, with one leg of each angle horizontal and the face of the other leg coinciding with the surface of the wall.

9. A steel I-beam having a span of 24 ft. carries a total load of 24,000 lb. This load varies uniformly from zero at the supports to a maximum at midspan. Select a suitable steel beam. The allowable stress is 18,000 lb. per sq. in.

10. This wrench (Fig. 187) is to have the same factor of safety with respect to bending stress in the arms and shearing stress in the stem. If the ultimate shearing strength of the material is $\frac{3}{4}$ the ultimate tensile strength, what should the diameter of the arms be?

11. It can be shown that the section modulus of a beam of square cross-section with the diagonal vertical is increased if the top and bottom corners are removed to a depth of one-ninth of the height. Calculate the allowable bending moment, for an allowable stress of 1,200 lb. per sq. in., for the beam shown in Fig. 188, and compare it with the allowable bending moment if the cross-section is the original square. Compare the shearing stress in the two cross-sections.

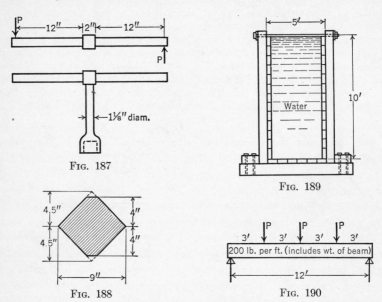

FIG. 187

FIG. 189

FIG. 188

FIG. 190

12. A water tank is constructed as shown in Fig. 189. The vertical beams are in pairs as shown and are 3 ft. apart along the length of the tank. Draw shear and bending-moment diagrams, and select a suitable beam of select grade cypress. (Assume it to be more or less continuously wet.)

13. A 21-in., 59-lb. wide-flange beam on supports 30 ft. on centers is to carry a concentrated load of 53,000 lb. at its midpoint. To increase the section modulus a 10-in.-by-$\frac{3}{4}$-in. cover plate is to be welded to each flange. These plates are obviously not necessary near the ends where the bending moment is small. What is the theoretical minimum length of each plate? ($S = 18,000$ lb. per sq. in.)

14. A 6-in.-by-10-in. (actual size) wooden beam carries loads as shown in Fig. 190. If the stress is not to exceed 1,600 lb. per sq. in., what is the maximum value of P?   Ans. $P = 1,620$ lb.

CHAPTER X

THE DEFLECTION OF STATICALLY DETERMINATE BEAMS

In this chapter the double integration method and the area moment method are both applied to the determination of beam deflections. The simpler cases are analyzed first by one method and then by the other. At the end of the chapter a number of more complex loadings are analyzed by the area moment method. In Chapter XI both methods are applied to the analysis of restrained beams, with the area moment method applied to a somewhat wider variety of loadings. In Chapter XVIII the theorem of three moments is derived by both methods. The authors recommend study of both methods, but both methods are independently presented and either one may be omitted if desired. In any event, however, Art. 107 (equation of the elastic curve) should be studied as a foundation for the theory of columns. At intervals in the text notations are made as to articles that may be omitted if only one of the methods is to be applied to beams.

103. Reasons for Calculating Beam Deflections. It has already been mentioned that a beam changes its shape when loads are applied. The vertical movement of a point on the neutral surface of a horizontal beam is called the *deflection* of the beam at that point. For several reasons an engineer should be able to calculate the amount of the deflection of a beam. In some cases a limitation upon the amount of deflection determines the size of a beam. For some machine parts and for the structural supports of some types of machinery, the deflections must not exceed certain very small amounts. For instance, in foundations for turbogenerator units it is sometimes specified that the deflection of any beam must not exceed 1/2,000 of the length of the beam. Another example is that of floor beams which carry plastered ceilings underneath. It is generally specified that the deflection of such beams must not exceed 1/360 of the span in order to avoid cracking the plaster. Beams which would be strong enough may be found to deflect too much. The designer must select a beam which will not deflect excessively even though this beam may be stronger than necessary. In certain other cases, any amount of deflection may be permissible, but it may be important to know how much the beam does deflect at some point.

One of the most important reasons for understanding a method of calculating deflections arises in connection with certain types of indeterminate beams which occur very frequently. Beams are said to be "indeterminate" (see Fig. 132) when the reactions cannot be found by the equations of equilibrium. In these cases the additional equations needed are obtained from deflections or slopes of the beam.

141

This chapter takes up methods by which deflections can be calculated and applies these methods to cantilever and simple beams under ordinary types of loading. Before taking up the actual calculation of deflections, however, certain fundamental relations between curvature, bending moment, and stresses will be considered.

104. Radius of Curvature and Stress. The line of intersection of the neutral surface of a beam and a vertical longitudinal plane is called the *elastic curve of the beam.*

A definite relation exists between the unit stress in the extreme fibers of a given beam and the radius of curvature of the elastic curve. It is

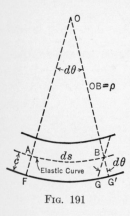

here assumed that the beam is straight when it is unloaded. In Fig. 191, AB is a short part of the elastic curve of a beam which has been bent by loads. Planes through A and B which were originally parallel (and vertical) now meet at O. A and B are very close together, the length ds being infinitesimal, and it may be assumed without any appreciable error that the bending moments at A and B are equal and also that the radii of curvature OA and OB are equal. If a plane BG is passed through B parallel to the plane AF, FG is the original length of the extreme fibers. These have increased in length by the amount GG'. The unit deformation of the extreme fibers is GG'/FG, which equals GG'/AB. If the proportional limit is not exceeded the unit stress equals the unit deformation multiplied by the modulus of elasticity, or

Fig. 191

$$S = \frac{GG'}{AB} E$$

But $AB = OB \times d\theta$ and, since $d\theta$ is small, $GG' = BG' \times d\theta$. Hence

$$\frac{GG'}{AB} = \frac{BG'}{OB}$$

But $BG' = c$ and $OB = \rho$, the radius of curvature. Hence

$$\frac{GG'}{AB} = \frac{c}{\rho}$$

Substituting c/ρ for GG'/AB in the expression for stress,

$$S = \frac{c}{\rho} E \quad \text{or} \quad \frac{S}{E} = \frac{c}{\rho}$$

That is, the stress in the extreme fibers of a beam is to the modulus of elasticity as the distance to the extreme fibers from the neutral axis is to the radius of curvature.

PROBLEMS

1. A small steel band saw is 0.018 in. thick. The pulleys on which it runs are 12 in. in diameter. What stress results in the extreme fibers?

Ans. $S = 45,000$ lb. per sq. in.

2. If the diameter of steel wire is d in., what is the diameter, D, of the coil in which it can be wound without causing a stress of more than 20,000 lb. per sq. in.?

105. Radius of Curvature and Bending Moment. The preceding article derived the relation $S = \dfrac{c}{\rho} E$, in which S is the unit stress in the extreme fibers of a beam. But $S = Mc/I$. Equating these two expressions for S,

$$\frac{c}{\rho} E = \frac{Mc}{I}$$

from which

$$M = \frac{EI}{\rho}$$

This simple relation makes it possible to compute the bending moment required to bend a beam to a given radius of curvature or to compute the radius of curvature of the elastic curve at any point in a beam if the bending moment is known. The formula $M = EI/\rho$ indicates that, if the bending moment is constant over part of the length of a beam, the radius of curvature is also constant and the elastic curve is the arc of a circle.

Where the bending moment varies, as it usually does, the curvature is sharper where the bending moment is larger.

PROBLEMS

1. A steel bar 1 in. square is loaded as shown in Fig. 192. Calculate the radius of curvature of the part between the supports.

Ans. $\rho = 104$ ft., 2 in.

2. A stick of oak 1 in. wide and $\frac{1}{2}$ in. thick is bent to a radius of curvature of 62 in. by a bending moment of 227 lb-in. Calculate E.

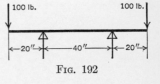

FIG. 192

106. Methods of Calculating Deflections in Beams; Assumptions Made. Several methods are available for calculating the deflection of a beam at any point.

In the method first used an equation for the elastic curve of the beam is written. This equation may be solved and the slope and deflection obtained.   This method was used by Leonhard Euler prior to 1750 and has been commonly used up to the present time.

In 1875 Professor Wilhelm Fraenkel of Dresden published a formula based upon the equality between work done by the movement of a load on the beam as the beam deflects and the work of resistance of the fibers of the beam (the product of the stress in the fibers and their change in length).   This method has many merits but is not widely used, except for indeterminate structures.

In 1873 Professor Charles E. Greene discovered a method which he called the *area moment* method.   This he taught in his classes at the University of Michigan and published it in 1874.   Professor Greene was unaware that a somewhat similar method had been published in 1868 by Professor Otto Mohr in Germany.

Assumptions.   In calculating deflections the following assumptions are commonly made.

1. It is assumed that the stresses caused by bending are below the proportional limit so that Hooke's law holds.

2. It is assumed that a plane section across the beam remains a plane after the beam is bent.

3. It is assumed that the length of the elastic curve is the same as the length of its horizontal projection.   For the actual beams in ordinary use this assumption is well within the limits of accuracy of ordinary methods of calculation.

4. It is assumed that deflections due to shear are negligible.   A more accurate statement is this: The deflection computed is that due to bending alone, and the deflection due to shearing stress must be calculated separately if necessary.   Deflections due to shearing stress are generally so much smaller than those due to bending that they may be entirely neglected without appreciable error.   They are discussed in Chapter XX.

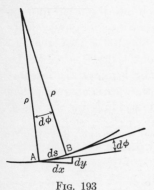

FIG. 193

BEAM DEFLECTIONS BY THE DOUBLE INTEGRATION METHOD

107. Equation of the Elastic Curve.   To derive a general expression for the elastic curve of a beam, consider two points, A and B, on a curve (Fig. 193), the length of the arc AB being ds.   At each of these points, the slope of the curve is the slope of the tangent at that point, and is equal to the value of dy/dx at that point.   The angle $d\phi$ between the two tangents is the change in the slope of the curve that has occurred in the distance ds. The rate of change of the slope with respect to s is $d\phi/ds$. But the rate of change of the slope of the curve with respect to s is also $\dfrac{d\dfrac{dy}{dx}}{ds}$ and hence $\dfrac{d\phi}{ds} = \dfrac{d\dfrac{dy}{dx}}{ds}$. But $d\phi$ is also the angle between the radii of curvature, so that $ds/\rho = d\phi$ or $d\phi/ds = 1/\rho$. Also *if the slope of the curve is small*, ds differs only slightly from dx and the second member of the equation $\dfrac{d\dfrac{dy}{dx}}{ds}$ may be written d^2y/dx^2. The equation[1] thus becomes

$$\frac{1}{\rho} = \frac{d^2y}{dx^2}$$

But $1/\rho = M/EI$. Hence

$$\frac{d^2y}{dx^2} = \frac{M}{EI}$$

This equation is commonly called the *general equation of the elastic curve* of a deflected beam. When M for a given beam has been expressed as a function of x (the x axis being parallel to the undeflected beam and a convenient origin having been chosen) the equation represents a definite curve. It is evidently not the common type of equation of this curve, expressing directly the relation between the abscissas, x, and the ordinates, y, of points on the curve. Instead, it defines the curve by giving *the sharpness of its curvature* (d^2y/dx^2) at any point in terms of x, the abscissa of the point. To convert the equation into the usual form of expression in x and y, it is necessary to perform two integrations, evaluating the resulting constants and inserting their values in the final equation.

In succeeding articles this general equation of the elastic curve will be applied to several important types of beams and loadings, the integrations will be performed, and the equation of the elastic curve for that particular type of beam and loading will be obtained in terms of x and y.

[1] Since this equation is based on the assumption that dx equals ds, it is approximate rather than exact. Textbooks on calculus show that the exact value is

$$\frac{1}{\rho} = \frac{\dfrac{d^2y}{dx^2}}{\left[1 + \left(\dfrac{dy}{dx}\right)^2\right]^{\frac{3}{2}}}$$

But if the slope of the curve, dy/dx, is small, it follows that $(dy/dx)^2$ is an extremely small quantity compared with unity and may be neglected in the above equation. In this case the denominator becomes unity and $1/\rho = d^2y/dx^2$.

108. Signs of Quantities in Equations for Elastic Curve. When writing an expression for M in terms of x the sign given to the expression for M should be consistent with the conventions previously given for the sign of bending moment.

The slope of the curve at a given point dy/dx is positive if the tangent to the curve at that point slopes upward and away from the origin. The quantity d^2y/dx^2 is the rate of change of the slope with respect to x, and a plus value of this corresponds to an increasing steepness of a plus slope or a decreasing steepness of a minus slope. Therefore a plus d^2y/dx^2 corresponds to plus bending moment, as will be seen by considering Fig. 194.

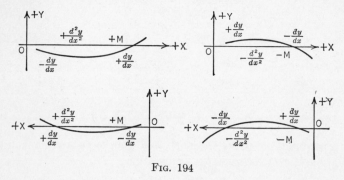

FIG. 194

If, in writing the equation $M/EI = d^2y/dx^2$, the quantity d^2y/dx^2 is always given a plus sign, then the values for the slope dy/dx and for the ordinate y will have the correct signs when the equation is solved.

The ordinate y will be the desired deflection only if the x axis is chosen so that it coincides with the original undeflected elastic curve. However, if the x axis is chosen above or below the undeflected elastic curve the deflection is readily found from the ordinate y.

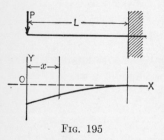

FIG. 195

In this book the positive direction of the y axis will always be considered as upward. The positive direction of the x axis may be taken as either to the right or to the left from the origin.

109. Cantilever Beam; Concentrated Load at End. (Arts. 109 to 114 inclusive, may be omitted if the double integration method is not to be applied to beam deflection.) The diagrams in Fig. 195 show the loaded beam, and below it is sketched the approximate shape of the elastic curve. The origin is taken at the free end of the unloaded beam with the x axis lying in the neutral surface. The value of the bending moment at a point x inches from the origin is $-Px$. Hence

$$\frac{d^2y}{dx^2} = -\frac{Px}{EI}$$

Integrating,

$$\frac{dy}{dx} = -\frac{Px^2}{2\,EI} + C_1$$

But dy/dx is the slope of the curve, and this is seen to be zero when $x = L$. Hence

$$-\frac{PL^2}{2\,EI} + C_1 = 0$$

or

$$C_1 = \frac{PL^2}{2\,EI}$$

and

$$\frac{dy}{dx} = -\frac{Px^2}{2\,EI} + \frac{PL^2}{2\,EI}$$

which is an equation giving the slope of the curve at any point in terms of the abscissa x of that point. Integrating,

$$y = -\frac{Px^3}{6\,EI} + \frac{PL^2x}{2\,EI} + C_2$$

It will be seen that $y = 0$ when $x = L$, from which

$$-\frac{PL^3}{6\,EI} + \frac{PL^3}{2\,EI} + C_2 = 0 \quad \text{or} \quad C_2 = -\frac{PL^3}{3\,EI}$$

This, substituted in the above value of y, gives

$$y = -\frac{Px^3}{6\,EI} + \frac{PL^2x}{2\,EI} - \frac{PL^3}{3\,EI}$$

This is the equation of the elastic curve of this beam with reference to the chosen axes. The maximum deflection is the value of y when $x = 0$ or

$$y_{\text{max.}} = -\frac{PL^3}{3\,EI}$$

The minus sign indicates that, with the origin and axes as chosen, the point of maximum deflection is below the x axis. Since E is in pounds per square inch, P must be in pounds and L must be in inches when solving for y, which will then be in inches.

110. Significance of the Constants of Integration. The equation

$$\frac{dy}{dx} = -\frac{Px^2}{2\,EI} + C_1$$

in the preceding example expresses the slope of the curve at any point in terms of the abscissa of the point.   If the value of x is zero, $dy/dx = C_1$. That is, *the first constant of integration is the value of the slope at the point on the curve where $x = 0$.*

The equation

$$y = -\frac{Px^3}{6\,EI} + \frac{PL^2x}{2\,EI} + C_2$$

gives the value of y in terms of x.   If $x = 0$, $y = C_2$, showing that *the second constant of integration is the value of the ordinate of the curve at the point where $x = 0$.*

In order to emphasize the significance of the constants of integration, the axes in the above example were chosen so that neither C_1 nor C_2 would be zero.   It is often possible and desirable, however, to choose an origin which makes one or both of these constants zero, thereby simplifying the solution.

In beams where E and I are both constant, as is nearly always the case, it is convenient to keep EI in the left-hand member of the equation as a coefficient.   When this is done C_1 is EI times the slope of the curve where $x = 0$; or C_1/EI is the slope of the curve where $x = 0$; and C_2/EI is the ordinate where $x = 0$.

PROBLEM

Solve the above example, taking the origin on the curve at the fixed end.

111. Cantilever Beam; Uniformly Distributed Load. The origin will be taken at the fixed end (Fig. 196).   Then $M_x = -\dfrac{w(L - x)^2}{2}$ and consequently

$$EI\frac{d^2y}{dx^2} = -\frac{w(L - x)^2}{2} = -\frac{wL^2}{2} + wLx - \frac{wx^2}{2}$$

Integrating,

$$EI\frac{dy}{dx} = -\frac{wL^2x}{2} + \frac{wLx^2}{2} - \frac{wx^3}{6} + C_1$$

but $dy/dx = 0$ when $x = 0$.   Hence $C_1 = 0$ as it must be with the origin as chosen. Integrating again,

$$EIy = -\frac{wL^2x^2}{4} + \frac{wLx^3}{6} - \frac{wx^4}{24} + C_2$$

but $y = 0$ when $x = 0$. Hence $C_2 = 0$. Hence the equation of this elastic curve referred to the chosen axes is

$$EIy = -\frac{wL^2x^2}{4} + \frac{wLx^3}{6} - \frac{wx^4}{24}$$

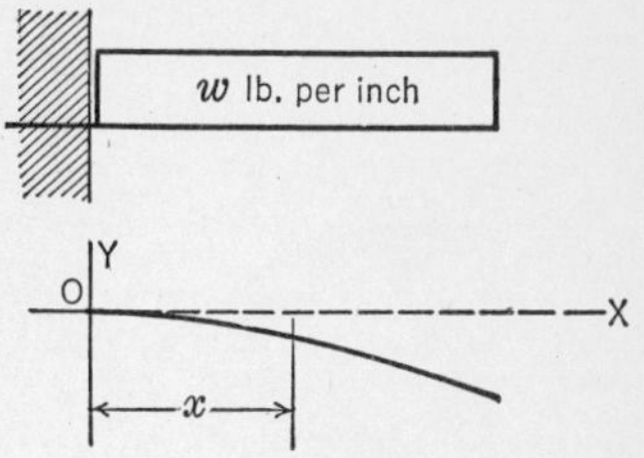

The maximum deflection is the value of y when $x = L$.

$$EIy_{\text{max.}} = -\frac{wL^4}{4} + \frac{wL^4}{6} - \frac{wL^4}{24} = -\frac{wL^4}{8}$$

or

$$y_{\text{max.}} = -\frac{wL^4}{8\,EI}$$

If $W = wL$, the total load, then

$$y_{\text{max.}} = -\frac{WL^3}{8\,EI}$$

Fig. 196

PROBLEMS

1. (a) Calculate the deflection of a wooden cantilever beam 4 in. deep, 2 in. wide, and 12 ft. long caused by a uniformly distributed load of 10 lb. per ft. (b) Calculate the slope at the end. ($E = 1,200,000$ lb. per sq. in.) *Ans.* (a) $y = 3.50$ in. (b) .0324 rad

2. Using the principle of summation of effects and the expressions for slope and deflection previously derived, calculate the deflection at the end of the beam shown in Fig. 197. 0.828

3. A cantilever beam is subjected to a moment of T lb-in. applied at the end. Using the equation for the elastic curve, calculate the slope and the deflection at the end. $slope = \frac{TL}{EI}$, $Defl = \frac{TL^2}{2EI}$

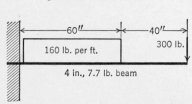

Fig. 197

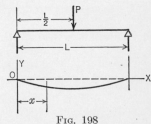

Fig. 198

112. Beam on Two Supports; Concentrated Load at Midpoint. For the left half of the beam shown in Fig. 198 (x between zero and $L/2$)

$$M_x = \frac{P}{2}x \text{ and}$$

$$EI\frac{d^2y}{dx^2} = \frac{Px}{2}$$

Integrating,

$$EI\frac{dy}{dx} = \frac{Px^2}{4} + C_1$$

but, because of symmetry, $dy/dx = 0$ when $x = L/2$. Therefore $C_1 = -PL^2/16$. Hence

$$EI\frac{dy}{dx} = \frac{Px^2}{4} - \frac{PL^2}{16}$$

Integrating,

$$EIy = \frac{Px^3}{12} - \frac{PL^2x}{16} + C_2$$

but $y = 0$ when $x = 0$. Therefore $C_2 = 0$.

The equation for the elastic curve (for values of x not more than $L/2$) is

$$EIy = \frac{Px^3}{12} - \frac{PL^2x}{16}$$

The maximum deflection is the value of y for $x = L/2$.

$$EIy = \frac{PL^3}{96} - \frac{PL^3}{32} = -\frac{PL^3}{48}$$

Therefore

$$y_{\text{max.}} = -\frac{PL^3}{48\,EI}$$

Note, too, that each half of this beam may be considered as a cantilever with a length $L/2$ and an *upward* concentrated load $P/2$ at its end. Substituting these values in the equation derived in Art. 109,

$$y_{\text{max.}} = -\frac{\left(\frac{P}{2}\right)\left(\frac{L}{2}\right)^3}{3\,EI} = -\frac{PL^3}{48\,EI}, \text{ as above}$$

PROBLEMS

1. A 4-in., 7.7-lb. American standard beam rests on supports 12 ft. center to center. Calculate the deflection caused by a load of 1,500 lb. at the midpoint of the beam.   *Ans.* $y = 0.518$ in.

2. Calculate the end slope of the beam in Problem 1 caused by this load.

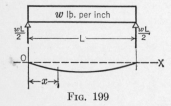

FIG. 199

113. Beam on Two Supports; Uniformly Loaded. The origin is taken at the left support (Fig. 199).

$$M_x = \frac{wLx}{2} - \frac{wx^2}{2}$$

and consequently

$$EI \frac{d^2y}{dx^2} = \frac{wLx}{2} - \frac{wx^2}{2}$$

Integrating,

$$EI \frac{dy}{dx} = \frac{wLx^2}{4} - \frac{wx^3}{6} + C_1$$

but $dy/dx = 0$ when $x = L/2$.   Therefore

$$C_1 = \frac{wL^3}{48} - \frac{wL^3}{16} = -\frac{wL^3}{24}$$

Therefore

$$EI \frac{dy}{dx} = \frac{wLx^2}{4} - \frac{wx^3}{6} - \frac{wL^3}{24}$$

Integrating,

$$EIy = \frac{wLx^3}{12} - \frac{wx^4}{24} - \frac{wL^3x}{24} + C_2$$

But $y = 0$ when $x = 0$, hence $C_2 = 0$ and

$$EIy = \frac{wLx^3}{12} - \frac{wx^4}{24} - \frac{wL^3x}{24}$$

The maximum deflection is the value of y corresponding to $x = L/2$

$$EIy = \frac{wL^4}{96} - \frac{wL^4}{384} - \frac{wL^4}{48} = -\frac{5\,wL^4}{384}$$

Therefore

$$y_{max} = -\frac{5\,wL^4}{384\,EI}$$

If the total load is W lb.

$$y_{max.} = -\frac{5\,WL^3}{384\,EI}$$

PROBLEMS

1. What is the greatest uniformly distributed load that a 10-in., 25.4-lb. American standard beam can carry if the deflection is not to exceed that commonly allowed for beams supporting plastered ceilings?   The span is 20 ft.   What will be the end slope of the beam?

2. A wooden beam $5\frac{1}{2}$ in. wide and $11\frac{1}{2}$ in. deep rests on supports 18 ft. center to center.   It carries a uniform load of W lb. and a concentrated load of P lb. at the midpoint.   If P and W are equal, calculate their values to cause a stress of 1,600 lb. per sq. in.   What deflection results from these loads if $E = 1,400,000$ lb. per sq. in.?

Ans. $P = 2,400$ lb.

114. Beam on Two Supports, with One Non-Central Load. This entire curve (Fig. 200) cannot be expressed by a single equation. The problem can be solved with one origin, but the following solution makes use of two origins, one at each support.

Between Left Reaction and Load

Between Right Reaction and Load (regard x' as $+$, as shown)

$$M = \frac{Pbx}{L} \qquad\qquad M = \frac{Pax'}{L}$$

Hence, $\quad EI \dfrac{d^2y}{dx^2} = \dfrac{Pbx}{L} \qquad\qquad EI \dfrac{d^2y'}{dx'^2} = \dfrac{Pax'}{L}$ (1)

Integrating, $\quad EI \dfrac{dy}{dx} = \dfrac{Pbx^2}{2L} + C_1 \qquad\qquad EI \dfrac{dy'}{dx'} = \dfrac{Pax'^2}{2L} + C_2$ (2)

Integrating again,

$$EIy = \frac{Pbx^3}{6L} + C_1 x + C_3 \qquad\qquad EIy' = \frac{Pax'^3}{6L} + C_2 x' + C_4 \quad (3)$$

when $x = 0$, $y = 0$, hence $C_3 = 0$ $\quad\big|\quad$ when $x' = 0$, $y' = 0$, hence $C_4 = 0$

When $x = a$, for left segment the deflection equals the deflection of the right-hand segment for $x' = b$. Equating these two values of EIy,

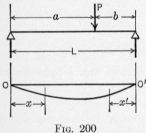

Fig. 200

$$\frac{Pba^3}{6L} + C_1 a = +\frac{Pab^3}{6L} + C_2 b \qquad (4)$$

The slope of the left segment at the load equals the slope of the right segment at the load, but one is upward and the other is downward. Hence the slope dy/dx of left segment for $x = a$ equals minus the slope of the right segment for $x' = b$, whence

$$\frac{Pba^2}{2L} + C_1 = -\frac{Pab^2}{2L} - C_2 \qquad (5)$$

Solving equations (4) and (5) for C_1,

$$C_1 = -\frac{Pab}{6L}(L + b) \qquad (6)$$

Substituting this value for C_1 in (3)

$$EIy = \frac{Pbx^3}{6L} - \frac{Pabx}{6L}(L + b) = \frac{Pbx}{6L}[x^2 - a(L + b)] \qquad (7)$$

Substituting the value for C_1 in (2),

$$EI\frac{dy}{dx} = \frac{Pbx^2}{2L} - \frac{Pab}{6L}(L+b) \tag{8}$$

The deflection is maximum where $dy/dx = 0$, from which

$$x = \sqrt{\frac{a}{3}(L+b)} = \frac{1}{3}\sqrt{3\,a(a+2\,b)}. \tag{9}$$

The maximum deflection is obtained by substituting this value for x in (7)

$$y = \frac{Pb\sqrt{3\,a(a+2\,b)}}{18\,LEI}\left[\frac{a}{3}(L+b) - a(L+b)\right]$$

$$= \frac{Pab(a+2\,b)\sqrt{3\,a(a+2\,b)}}{27\,LEI} \tag{10}$$

PROBLEMS

1. A beam rests on two supports 100 in. apart and carries a load P 20 in. from one reaction. Using equation (7) above, calculate the deflection at the midpoint of the beam and compare with the maximum deflection. How many inches from the midpoint does the maximum deflection occur? See equation (9).

2. Referring to equation (9) of this article, it is apparent that the distance to the point of maximum deflection increases as a increases. Show that the point of maximum deflection in a beam on two supports, without overhang, and carrying a single concentrated load, cannot be more than $0.077\,L$ from the midpoint.

BEAM DEFLECTIONS BY THE AREA MOMENT METHOD

(Arts. 115 to 122, inclusive, may be omitted if the area moment method is not to be studied.)

115. The Area Moment Method. The principles employed in the area moment method of determining beam slopes and deflections afford a simple means of calculating the angle θ (in radians) between the

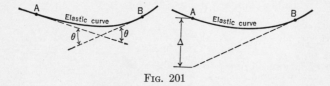

FIG. 201

tangents to the elastic curve at any two points. They also afford a simple means of calculating the displacement (in a direction perpendicular to the length of the undeflected beam) of any point on the elastic curve of the beam from the tangent to the elastic curve at any other point. These two quantities are illustrated in Fig. 201. *AB* is part of the elastic curve of a beam which was originally straight and horizontal.

The application of these principles to an actual problem is illustrated in Fig. 202. The maximum deflection of the cantilever beam evidently equals the displacement of point A from the tangent at point B. The slope of the beam at A (which may be needed for some purposes) equals the angle between the tangent at A and the tangent at B.

The area moment method makes use of a diagram called "the M/EI diagram." The M/EI diagram for a beam is one having ordinates equal to M/EI at any point.

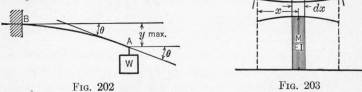

FIG. 202   FIG. 203

116. The First Area Moment Proposition.

The angle between the tangents to the elastic curve of a beam at any two points A and B equals the area of the part of the M/EI diagram between A and B.

Proof: AB in Fig. 203 is part of the elastic curve of a beam originally straight and horizontal. Radii of curvature are shown at A and B. Note that the angle between the radii of curvature at A and B is equal to the angle between the tangents at A and B. MN is any part of the elastic curve of differential length, ds, between A and B. The angle $d\phi$ is the angle between the radii of curvature to the curve at M and N. If $d\phi$ is in radians, $\rho \, d\phi = ds$. Hence $1/\rho = d\phi/ds$. But in Art. 105 it was shown that $1/\rho = M/EI$. Hence

$$\frac{d\phi}{ds} = \frac{M}{EI}$$

The assumption is made that ds equals dx. This assumption is justified for any ordinary beam where the curvature is very slight. Then

$$\frac{d\phi}{dx} = \frac{M}{EI}$$

or

$$d\phi = \frac{M \, dx}{EI}$$

Mdx/EI is the area (shaded in Fig. 203) of the part of the M/EI diagram between M and N. This area is the product of the width dx and the height M/EI.

The angle θ between the radii of curvature at A and B is the sum of all the differential angles $d\phi$ as ϕ varies from zero to θ. Each of these differential angles equals the corresponding differential area, Mdx/EI. Hence the sum of all the differential angles equals the sum of all the differential areas or θ equals the area of the M/EI diagram between A and B.

Mathematically this may be stated thus:

$$\theta = \int_0^\theta d\phi = \int_A^B \frac{Mdx}{EI}$$

The expression $\int_A^B \frac{Mdx}{EI}$ (the integral of all the differential areas between A and B) is the area of the M/EI diagram between A and B. Hence the first area moment proposition is proved.

In most cases E and I are constant throughout the length of the beam. If E and I are constant between the two points A and B, the angle θ between the tangents at A and B equals the area of the *bending-moment* diagram between A and B divided by EI. The bending-moment diagram is often called the M diagram. If E and I change in value between A and B it is necessary to use the M/EI diagram.

Example. A 10-in., 30-lb. I-beam with a span of 15 ft. carries a concentrated load of 10,000 lb. at the midpoint. Calculate the angle between the tangents at the center and at one end due to the concentrated load only.

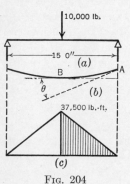

Solution: Fig. 204 (a) shows the beam and the load. The elastic curve is evidently symmetrical as shown in (b), and the desired angle θ is indicated. The bending-moment diagram is shown in (c). According to the first area moment proposition, the area of the shaded part of the M diagram divided by EI is the value of the angle θ. Since E and I are used in inch units

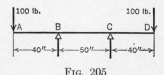

FIG. 204   FIG. 205

it is also necessary to use inch units for the bending moment and length.

$$\theta = \frac{37,500 \times 12 \times \frac{9.0}{2}}{30,000,000 \times 133.5} = 0.00505 \text{ radian}$$

The value of θ in degrees is $0.00505 \times 360/2\,\pi = 0.29°$.

PROBLEMS

1. A 1-in.-by-1-in. steel bar is loaded as shown in Fig. 205. Calculate the angle (in radians) between the radii of curvature at B and C. Give the answer in degrees also. *Ans.* $\theta = 0.08$ radian.

2. With the data of Problem 1, calculate the slope (angle with the horizontal) of the elastic curve at A. (Note that because of symmetry the tangent to the elastic curve is horizontal at the midpoint of the beam.)

117. The Second Area Moment Proposition.

The vertical displacement, Δ, of any point A on the elastic curve of a beam (originally straight and horizontal) from the tangent to the elastic curve at any point B equals the statical moment about A of the part of the M/EI diagram between A and B (Fig. 206).

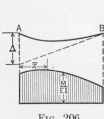
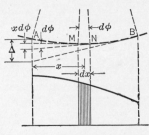

FIG. 206   FIG. 207

Proof: AB in Fig. 207 is part of the elastic curve of a beam originally straight and horizontal. M and N are any two points on the elastic curve, the distance MN being an infinitesimal distance ds. The angle between the tangents to the elastic curve at M and N is $d\phi$. The horizontal distance from A to MN is x. If $d\phi$ is in radians then $xd\phi$ is the part of the vertical through A intercepted between these two tangents.[1]

The sum of all such intercepts as x varies from 0 to AB equals Δ, or expressed as an equation

$$\Delta = \int_A^B x d\phi$$

But from the preceding article

$$d\phi = \frac{M dx}{EI}$$

---

[1] It should be kept in mind that in the diagram (Fig. 207) the distance MN is very greatly exaggerated, being actually infinitesimal. AB, on the other hand, is a finite distance (perhaps several feet). The distance x varies from zero to the distance AB. In any practical case the curvature is very slight and the tangents at M, N, and B are all very nearly horizontal.

Hence

$$\Delta = \int_A^B \frac{Mxdx}{EI}$$

But Mdx/EI is an elementary area (the part of the M/EI diagram with a width dx), and this multiplied by x is the statical moment of this elementary area with respect to A. The right-hand member of the last equation is, therefore, the statical moment (with respect to A) of the M/EI diagram between A and B. Proposition II is thus proved. If E and I are constant between A and B, the statical moment of the M diagram may be calculated and then divided by E and I.

In the next five articles, the area moment method will be used for determining the deflections of the same types of beams (and loadings) as were analyzed in Art. 109 to 114, using the double integration method.

118. Cantilever Beam; Concentrated Load at End. Fig. 208 shows the loaded beam, the approximate shape of the elastic curve, and the M diagram. The ordinate $y_{\max.}$ is evidently the displacement of B from the tangent at A and, according to the second area moment proposition, is equal to the statical moment, with respect to b, of the area of the M diagram, divided by EI. Thus

$$y_{\max.} = \frac{(\text{Area of } M \text{ diagram}) \, \bar{x}}{EI} = \frac{\left(-PL \times \dfrac{L}{2}\right) \times \left(\dfrac{2}{3}L\right)}{EI} = -\frac{PL^3}{3\,EI}$$

The minus sign indicates that the deflection is downward.

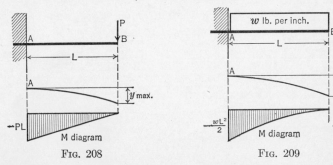

FIG. 208   FIG. 209

The slope of the curve at B is the angle between the tangents to the curve at A and B and according to the first area moment proposition is the area of the M diagram divided by EI. Thus

$$\theta_B = -\frac{PL \times \dfrac{L}{2}}{EI} = -\frac{PL^2}{2\,EI} \text{ radians}$$

119. Cantilever Beam; Uniformly Distributed Load. In Appendix A it is proved that the parabolic shaded area shown in Fig. 209 equals one-third of the base times the altitude and that the centroid is $\frac{3}{4} L$ from the small end. Using these values,

$$y_{\text{max.}} = \frac{-\dfrac{wL^2}{2} \times \dfrac{L}{3} \times \dfrac{3}{4} L}{EI} = -\frac{wL^4}{8\,EI} = -\frac{WL^3}{8\,EI}$$

where W equals the total load on the beam.

The slope at the end,

$$\theta_B = \frac{-\dfrac{wL^2}{2} \times \dfrac{L}{3}}{EI} = -\frac{wL^3}{6\,EI} = -\frac{WL^2}{6\,EI}$$

120. Beam on Two Supports; Concentrated Load at Midpoint. It will be noticed in Fig. 210 that the maximum deflection (at the mid-point of the beam) equals the displacement of either end from the tangent at the midpoint since, from symmetry, the tangent at the midpoint of the elastic curve is horizontal. Therefore

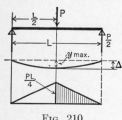

Fig. 210

$$\Delta = \frac{\dfrac{PL}{4} \times \dfrac{L}{4} \times \dfrac{2}{3} \dfrac{L}{2}}{EI} = \frac{PL^3}{48\,EI}$$

But $\Delta = -y_{\text{max.}}$. Therefore

$$y_{\text{max.}} = -\frac{PL^3}{48\,EI}$$

The slope at the end,

$$\theta_B = \frac{\dfrac{PL}{4} \times \dfrac{L}{4}}{EI} = \frac{PL^2}{16\,EI}$$

121. Beam on Two Supports; Uniformly Distributed Load. Again it is evident (Fig. 211) that the maximum deflection equals the displacement, Δ, of point B on the elastic curve from the tangent at the midpoint. Also, Δ equals the statical moment of the right-hand half of the bending-moment diagram (with respect to the end B), divided by EI.

Although a simpler method of finding this statical moment will be given later, it will now be found by integration. At a distance x from the end of the beam, $M_x = \dfrac{wLx}{2} - \dfrac{wx^2}{2}$, and the area of the elementary strip shown is

$$\left(\frac{wLx}{2} - \frac{wx^2}{2} \right) dx$$

The statical moment of the strip is the area multiplied by x, and for the area between C and B the statical moment is

$$\int_0^{L/2} x \left(\frac{wLx}{2} - \frac{wx^2}{2} \right) dx = \left(\frac{wLx^3}{6} - \frac{wx^4}{8} \right) \Big]_0^{L/2} = \frac{wL^4}{48} - \frac{wL^4}{128} = \frac{5\,wL^4}{384}$$

Therefore the deflection

$$y_{\max.} = - \frac{5\,wL^4}{384\,EI} \quad \text{or} \quad - \frac{5\,WL^3}{384\,EI}$$

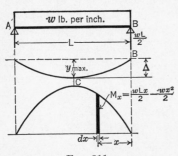

Fig. 211

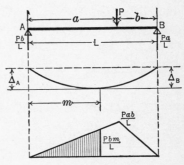

Fig. 212

Similarly,

$$EI\theta_B = \int_0^{L/2} \left(\frac{wLx}{2} - \frac{wx^2}{2} \right) dx = \left(\frac{wLx^2}{4} - \frac{wx^3}{6} \right) \Big]_0^{L/2}$$

$$= \frac{wL^3}{16} - \frac{wL^3}{48} = \frac{wL^3}{24} \quad \text{or} \quad \frac{WL^2}{24}$$

and

$$\theta_B = \frac{WL^2}{24\,EI} \text{ radians}$$

122. Beam on Two Supports; Concentrated Load Not at Midpoint. The beam with load and reactions, the approximate shape of the elastic curve, and the bending-moment diagram are shown in Fig. 212. At the point of maximum deflection the tangent to the elastic curve is horizontal, and consequently $\Delta_A = \Delta_B$.

Let m = the distance (inches) from A to the point of maximum deflection (which occurs in the longer segment).

$EI\Delta_A$ = the statical moment of the shaded area with respect to A.

$EI\Delta_B$ = the statical moment of the unshaded part of the moment diagram with respect to B.

But the statical moment of the unshaded part of the bending-moment diagram equals the statical moment of the entire diagram (two triangles) minus the statical moment of the shaded area.

Equating these values for $EI\Delta_A$ and $EI\Delta_B$,

$$\frac{Pbm}{L} \times \frac{m}{2} \times \frac{2}{3}m = \frac{Pab}{L} \times \frac{b}{2} \times \frac{2}{3}b + \frac{Pab}{L} \times \frac{a}{2}\left(L - \frac{2}{3}a\right)$$
$$- \frac{Pbm}{L} \times \frac{m}{2}\left(L - \frac{2}{3}m\right)$$

Hence

$$\frac{Pbm^2}{2L}\left(\frac{2}{3}m + L - \frac{2}{3}m\right) = \frac{Pab}{3L}\left(b^2 + \frac{3\,aL}{2} - a^2\right)$$

But

$$b^2 - a^2 = (b - a)(b + a) = (b - a)L$$

Therefore

$$m^2 = \frac{2}{3}\frac{a}{L}\left[\frac{3\,aL}{2} + (b - a)L\right] = \frac{a}{3}(3\,a + 2\,b - 2\,a) = \frac{a}{3}(a + 2\,b)$$

and

$$m = \tfrac{1}{3}\sqrt{3\,a\,(a + 2\,b)}$$

The maximum deflection is most easily found by substituting this value of m in the expression for Δ_A used above,

$$y_{\text{max.}} = \frac{-\dfrac{Pbm}{L} \times \dfrac{m}{2} \times \dfrac{2}{3}m}{EI} = -\frac{Pbm^3}{3\,EIL}$$

$$= -\frac{Pb}{3\,EIL} \times \frac{1}{9}[3\,a(a + 2\,b)] \times \frac{1}{3}\sqrt{3\,a(a + 2\,b)}$$

$$= -\frac{Pab(a + 2\,b)\sqrt{3\,a(a + 2\,b)}}{27\,EIL}$$

A more general method for calculating the maximum deflection in unsymmetrical beams by the area moment method will be given in Arts. 130 and 131.

123. Relation Between Deflection and Bending Stress. At times it is desirable to know what the maximum deflection of a beam will be when it is loaded so that the maximum bending stress in it has a known value, or to know what the maximum bending stress in the beam will be when the maximum deflection has a known value. This relationship is easily obtained for any one of the preceding cases by expressing the load P or W in terms of the maximum stress which it causes, and inserting the quantity in this form into the deflection equation. Thus for a cantilever beam carrying a concentrated load P at the end, the maximum bending moment is PL lb-in. But $M = SI/c$, from which $P = S_{max.}I/cL$. Inserting this value in the equation for the maximum deflection of the beam,

$$y_{max.} = \frac{S_{max.}\dfrac{I}{cL} \times L^3}{3\,EI} = \frac{S_{max.}L^2}{3\,Ec}$$

Corresponding relationships can be similarly developed for other types of beams and loadings.

124. Errors in Calculated Deflections. The calculation of the true deflection of a beam by the exact equation

$$\frac{M}{EI} = \frac{\dfrac{d^2y}{dx^2}}{\left[1 + \left(\dfrac{dy}{dx}\right)^2\right]^{\frac{3}{2}}}$$

is, in general, very laborious. However, for a beam resting on two supports and bent by equal couples at the supports, as shown in Fig. 213, it is not difficult to compare the true deflection with the deflection as calculated either by the simplified equation for the elastic curve or by the area moment method. Both these methods give the same relation between x and y, which is expressed by the equation $y = \dfrac{Mx^2}{2EI}$, and both methods give for the max-

M diagram

Fig. 213

imum deflection, $\Delta = \dfrac{ML^2}{8\,EI}$. It is therefore evident that the simplifying assumptions make the equation of the elastic curve for this case a parabola, when the curve is, in fact, a circular arc. How serious is this error?

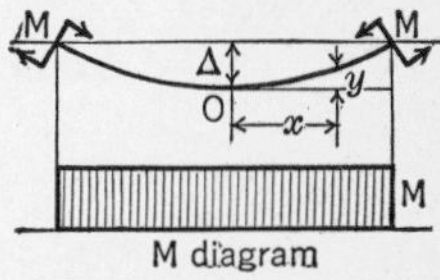

Tabulated on page 162 are deflections for a beam 100 in. (8 ft. 4 in.) long, subject to bending moments such that EI/M (the radius of curvature)

has the values given.   The values designated as " True Δ " are the·
calculated middle ordinates of circular arcs 100 in. long with the given
radii of curvature; the values designated as " Approx. Δ " are calculated
by the formula $\Delta = \dfrac{ML^2}{8\,EI}$.

PERCENTAGE OF ERROR IN DEFLECTION OF A BEAM AS CALCULATED BY
METHODS INVOLVING THE COMMON SIMPLIFICATION

$\rho = \dfrac{EI}{M}$ (in.)	5,000	1,000	200	100	50
True Δ (in.)	0.250	1.250	6.22	12.24	23.00
Approx. Δ (in.)	0.250	1.250	6.25	12.50	25.00
% Error	....	....	$\frac{1}{2}$ of 1%	2%	9%
$\dfrac{\text{Approx. } \Delta}{L}$	$\frac{1}{400}$	$\frac{1}{80}$	$\frac{1}{16}$	$\frac{1}{8}$	$\frac{1}{4}$

For the same ratios of calculated deflection to length of beam, but with
different loadings, the percentage errors will be of about the *same order*
of magnitude.

Another source of errors in calculated deflections is the change in the
moment arms of the loads and reactions as the beam deflects.   This is
illustrated in Fig. 214.   If the elastic curve of the beam is the same

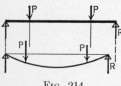

length as the unloaded straight beam, then the
moment arms are slightly decreased in the deflected beam and the bending moment at every
point is less than assumed.   The error resulting
from disregarding the decrease in bending moments also makes the computed deflections
too large.   This type of error does not occur

FIG. 214

in beams bent only by couples at the ends, such as the one assumed
at the beginning of this article.   For small deflections this type of error
is entirely negligible, but for beams with very large deflections the errors
may be as great as those resulting from use of the approximate equation
of the elastic curve.

The errors in computed values of the deflections which result from the
circumstances just mentioned can be serious only in relatively slender
beams (for which the ratio of length to depth is large).   Unless the beam
is slender, the stresses accompanying a large deflection will exceed the

proportional limit of the material, and neither method of finding the deflections will be valid.

In short beams heavily loaded, the deflection due to shearing stresses (which, as noted in Art. 106, is not included in the expressions for deflection that have been worked out) may be fairly large in comparison with the deflections due to bending. This matter is discussed in Chapter XX.

DEFLECTIONS BY AREA MOMENTS; ADDITIONAL CASES[1]

125. Steps in Using the Area Moment Method. The previous articles have taken up, both by double integration and by area moments, the derivation of expressions for the deflections which cantilever and simple beams have under a number of elementary loadings. The remainder of this chapter is devoted to the calculation, by area moments, of deflections that result from more complex loadings. Overhanging beams, as well as cantilever and simple beams, are considered.

The data of most of the examples and problems in the following articles of the chapter are numerical, and it will be found that numerical solutions are most easily made. In many cases, general expressions for deflections are difficult to derive.

In the solution of *all* problems in deflections by the area moment method, the following steps are desirable:

(*a*) Sketch, approximately to scale, the beam with loads and dimensions.

(*b*) Draw below this the approximate shape of the elastic curve (exaggerating the deflection). On this, indicate the tangent (or tangents) used in the application of the area moment proposition.

(*c*) Draw below this the bending-moment diagram approximately to scale. If this is divided into elementary shapes for easy calculation, indicate these divisions by dotted lines.

(*d*) Perform necessary calculations at one side of these diagrams.

126. Cantilever Beams. The deflection at A (Fig. 215) is found by calculating the statical moment, with respect to A, of the M diagram, and dividing by EI.

If a cantilever beam (Fig. 216) carries two loads, the bending-moment diagram may conveniently be drawn as two separate areas. If one load is an upward load, the areas are opposite in sign and should be so drawn. To calculate Δ_C the part of the lower diagram between B and C may be divided into a rectangle and a triangle, as indicated in Fig. 216.

---

[1] The remainder of this chapter may be omitted, if desired, without causing any complication except that Art. 128 is referred to in Chapter XI.

For the type of loading shown in Fig. 217, the bending-moment diagram may be divided into three parts as shown, the parabolic area, a rectangle, and a triangle.

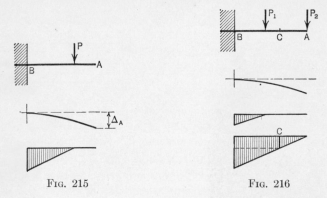

FIG. 215   FIG. 216

If the beam is made up of sections with different values of EI (Fig. 218) the M/EI diagram (instead of the M diagram) may be drawn and used in determining slopes and deflections.

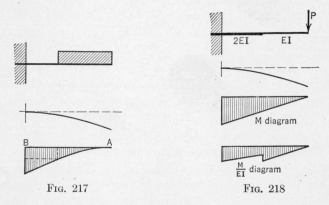

FIG. 217   FIG. 218

PROBLEMS

1. A 4-in., 7.7-lb. I-beam is used as a cantilever projecting 12 ft. from the fixed end.   What deflection at the end is caused by the two loads shown in Fig. 219?

Ans. $y = 1.45$ in.

2. How many pounds must the load P be to cause zero deflection at the end of the 4-in., 7.7-lb. I-beam shown in Fig. 220?   (NOTE: Draw the bending-moment diagram as two separate triangles, one positive and one negative, as shown.)

3. Two 14-in., 34-lb. wide-flange beams are to project 14 ft. from a framework of which they are a part and are to carry a load of 16,000 lb. which is distributed uniformly over the end 8 ft. of the two beams.   (*a*) Calculate the deflection at the ends of the beams.   (*b*) Calculate the deflection 8 ft. from the end.

4. If the two beams of Problem 3 are to carry the same distributed load on 8 ft. nearer the fixed end, what deflection results at the end of the beam?

Ans. $y = 0.174$ in.

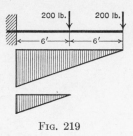

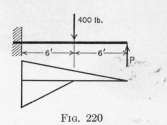

FIG. 219   FIG. 220

5. It is desired to calculate the deflection at a point B, which is a ft. from the end of a cantilever beam carrying a uniformly distributed load of w lb. per ft. Show that the part of the M diagram between the fixed end and B may be divided into a rectangle, a triangle, and a parabolic area as shown in Fig. 221. What are the ordinates of each of these areas at the fixed end?

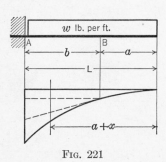

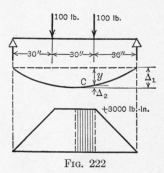

FIG. 221   FIG. 222

127. Symmetrical Beams on Two Supports — Concentrated Loads.

In all symmetrical beams on two supports, carrying symmetrical loads, the tangent to the elastic curve is horizontal at the midpoint. This horizontal tangent may be used as the reference tangent. The maximum deflection (at the midpoint) is found by determining the displacement, from the tangent at the midpoint, of the point on the elastic curve at either support. This procedure is illustrated in the following example, which also illustrates the process of finding the deflection at any other point on the curve.

Example. A steel bar 1 in. square rests on two supports 90 in. apart. (*a*) Calculate the deflection at the midpoint caused by two loads of 100 lb. each, 15 in. from the midpoint of the beam. (*b*) Calculate the deflection at one of the loads.

Solution: (*a*) The deflection $y_{max.}$ is wanted. This is equal to Δ_1, Fig. 222, the displacement of B from the tangent at the midpoint. This, in turn, is the statical moment of half the bending-moment diagram with respect to B, divided by EI. For convenience in calculating, this is divided into a triangle and a rectangle.

$$y_{max.} = \Delta_1 = \frac{(3,000 \times 15) \times 20 + (3,000 \times 15) \times 37.5}{30,000,000 \times \frac{1}{12}} = 1.035 \text{ in.}$$

(b) The deflection, y, is wanted. It will be observed that this equals Δ_1 (computed above) minus Δ_2, the displacement of point C on the elastic curve from the tangent at the midpoint. Applying the area moment principle,

$$\Delta_2 = \frac{(3,000 \times 15) \times 7.5}{30,000,000 \times \frac{1}{12}} = 0.135 \text{ in.}$$

$$y = \Delta_1 - \Delta_2 = 1.035 - 0.135 = 0.900 \text{ in.}$$

In general, the deflection of any point on a symmetrical simple or overhanging beam may be computed as the difference between the two displacements. One of these is the displacement of the reaction from the tangent at the center, the other being the displacement of the point at which the deflection is wanted, from the same tangent.

PROBLEMS

1. The beam shown in Fig. 223 is a 14-in., 53-lb. wide-flange beam. Calculate the maximum deflection caused by the concentrated loads.

2. Calculate the deflection at one of the 8,000-lb. loads in the beam shown in Fig. 223.

3. The beam shown in Fig. 224 is a 2-in. standard steel pipe. Calculate the deflection at the end. *Hint:* Calculate the deflections from the tangent at midpoint of end and of reaction. The difference is the desired deflection.

FIG. 223   FIG. 224

128. Bending-Moment Diagrams " by Parts." Before proceeding further with problems involving beams on two supports, a useful method of drawing bending-moment diagrams will be shown. This method is generally convenient for concentrated loads, and is almost necessary in many cases of uniformly distributed loading. Consider the beam AB (Fig. 225) with a uniform load of w lb. per ft. The bending moment at any point distant x from A is

$$M = R_L x - wx^2/2$$

Heretofore in drawing bending-moment diagrams the subtraction has been performed and the difference of the terms has been plotted (as in the shaded diagram). However, the two terms may be plotted separately as shown in (b). If ordinates equal to $R_L x$ are laid off at all points, a triangular positive area results. If ordinates equal to $-wx^2/2$ are laid off at all points, a negative parabolic area results. This is exactly the same parabolic area that is the M diagram for a cantilever beam. The area of this is one-third the height times the length, as was stated in Art. 119.

Hence the bending-moment diagram may be represented by a triangle and a parabolic area, the areas and centroids of both of which are known. The method illustrated above may be used for any kind of loading and frequently gives bending-moment diagrams much more convenient for the area moment method.

It is interesting to note that the " combined " bending-moment diagram may be regarded as a triangle from the ordinates of which the negative ordinates of the parabola have been laid off (Fig. 225(c)).

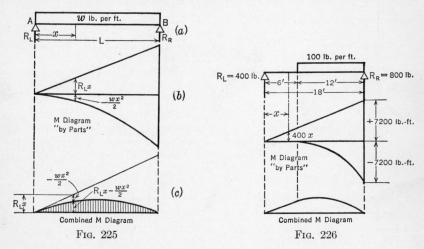

Fig. 225   Fig. 226

Example. Draw the bending-moment diagram by parts for the beam shown in Fig. 226.

Solution: At any point in the left-hand 6 ft. the bending moment is due to the left reaction alone and is $M = 400\ x$. For values of x greater than 6 ft., $M = 400\ x - 50(x - 6)^2$. The term $400\ x$ occurs as all or part of the bending moment at every point in the beam. These ordinates vary with x, being zero at the left end and 7,200 lb-ft. at the right end. When plotted, they form a positive triangle. The negative ordinates $50(x - 6)^2$ when plotted form the negative area bounded by the parabolic curve shown. The maximum ordinate of this area is $-7,200$ lb-ft.

In drawing moment diagrams by parts, it is not necessary to write equations for bending moments as was done above. The equations were given to show that each term in such an equation is represented by an area.

A moment diagram "by parts" can be started at either end of the beam. At each concentrated load, a triangular area begins — positive for an upward load or reaction and negative for a downward load. The beginning of a uniformly distributed load on the beam marks the beginning of an area in the moment diagram which is bounded by a parabolic curve. This area is negative for a downward uniform load. If the uniform load ends before the end of the beam is reached, the parabolic boundary line ends at the end of the uniform load. The area continues with a straight line tangent to the end of the curve.

The advantage of this method of drawing a bending-moment diagram is evident in the foregoing example. It would be difficult to calculate accurately the area of the "combined" bending-moment diagram, or of part of it. The distance to the centroid would also be difficult to compute. But the parabola and the triangle of the diagram "by parts" are figures of known areas, and the positions of the centroids of these figures are also known.

Because it is important to be able readily to draw bending-moment diagrams by parts, an additional illustration of a simple loading is given in Fig. 227. These examples should be carefully studied and thoroughly understood.

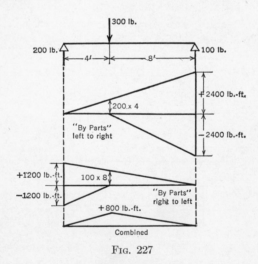

Fig. 227

129. Symmetrical Beams on Two Supports — Distributed Loads.

The bending-moment diagram "by parts" will be found most convenient to use in deflection problems dealing with beams having uniformly distributed loads.

In other respects the method of calculating the deflection at any point is the same as that explained in Art. 127 for beams with concentrated loads.

Example. A 4-in., 7.7-lb. American standard I-beam rests on two supports 10 ft. apart and carries a load of 2,000 lb. uniformly distributed over the middle 5 ft. Calculate the deflection at the midpoint caused by the 2,000-lb. load.

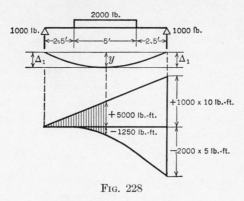

Fig. 228

Solution: The beam, Fig. 228, is symmetrical, and y, the deflection at the midpoint, equals Δ_1, the displacement of either end from the tangent at the midpoint. Only one half of the bending-moment diagram is needed. As drawn, the left half (shaded) is more easily used.

$$y = \Delta_1 = \frac{5{,}000 \times 12 \times 30 \times 40 - 1{,}250 \times 12 \times 10 \times 52.5}{30{,}000{,}000 \times 6}$$

$$= \frac{2{,}400 - 262.5}{6{,}000} = 0.356 \text{ in.}$$

PROBLEMS

1. A 12-in., 65-lb. wide-flange beam carries 2 loads W of 32,000 lb. each as shown in Fig. 229. Calculate the maximum deflection. *Ans.* $y = 0.92$ in.

2. Calculate the deflection 8 ft. from the end in the beam of Problem 1.

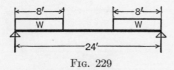

Fig. 229

130. Deflection of Unsymmetrical Simple or Overhanging Beams. In unsymmetrically loaded simple and overhanging beams the position of the horizontal tangent to the elastic curve of the deflected beam is unknown. Therefore it is generally desirable to take some other tangent as the reference tangent. Usually this will be the tangent at one of the supports. The procedure to be followed in calculating the deflection at any given point in a simple or overhanging beam will be illustrated by a numerical example.

Example. For the beam shown in Fig. 230, calculate the deflection at a point 8 ft. from the right reaction.

Solution: The approximate elastic curve is sketched in, and below it the bending-moment diagram " by parts " is drawn from right to left.[1] The reference tangent used will be the tangent at the right reaction. First calculate Δ_1, the displacement of the left support from the tangent at the right support.

$$\Delta_1 = \frac{700 \times 240 \times 120 \times 80 - 2,000 \times 96 \times 48 \times 32}{1,200,000 \times 256} = 4.29 \text{ in.}$$

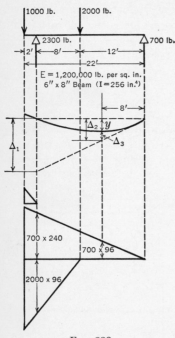

By proportion calculate Δ_2. $\Delta_2/\Delta_1 = 8/20$. Therefore $\Delta_2 = 8/20 \times 4.29 = 1.72$ in. Calculate Δ_3, the displacement of a point on the elastic curve from the reference tangent.

$$\Delta_3 = \frac{700 \times 96 \times 48 \times 32}{1,200,000 \times 256} = 0.336 \text{ in.}$$

$$y = \Delta_2 - \Delta_3 = 1.72 - 0.34 = 1.38 \text{ in.}$$

From the foregoing example it can be seen that the deflection at any point in an unsymmetrical beam on two supports is calculated in the following steps:

(*a*) Assume the reference tangent at one reaction, and draw the bending-moment diagram.

(*b*) Calculate Δ_1, the displacement of the other reaction (a point on the elastic curve) from the tangent.

(*c*) Calculate by proportion Δ_2, the distance, at the point where the deflection is wanted, between the original horizontal line of the beam and the reference tangent.

Fig. 230

[1] In cases of unsymmetrically loaded beams on two supports, the difficulty of the computation necessary for the solution of a problem frequently depends greatly on whether the moment diagram is drawn from left to right, or vice versa. It should always be drawn in the way which will render the computations as simple as possible. Sometimes it may be desirable, before actually attempting the solution of a problem, to sketch the diagram both ways, and then to determine which is more suitable. No simple rule can be laid down to cover all cases. For a simple beam with a single concentrated or distributed load, however, it will be found desirable to draw the diagram *from* the reaction which is most distant from the load, and to take the tangent at that reaction. With overhanging beams it is sometimes desirable to draw the diagram *from* both ends of the beam *to* one or the other of the reactions.

(d) Calculate Δ_3, the displacement from the reference tangent of the point on the elastic curve where the deflection is wanted.

(e) The deflection wanted is $\Delta_2 - \Delta_3$.

PROBLEMS

1. A 10-in., 35-lb. American standard beam 30 ft. long rests on two supports, one at one end and one 10 ft. from the other end. It carries a uniformly distributed load of 720 lb. per ft. Calculate the deflection of the overhanging end.

0.35 8

2. A small beam for which $EI = 100,000$ is 48 in. long and rests on supports 36 in. apart overhanging 12 in. It carries 200 lb. at the overhanging end, and 400 lb. 24 in. from the overhanging end. Calculate the deflection at the 400-lb. load.

1.16"

131. Location and Amount of Maximum Deflection, Simple or Overhanging Beams. It is obvious that a tangent to the elastic curve is horizontal at the point where the deflection is greatest. This fact may be used to determine where the maximum deflection occurs.

In the beam shown in Fig. 231, the angle θ between the tangent at the right reaction and the original horizontal line of the beam may be computed from

$$\theta = \frac{\Delta_1}{L} \text{ radians}$$

(It should be kept in mind that this angle in an actual beam is very small. It is greatly exaggerated in the sketch.)

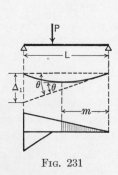

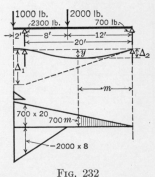

FIG. 231   FIG. 232

Since the tangent at the point of maximum deflection is horizontal it also makes the angle θ with the reference tangent at the right reaction. By the first area moment proposition the area of the shaded part of the bending-moment diagram divided by EI equals θ, the angle between these two tangents. The shaded area therefore equals $EI\theta$. If this area can be expressed in terms of its unknown length m, and equated to $EI\theta$, it will be possible to solve for m.

A numerical example will illustrate the application of this method.

Example.   A wooden beam 6 in. wide, 8 in. deep, and 22 ft. long is supported and loaded as shown in Fig. 232.   Calculate the maximum deflection due to the two concentrated loads.   Assume $E = 1{,}200{,}000$ lb. per sq. in.
Solution:

$$\Delta_1 = \frac{700 \times 20 \times 12 \times 120 \times 80 - 2{,}000 \times 8 \times 12 \times 48 \times 32}{1{,}200{,}000 \times 256} = 4.29 \text{ in.}$$

Also $\theta = \Delta_1/L = 4.29/240 = 0.0179$ radian.   But $EI\theta =$ shaded area $= 700 \ m^2/2$; whence $m^2 = 15{,}660$, and $m = 125$ in.

Obviously y, the maximum deflection, is equal in amount to Δ_2, the displacement of the right reaction from the tangent at the point of maximum deflection.   But Δ_2 equals the statical moment of the shaded area with respect to the right reaction, divided by EI.   Or

$$y = \Delta_2 = \frac{700 \times 125 \times \frac{125}{2} \times \frac{2}{3} \times 125}{1{,}200{,}000 \times 256} = 1.49 \text{ in.}$$

The steps to be taken in calculating the maximum deflection of an unsymmetrically loaded beam on two supports are:

(*a*) Assume the tangent at one support as the reference tangent.

(*b*) Draw the bending-moment diagram in the simplest way.

(*c*) Calculate Δ_1, the displacement of the other support from the reference tangent.

(*d*) Compute the angle θ between the reference tangent and the horizontal.

(*e*) Express the area of the part of the bending-moment diagram between the point of tangency and the point of maximum deflection in terms of the unknown distance, m, to the point of maximum deflection.

(*f*) Equate this to $EI\theta$, and solve for m.

(*g*) Having found m, solve for deflection.

PROBLEMS

1. A 6-in.-by-8-in. timber beam (8-in. side vertical) rests on two supports 20 ft. apart and carries a load of 2,000 lb. 8 ft. from one support.   Calculate the maximum deflection caused by the 2,000-lb. load.   Assume $E = 1{,}200{,}000$ lb. per sq. in.

FIG. 233   FIG. 234

⊢   **2.** A steel rod is used for the beam shown in Fig. 233. $EI = 1{,}000$.   Calculate the maximum upward deflection between A and B caused by the 6-lb. load.   .055"

⊢   **3.** Calculate the location and amount of the maximum deflection of the beam shown in Fig. 234. $EI = 180{,}000{,}000$.   *Ans. $y = 0.237$ in.*

GENERAL PROBLEMS

1. A 4-in., 7.7-lb. I-beam is anchored down at one end and rests on a support 10 ft. from this end. It projects 5 ft. beyond the support. A load of 1,000 lb. is applied at the overhanging end. Calculate the maximum upward deflection caused by the concentrated load. *Ans.* $y = 0.308$ in.

2. A 6-in.-by-8-in. (nominal size) wooden beam ($E = 1,200,000$ lb. per sq. in.) rests on supports 20 ft. apart. The 8-in. sides are vertical. A uniformly distributed load of 3,000 lb. covers 12 ft. of the beam at one end. Calculate the deflection at the center caused by this load.

3. A 12-in., 31.8-lb. American standard beam is used as a cantilever projecting 22 ft. A concentrated load applied 4 ft. from the free end causes a maximum bending stress of 18,000 lb. per sq. in. Calculate the deflection at the end of the beam.

4. A simple beam L in. long carries a concentrated load of P lb. at a distance b from one reaction. (*a*) Prove that, at a point between the load and the other reaction and k in. from the other reaction, the deflection is $y = \dfrac{Pbk}{6\,EIL}\,(L^2 - b^2 - k^2)$.

(*b*) A and B are two points on a simple beam. Prove that the deflection of point A caused by a load P applied at B equals the deflection of point B caused by the load P applied at A.

5. A floor is to carry a live load of 60 lb. per sq. ft., and the weight of the floor itself, the joists, and the ceiling below may be taken as 18 lb. per sq. ft. The floor is carried on 2-in.-by-10-in. (nominal size) joists of southern pine, common grade, spaced 16 in. on centers and with a span of 15 ft. For long-continued loading, the modulus of elasticity of these joists may be taken as 800,000 lb. per sq. in. (*a*) Does the maximum deflection of these joists, caused by the live load alone, exceed $\frac{1}{360}$ of the span? (*b*) Do the maximum stresses in the joists exceed the allowable stresses given in Table XI?

6. A and B (Fig. 235) are two similar beams. A screw-jack, C, is inserted between the beams and it exerts an upward load of P lb. upon A and a downward load of P lb. upon B. The strength of each beam is such that a central load of $4\,P$ causes a stress equal to the proportional limit. What downward load can be applied to the top of beam A at its midpoint without causing a stress greater than the proportional limit in either beam?

7. Derive an expression for the deflection at the end of a cantilever beam carrying a total load of W which varies as shown in Fig. 236. (*Hint:* The part of the load on a length x of the beam is Wx^2/L^2.)

$$\frac{W\ell^3}{15\,EI}$$

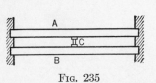

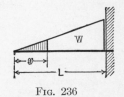

FIG. 235   FIG. 236

8. Each of two cantilever beams is L in. long and loaded at the end with a load of P lb. One is of circular cross-section, the diameter being D at all sections. The other is circular, the diameter being $D/2$ for the half length nearer the load and D for the other half. How do the deflections compare?

9. Two wooden cantilever beams, each 6 in. by 6 in. in cross-section, extend a distance of 8 ft. from the face of the wall. One beam is exactly over the other, and is 3 in. above it. At the free end, a roller is placed between the two beams to keep them 3 in. apart, without exerting any other restraint on them. A load of 500 lb. is placed on the upper beam, directly over the roller. (*a*) Does this cause a reaction of 250 lb. on the lower beam, or not? (*b*) What is the reaction of the roller if in addition to the 500-lb. load on the upper beam a load of 100 lb. is applied to the lower beam at a point 2 ft. from the wall? (Assume $E = 1,200,000$ lb. per sq. in.)

Ans. (*b*) $R = 246.1$ lb.

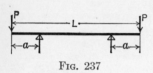

Fig. 237   Fig. 238

10. Prove that the deflection of the end of the beam shown in Fig. 237 is
$$\frac{Pa}{6\,EI}\,(3\,aL - 4\,a^2).$$

11. A beam L in. long is bent by a couple of T lb-in. applied at the midpoint, as shown in Fig. 238. Calculate the maximum slope of the beam. Calculate the end slope of the beam.

12. Prove that the maximum deflection of the beam shown in Fig. 239 is
$$\frac{Pa}{6\,EI}\,(\tfrac{3}{4}\,L^2 - a^2).$$

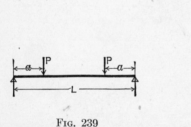

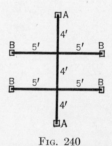

Fig. 239   Fig. 240

NOTE: The following problems are statically indeterminate. The solutions depend upon the fact that the beams which are in contact deflect equal amounts at the point of contact.

13. A 12-in., 31.8-lb. I-beam projects 15 ft. from the face of a wall into which the other end is rigidly fixed. The free end of the cantilever is just in contact with the midpoint of the top flange of another 12-in., 31.8-lb. I-beam 15 ft. long which rests on supports at its ends, no force being exerted between the two beams. A load of 15,000 lb. is placed on the cantilever beam 12 ft. from the wall. What reactions does this load cause at the ends of the simple beam?

Ans. $R = 4,975$ lb.

14. A beam of length L rests on two supports at the ends, and at its midpoint its lower surface is in contact with the top surface of the end of a cantilever beam $L/2$ in length. If a load of P lb. is applied to the upper beam at each quarter-point, calculate the force F exerted by the cantilever beam on the simple beam. E and I are the same for both beams.

15. A 5-in., 14.75-lb. beam 10 ft. long rests upon supports at the ends. In contact with its upper surface at the midpoint is a 4-in., 7.7-lb. I-beam which rests on two supports each 4 ft. from the point of contact of the two beams. The two beams are just in contact when unloaded. If a uniformly distributed load of 4,000 lb. is applied to the upper beam, what is the pressure of the lower beam against the upper beam? *Ans.* $P = 1,400$ lb.

16. In Fig. 240, A–A is a simply supported beam and the two beams B–B are simply supported beams which are just in contact with the upper surface of A–A when unloaded. A load of 1,000 lb. is applied to the midpoint of each of the beams B–B. The beams are all of the same cross-section. Calculate the reactions at A and B due to the loads. EI is the same for all three beams.

CHAPTER XI

RESTRAINED BEAMS

132. Introduction. The simple and overhanging beams so far considered have been assumed to rest on supports which offer no *restraint* as the beam deflects, so that the elastic curve is free to assume any slope at the support. Knife-edges and frictionless pins are examples of such supports. Ordinary bearing plates and many riveted connections approximate the condition, and the shears and moments in beams supported on them are customarily calculated on the assumption that there is no restraint at the support.

In this chapter two types of *statically indeterminate beams* will be considered. These are commonly called " beams fixed at one end " and " beams fixed at both ends." A third type — " continuous beams " — will be considered in Chapter XVIII.

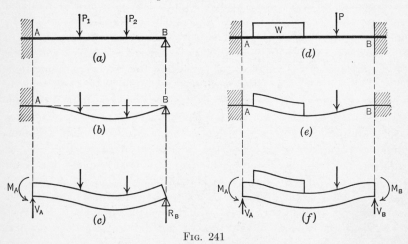

Fig. 241

In Fig. 241 these two types of beams are shown. The restraint may actually be furnished by other means than by embedding the end in a wall. The diagrams at the top show the conventional way of representing the beams. Below these are shown the shapes of the elastic curves. The diagrams at the bottom show the beams as free bodies with the external forces and moments which hold the free bodies in equilibrium.

For purposes of analysis the important fact about restraint is that the

176

slope of the beam remains zero (the tangent to the elastic curve remains horizontal) at the point of restraint as the beam is loaded. In the conventional representation of the beam, the point of restraint is considered to be at the " face of the wall." Consequently the beam is regarded as extending to the face of the wall (or walls, if the beam is fixed at both ends) and to be in equilibrium under the loads applied to it and the shears and moments that act on it in the plane of the wall as in Fig. 241 (c) and (f).

The reason for calling these beams " statically indeterminate " can now be understood. Consider the beam which is fixed at one end and supported at the other end. Only two equations of statics exist for the determination of the forces acting on this beam (since there are no horizontal forces). But the free body shows that, in addition to the vertical forces at A and B, the beam is acted on by a moment of unknown amount at A. The two available equations are not sufficient to determine these three unknowns. That is, there are any number of combinations of values of M_A, V_A, and R_B which will satisfy the conditions of equilibrium. This can easily be seen if one imagines that some value for R_B is arbitrarily assumed. Whatever this assumed value of R_B, use of $\Sigma M = 0$ and $\Sigma V = 0$ will establish values of M_A and of V_A consistent with it. Therefore some condition in addition to the two given by the equations of statics is required to establish which one of the possible sets of values is the correct one for the beam in question.

In the most usual case, this additional condition is that the tangent to the elastic curve at A continues, as the beam deflects, to pass through the point B (in other words, the deflection of B is zero). In cases which are of less frequent occurrence, the point B may shift by some amount, either above or below the tangent at A, when the beam is loaded. For example, if the restraint at A is not complete, the beam will rotate until it is no longer horizontal at that end, and if the support at B has not " settled," B will then lie above the tangent at A. Or conversely, if the support at A is rigid, but the support at B settles under load, the tangent to the curve at A will pass above the point B on the elastic curve of the loaded beam. If the nature of the supports is such that the position of B relative to the tangent at A is known or can be satisfactorily assumed for the loaded beam, that fact can be used in determining the forces and moments on the beam.

In the case of a beam fixed at *both* ends, there are *two* reaction elements in addition to those required for equilibrium, and *two* equations in addition to those of statics are needed.

In the design or investigation of statically indeterminate beams, the first step is to find the values of the moments and forces that act on the beam at the supports.   After these have been found, bending moments and shears and deflections at points along the length of the beam can be determined by principles given in previous chapters.

Succeeding articles will outline methods of determining the external moments and forces on restrained beams, and the deflections given them by certain loadings.   The double integration method will first be used for these analyses, and then the area moment method.

133. Bending Moments in Beams Fixed at Both Ends.   Whichever method (double integration of the elastic curve, or area moments) is used for determining the moments and forces exerted on a restrained beam, it

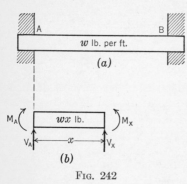

(a)

(b)

Fig. 242

is necessary to set up a general expression for the bending moment at a variable distance x from one of the fixed ends of the beam. This can be done by substituting M_A and V_A in the *general moment equation* which was derived in Art. 79. For a beam fixed at both ends and uniformly loaded (Fig. 242) this gives

$$M_x = M_A + V_A x - \frac{wx^2}{2}$$

For a beam with other loading the last term (which represents the moment of the intervening loads) must be written to agree with the loading.   In this equation M_A and V_A are the unknowns and they may be found by the methods given later in the chapter. M_A and V_A having been solved for, the general moment equation can be written for the entire beam (letting $x = L$) and solved for M_B. Although M_A will be found to be negative bending moment in beams with downward loads, it is desirable to write it as a plus quantity in the expression for M_x.   If this is done, the sign which it has when its value is found will be the true sign.[1]

---

[1] This is an illustration of the general principle that a *sense* may be assumed for any quantity, and equations may be set up in accordance with that assumption, irrespective of whether the assumption is correct or not.   If solution of the equation yields a positive value for the quantity, the assumed sense is thereby shown to be correct; if a negative value is obtained, the assumed sense is shown to be incorrect.   Therefore, if in drawing diagrams and writing equations, unknown bending moments are assumed positive (in accordance with the convention for signs of bending moments, as given above), those that are actually positive will have positive signs when the equations are solved, and those that are negative will have negative signs.   To assume unknown bending moments positive in writing equations is therefore a convenient procedure.

DOUBLE INTEGRATION METHOD

(Arts. 134 to 136, inclusive, may be omitted if the double integration method is omitted.)

134. Beam Fixed at One End; Uniform Load. To find the amount of the reaction, R (Fig. 243), the equation of the elastic curve may be utilized, employing the condition specified in Art. 132, that the deflection at the supported end is zero. After R has been found, the conditions of equilibrium are sufficient to permit determination of shears and moments throughout the length of the beam and the equation of the elastic curve can be used to determine the maximum deflection.

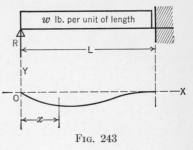

FIG. 243

If the origin is chosen at the unrestrained end, the value of M at a distance x from the origin is

$$M_x = Rx - \frac{wx^2}{2}$$

The equation for the elastic curve is therefore

$$EI\frac{d^2y}{dx^2} = Rx - \frac{wx^2}{2} \tag{1}$$

Integrating,

$$EI\frac{dy}{dx} = \frac{Rx^2}{2} - \frac{wx^3}{6} + C_1 \tag{2}$$

When $x = L, \dfrac{dy}{dx} = 0$; therefore $C_1 = -\dfrac{RL^2}{2} + \dfrac{wL^3}{6}$, and

$$EI\frac{dy}{dx} = \frac{Rx^2}{2} - \frac{wx^3}{6} - \frac{RL^2}{2} + \frac{wL^3}{6} \tag{3}$$

Integrating again,

$$EIy = \frac{Rx^3}{6} - \frac{wx^4}{24} - \frac{RL^2x}{2} + \frac{wL^3x}{6} + C_2 \tag{4}$$

But $y = 0$ when $x = 0$, hence $C_2 = 0$, and

$$EIy = \frac{Rx^3}{6} - \frac{wx^4}{24} - \frac{RL^2x}{2} + \frac{wL^3x}{6} \tag{5}$$

But also, $y = 0$ when $x = L$. Hence

$$\frac{RL^3}{6} - \frac{wL^4}{24} - \frac{RL^3}{2} + \frac{wL^4}{6} = 0 \tag{6}$$

Solving for R,

$$R = \frac{3}{8} wL = \frac{3}{8} W \tag{7}$$

The bending moment at the fixed end is

$$M = \frac{3}{8} wL^2 - \frac{wL^2}{2} = -\frac{wL^2}{8}$$

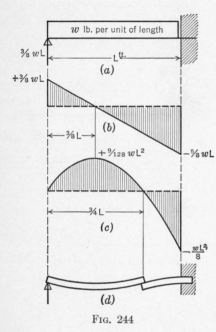

FIG. 244

The shear and bending-moment diagrams are shown in Fig. 244. The maximum + bending moment occurs when the shear changes sign, which is $\frac{3}{8} L$ from the support.

At this point $M = \frac{3}{8} wL \times \frac{3}{8} L -$

$$\frac{\frac{9}{64} wL^2}{2} = \frac{9}{128} wL^2.$$

To find the location and amount of the maximum deflection of this beam, the value $R = \frac{3}{8} wL$ is substituted in equation (3) above. Then

$$EI \frac{dy}{dx} = \frac{3}{16} wLx^2 - \frac{wx^3}{6} -$$

$$\frac{3}{16} wL^3 + \frac{wL^3}{6} \tag{8}$$

But since the slope of the elastic curve is zero at the point of maximum deflection, the abscissa of this point can be found by equating the right-hand member of equation (8) to zero. Hence

$$\frac{3}{16} wLx^2 - \frac{wx^3}{6} - \frac{1}{48} wL^3 = 0 \tag{9}$$

One of the roots of this equation is $x = 0.4215 L$, which is the distance from the supported end of the beam to the point of maximum deflection. Substituting $\frac{3}{8} wL$ for R in equation (5),

$$EIy = \frac{wLx^3}{16} - \frac{wx^4}{24} - \frac{3}{16} wL^3 x + \frac{wL^3 x}{6} = -\frac{wL^3 x}{48} + \frac{wLx^3}{16} - \frac{wx^4}{24} \tag{10}$$

The value of y for $x = 0.4215\,L$ is the maximum deflection, which is

$$y_{\text{max.}} = \frac{wL^4}{185\,EI} = \frac{WL^3}{185\,EI} \tag{11}$$

The same slopes, deflections, and stresses would result in the two beams shown in Fig. 244 (d).

PROBLEMS

1. A 4-in., 7.7-lb. I-beam is fixed at one end and supported at the other end, the distance between the fixed point and the support being 12 ft. Calculate the maximum bending stress caused by a load of 240 lb. uniformly distributed.

Ans. $S = 1,440$ lb. per sq. in.

2. A beam fixed at one end and simply supported at the other end is 22 ft. long and carries a load of 1,000 lb. per ft. Select a suitable steel beam.

135. Beam Fixed at One End; Concentrated Load at Midpoint. In this case the equation of the elastic curve between the support and the load differs from the equation of the elastic curve from the load to the fixed end. With the origin at the unrestrained end (Fig. 245), the equations are those given below.

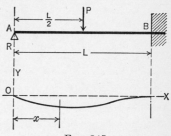

FIG. 245

For values of x
between zero and $L/2$

$$M_x = Rx$$

$$EI\frac{d^2y}{dx^2} = Rx$$

Integrating,

$$EI\frac{dy}{dx} = \frac{Rx^2}{2} + C_1$$

For values of x
between $L/2$ and L

$$M_x = Rx - P\left(x - \frac{L}{2}\right)$$

$$EI\frac{d^2y}{dx^2} = Rx - Px + \frac{PL}{2}$$

Integrating,

$$EI\frac{dy}{dx} = \frac{Rx^2}{2} - \frac{Px^2}{2} + \frac{PLx}{2} + C_2$$

But $dy/dx = 0$ when $x = L$. Hence

$$C_2 = \frac{PL^2}{2} - \frac{RL^2}{2} - \frac{PL^2}{2} = -\frac{RL^2}{2}$$

and

$$EI\frac{dy}{dx} = \frac{Rx^2}{2} - \frac{Px^2}{2} + \frac{PLx}{2} - \frac{RL^2}{2}$$

Both of these curves have the same slope at the load where $x = L/2$. Hence

$$\frac{RL^2}{8} + C_1 = \frac{RL^2}{8} - \frac{PL^2}{8} + \frac{PL^2}{4} - \frac{RL^2}{2}$$

whence

$$C_1 = \frac{PL^2}{8} - \frac{RL^2}{2}$$

and

$$EI\frac{dy}{dx} = \frac{Rx^2}{2} + \frac{PL^2}{8} - \frac{RL^2}{2}$$

Integrating again,

For values of x between 0 and $L/2$

$$EIy = \frac{Rx^3}{6} + \frac{PL^2x}{8} - \frac{RL^2x}{2} + C_3$$

But $y = 0$ when $x = 0$. Therefore $C_3 = 0$. Hence

$$EIy = \frac{Rx^3}{6} + \frac{PL^2x}{8} - \frac{RL^2x}{2}$$

For values of x between $L/2$ and L

$$EIy = \frac{Rx^3}{6} - \frac{Px^3}{6} + \frac{PLx^2}{4} - \frac{RL^2x}{2} + C_4$$

But $y = 0$ when $x = L$. Therefore

$$C_4 = -\frac{RL^3}{6} + \frac{PL^3}{6} - \frac{PL^3}{4} + \frac{RL^3}{2}$$

$$= \frac{RL^3}{3} - \frac{PL^3}{12}$$

And

$$EIy = \frac{Rx^3}{6} - \frac{Px^3}{6} + \frac{PLx^2}{4} - \frac{RL^2x}{2} + \frac{RL^3}{3} - \frac{PL^3}{12}$$

Both of these curves have the same ordinate when $x = L/2$. Equating these values,

$$\frac{RL^3}{48} + \frac{PL^3}{16} - \frac{RL^3}{4} = \frac{RL^3}{48} - \frac{PL^3}{48} + \frac{PL^3}{16} - \frac{RL^3}{4} + \frac{RL^3}{3} - \frac{PL^3}{12}$$

Solving for R,
$$R = \tfrac{5}{16}P$$

With the reaction at the end known it is possible by $\Sigma M = 0$ and $\Sigma V = 0$ to calculate the moment at the fixed end and the shear at the fixed end.

$\Sigma M = 0$

$$-M_B + \tfrac{5}{16}PL - P\frac{L}{2} = 0$$

$$M_B = -\tfrac{3}{16}PL$$

$\Sigma V = 0$

$$V_B - P + \tfrac{5}{16}P = 0$$

$$V_B = \tfrac{11}{16}P$$

The shear and bending-moment diagrams are shown in Fig. 246. Substituting $\tfrac{5}{16}P$ for R in the equations for the curve:

$$EIy = \frac{5\,Px^3}{96} + \frac{PL^2x}{8} - \frac{5\,PL^2x}{32} = \frac{5\,Px^3}{96} - \frac{PL^2x}{32}$$

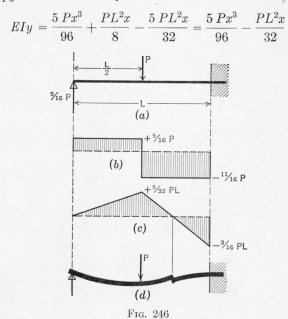

FIG. 246

Substituting $\tfrac{5}{16}P$ for R in the value of dy/dx above

$$EI\frac{dy}{dx} = \frac{5\,Px^2}{32} + \frac{PL^2}{8} - \frac{5\,PL^2}{32} = \frac{5\,Px^2}{32} - \frac{PL^2}{32}$$

The deflection is a maximum where the slope is zero, or

$$\frac{5\,Px^2}{32} - \frac{PL^2}{32} = 0$$

whence $x = \sqrt{\dfrac{L^2}{5}} = 0.447\,L$. Substituting this value for x in the equation for y, there results

$$EIy_{\text{max.}} = \frac{5\,PL^3}{96} \times 0.0894 - \frac{PL^3 \times 0.447}{32}$$

or

$$y_{\text{max.}} = -\frac{0.00931\,PL^3}{EI}$$

PROBLEMS

1. Compare the weights of two steel beams of square cross-section, each to carry a load of 2,000 lb. at the midpoint of a span of 10 ft. and with a unit stress of 18,000 lb. per sq. in., one beam being simply supported at the ends, and the other being fixed at one end and supported at the other.

2. A beam 40 ft. long on three supports, with two equal spans, carries a central load of 4,000 lb. on each span. The beam weighs 60 lb. per ft. Calculate the maximum bending moment and the amount of the center reaction. (*Hint:* Bending moments and end reactions in each span of a *symmetrical* continuous beam on three supports are the same as for a beam fixed at one end and simply supported at the other end. Why?)

136. Beam Fixed at Both Ends — Uniform Load. In this case there

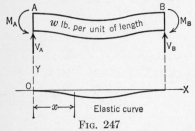

FIG. 247

are four unknowns acting on the beam: M_A, M_B, V_A, and V_B (Fig. 247). These are two more than the available conditions of static equilibrium. But because of the symmetry of the restraints and the loading $V_A = V_B = wL/2$ and $M_A = M_B$. The equation of the elastic curve can be used to establish the value of M_A.

After that has been done shears and moments can easily be determined throughout the length of the beam.

As was explained in Art. 133,

$$M_x = M_A + \frac{wLx}{2} - \frac{wx^2}{2}$$

Hence,

$$EI\frac{d^2y}{dx^2} = M_A + \frac{wLx}{2} - \frac{wx^2}{2}$$

Integrating,

$$EI\frac{dy}{dx} = M_A x + \frac{wLx^2}{4} - \frac{wx^3}{6} + C_1$$

But $dy/dx = 0$ when $x = 0$. Therefore $C_1 = 0$.

Also, because of symmetry $dy/dx = 0$ when $x = L/2$. Hence
$\dfrac{M_A L}{2} + \dfrac{wL^3}{16} - \dfrac{wL^3}{48} = 0$, and

$$M_A = -\frac{wL^2}{8} + \frac{wL^2}{24} = -\frac{wL^2}{12} = -\frac{WL}{12}$$

At the midspan,

$$M = -\frac{wL^2}{12} + \frac{wL}{2} \times \frac{L}{2} - \frac{wL}{2} \times \frac{L}{4} = +\frac{wL^2}{24} = +\frac{WL}{24}$$

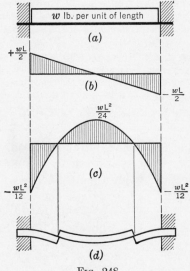

w lb. per unit of length

(a)

$+\frac{wL}{2}$

(b)

$-\frac{wL}{2}$

$\frac{wL^2}{24}$

(c)

$-\frac{wL^2}{12}$ $-\frac{wL^2}{12}$

(d)

Fig. 248

The shear and bending-moment diagrams are as shown in Fig. 248 (b) and (c). Substituting the value of M_A in the equation for the slope,

$$EI \frac{dy}{dx} = -\frac{wL^2 x}{12} + \frac{wLx^2}{4} - \frac{wx^3}{6}$$

and integrating,

$$EIy = -\frac{wL^2 x^2}{24} + \frac{wLx^3}{12} - \frac{wx^4}{24} + C_2$$

But $y = 0$ when $x = 0$. Therefore $C_2 = 0$. At center

$$y_{\text{max.}} = -\frac{wL^4}{384\, EI} = -\frac{WL^3}{384\, EI}$$

The same slopes, deflections, and stresses would result in the three beams shown in Fig. 248 (d).

PROBLEM

A beam L in. long and fixed at both ends carries a single concentrated load, P, at the midpoint. Calculate the bending moments at the ends and at the midpoint, and draw shear and bending-moment diagrams. Find the deflection at the midpoint, in terms of E and I.

$$Ans. \quad y_{max.} = -\frac{PL^3}{192\,EI}.$$

AREA MOMENT METHOD

(Arts. 137 to 143, inclusive, may be omitted if the area moment method is omitted.)

Because of the simplicity of the area moment method, it will be applied to restrained beams with a wider variety of loadings than was done with the double integration method. Also beams fixed at one end will be considered in which the support is either above or below the level of the tangent at the fixed end. Most of these cases will be presented in the form of numerical problems. However, in order to illustrate the method of solving a problem in general terms by area moments, the following article gives such a solution.

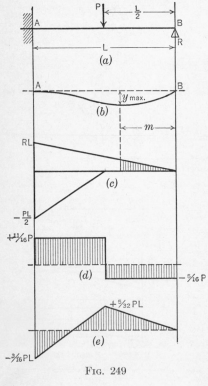

Fig. 249

137. Beam Fixed at One End — Concentrated Load at Midpoint. The beam and loading are shown in Fig. 249 (a) and the approximate shape of the elastic curve is shown in (b). The bending-moment diagram is drawn in two parts as shown in (c), the ordinates of the upper triangle representing the moments due to the unknown reaction R.

If the support at B is on the level of the horizontal tangent at A, the displacement of B from the tangent at A is zero. Therefore the statical moment, with respect to B, of the bending-moment diagram, divided by EI, is zero. Hence

$$\frac{RL \times \dfrac{L}{2} \times \dfrac{2}{3}L - \dfrac{PL}{2} \times \dfrac{L}{4} \times \dfrac{5}{6}L}{EI} = 0$$

Solving for R, $\qquad R = \frac{5}{16}P$

The shear diagram and the combined bending-moment diagram are shown in (*d*) and (*e*).   At the point of maximum deflection the tangent to the elastic curve is horizontal and therefore parallel to the tangent at *A*.   From this fact it follows that the area of the bending-moment diagram between the point of maximum deflection and *A*, the fixed end, is zero.   This fact may be used to determine the location of the point where the deflection is maximum.   The total plus area in the *M* diagram is $\frac{5}{16} PL \times L/2 = \frac{5}{32} PL^2$.

The total minus area is $PL/2 \times L/4 = \frac{1}{8} PL^2$.

Let *m* be the number of inches from *B* to the point of maximum deflection, then

$$\frac{5}{32} PL^2 - \frac{1}{8} PL^2 - \frac{5}{16} Pm \times \frac{m}{2} = 0$$

from which $$m^2 = \frac{L^2}{5}$$

and $$m = 0.447 \, L$$

But the maximum deflection equals the displacement of *B* from the horizontal tangent.   Hence

$$\Delta = \frac{\frac{5}{16} P \times 0.447 \, L \times \frac{0.447 \, L}{2} \times \frac{2}{3} \times 0.447 \, L}{EI}$$

and

$$y_{max.} = -0.00931 \frac{PL^3}{EI}$$

138. Beam Fixed at One End — Concentrated Load not at Midpoint.   The area moment method can be applied just as easily when the concentrated load is at some point other than the midpoint of the span, as illustrated by the following numerical example.

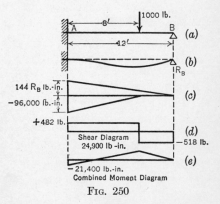

Fig. 250

Example. A 4-in., 7.7-lb. I-beam fixed at one end is loaded and supported as shown in Fig. 250.   Calculate the reaction at *B*, the resultant vertical force on the beam at the fixed end, and the resultant external couple or moment at the fixed end, caused by the 1,000-lb. load.

Solution: The bending-moment diagram is drawn as two triangles.   The ordinates of the positive triangle must be expressed in terms of R_B since the numerical value of the reaction is unknown. Determination of the value of R_B is the first step in the solution of the problem.

The deflection of B from the tangent at A equals zero. Therefore the statical moment with respect to B of the bending-moment diagram, divided by EI, equals zero. Or,

$$\frac{144\, R_B \times 72 \times 96 - 96{,}000 \times 48 \times 112}{30{,}000{,}000 \times 6} = 0$$

Whence $\qquad R_B = \dfrac{96{,}000 \times 48 \times 112}{144 \times 72 \times 96} = 518 \text{ lb.}$

With R_B known, the resultant vertical force on the beam at A and the resultant external couple at A are readily determined. Applying $\Sigma V = 0$ to the portion of the beam which projects from the wall, and letting V_A be the resultant vertical force (that is, the total shear) at A,

$$518 - 1{,}000 + V_A = 0$$
$$V_A = 482 \text{ lb.}$$

The resultant external couple at A is evidently equal to the bending moment at A. Since R_B is known, this can be found.

$$M_A = 518 \times 144 - 1{,}000 \times 96 = -21{,}400 \text{ lb-in.}$$

With R_B, V_A, and M_A known, the shear and combined bending-moment diagrams can be drawn. They are shown at (d) and (e). As with simple beams, it is evident that " dangerous sections " occur at points where the shear line passes through zero. The combined bending-moment diagram shows a point of zero bending moment between the fixed end and the load. Between this point and the fixed end the bending moment is negative and the beam is bent concave down, and between this point and the other end of the beam the beam is bent concave up.

In examples like this, where the deflection of the support is zero from the tangent at the fixed end, it is evident from the deflection equation that the amount of the reaction at the support is independent of E and I. This means that the reaction will be the same for a beam of any cross-section and material carrying this load (provided, of course, that the proportional limits of the material is not exceeded). In such cases the equation may be written in foot units instead of inch units, which simplifies the arithmetic slightly.

PROBLEMS

1. For the beam shown in Fig. 251, calculate the amount of R_R. Draw shear diagram and combined bending-moment diagram.

Ans. $R_R = 554$ lb.

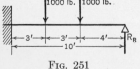

2. A beam L in. long is fixed at one end and supported at the other. It carries a load of P lb. $\frac{1}{3} L$ from the reaction. Calculate the amount of the reaction.

3. A beam L in. long is fixed at one end and supported at the other. It carries a uniformly distrib-

Fig. 251

uted load of W lb. Calculate the amount of the reaction. Draw the shear diagram and the combined bending-moment diagram.

4. The reaction R (Fig. 252) is on the level of the tangent at the fixed end.   Calculate R due to the load of 10,000 lb.   Draw combined bending-moment diagram and select the lightest steel wide-flange beam to carry this load with a stress not exceeding 18,000 lb. per sq. in.

16 WF 45

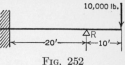

Fig. 252

139. Support Not on Level of Tangent at Fixed End.   If a beam fixed at one end is supported at some point and the support is pushed up above the line of the tangent at the fixed end, the amount of this reaction increases. If the support settles below the level of the tangent the amount of the reaction decreases.   The reaction becomes zero when the support is lowered until the beam carries the loads as a cantilever — if it is able to do so.

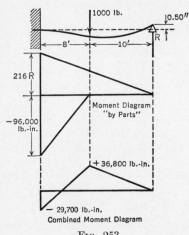

Combined Moment Diagram

Fig. 253

The method of solving for the amount of the reaction in such cases is the same as where the support remains on the " level." E and I must be known (or assumed) since they do not go out of the equation as they do when the support is at the same level as the fixed end.

Example.   A 5-in., 10-lb. I-beam is fixed at one end and loaded as shown in Fig. 253.   The other end is supported and the support is jacked up 0.50 in. above the tangent.   Calculate the amount of the reaction.

Solution:

$$0.50 = \frac{216\,R \times 108 \times 144 - 96,000 \times 48 \times 184}{30,000,000 \times 12.1}$$

$$181,500,000 + 848,000,000 = 216 \times 108 \times 144\,R$$

$$R = 253 + 54 = 307\ \text{lb.}$$

In following through this solution it will be observed that 54 lb. of this reaction is due to the fact that the support is elevated.

PROBLEMS

1. Solve the above example if the support is level with the tangent at A.   Draw combined M diagram.

2. Solve the above example if the support is lowered 0.50 in. below the tangent. Draw combined M diagram.   *R = 199 #*

3. By what amount does the lowering of the support in Problem 2 increase the maximum stress in the beam?

140. Beams Fixed at Both Ends. As pointed out in Art. 132, in a beam fixed at both ends, there is an unknown moment and an unknown shear at each support (Fig. 254). The determination of these four unknown quantities requires four equations. $\Sigma M = 0$ and $\Sigma V = 0$ furnish two of these equations. In the general case of unsymmetrical loading, the other two equations are furnished by the area moment propositions, utilizing the conditions of restraint that are present.

As shown in Art. 133, the bending moment at a distance x ft. from the end, A, of the beam is

$$M_x = M_A + V_A x - \text{Moments of intervening loads}$$

In drawing a bending-moment diagram for the beam, it is convenient to plot these terms separately, as shown in Fig. 255 (a). The moment M_A is the same for all values of x, and appears as a rectangle in the bending-moment diagram. The term $V_A x$ results in a triangle, since the moment of V_A increases as x increases. The moment of each intervening load results in a triangle if the load is concentrated, and

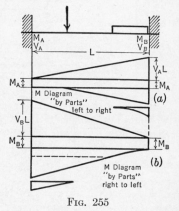

Fig. 254   Fig. 255

in a parabolic area where the load is uniformly distributed.

If more convenient, the distance x may be measured from the B end of the beam. In this case the moment equation is

$$M_x = M_B + V_B x - \text{Moments of intervening loads}$$

With x measured from the B end of the beam, the bending-moment diagram is as shown in Fig. 255 (b).

141. Beams Fixed at Both Ends — Symmetrical Loading. Because of the symmetry of loading, V_A and V_B each equals one half the sum of the loads. Since V_A is known, only one equation based on the conditions of restraint is necessary. The simplest equation is based on the fact that in a symmetrical beam the tangent at the midpoint is horizontal and therefore parallel to the tangent at either fixed end.

Example. Calculate the shear and bending moment at the left end of the beam in Fig. 256, caused by the concentrated loads. Draw shear and combined bending-moment diagrams.

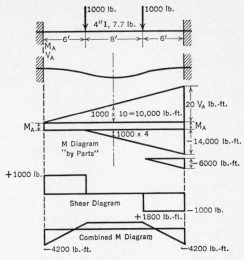

Fig. 256

Solution: Since the beam is symmetrical, $V_A = 1,000$ lb. Since the tangent at the midpoint is parallel to the tangent at the left end, the area of the M diagram between these two points is zero. Therefore

$$10,000 \times 5 + 10\ M_A - 4,000 \times 2 = 0$$
$$M_A = 800 - 5,000 = -4,200 \text{ lb.-ft.}$$
$$M_6 = M_A + 6\ V_A = -4,200 + 6,000 = +1,800 \text{ lb.-ft.}$$

PROBLEMS

1. Calculate the deflection at the midpoint of the beam in the preceding example.

2. Calculate bending moment at ends and deflection at center of the beam shown in Fig. 257. Draw combined bending-moment diagram. What maximum bending stress results in this beam?   *Ans.* $S_{max} = 9,167$ lb. per sq. in.

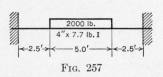

Fig. 257

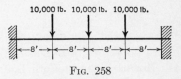

Fig. 258

3. Select the lightest steel, wide-flange beam for Fig. 258. Stress not to exceed 16,000 lb. per sq. in.

4. A beam L in. long, fixed at both ends, carries a concentrated load of P pounds at the midpoint. Using the area moment method, calculate the bending moments at the ends and at the midpoint, and the maximum deflection, in terms of E and I.

Compare these with the corresponding values for a simple beam loaded in the same way.

5. A beam L in. long, fixed at both ends, carries a load of W lb. uniformly distributed over its entire length. Using the area moment method, calculate the bending moments at the ends and at the midpoint, and the maximum deflection, in terms of E and I. Compare these with the corresponding values for a simple beam loaded in the same way.

142. Beams Fixed at Both Ends — Unsymmetrical Loading. In this case two unknown quantities must be solved for by equations based on the conditions of restraint. The method of drawing the bending-moment diagram which has been shown makes it most convenient to solve for the bending moment and shear at one end. There are three conditions of restraint, and the two which result in the simplest equations should be chosen. Those available are:

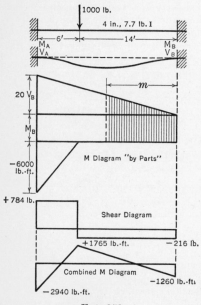

FIG. 259

(1) The tangent at one end is parallel to the tangent at the other end.

(2) The deflection of the right end from the tangent at the left end equals zero.

(3) The deflection of the left end from the tangent at the right end equals zero.

Example 1. The beam used in the previous example, with one of the loads omitted, will be considered. This is shown in Fig. 259. Solve for the shear and moment at each end, and draw a combined M diagram.

Solution: The equation based on the first condition of the three listed is:

$$20\ V_B \times 10 + 20\ M_B - 6{,}000 \times 3 = 0$$
$$10\ V_B + M_B = 900 \qquad (1)$$

The equation based on the third condition listed is:

$$20\ V_B \times 10 \times \tfrac{2\,0}{3} + 20\ M_B \times 10 - 6{,}000 \times 3 \times 2 = 0$$
$$\tfrac{2\,0}{3}\ V_B + M_B = 180 \qquad (2)$$

Subtracting equation (2) from equation (1),

$$\tfrac{1\,0}{3}\ V_B = 720$$
$$V_B = 216 \text{ lb.}[1]$$

[1] The positive value found for V_B indicates that V_B causes positive bending moment as assumed in the first equation. It is therefore an upward force on the right-hand end of the segment and, according to the usual shear convention, this is negative shear, and it is so shown in the shear diagram.

Therefore, since $\Sigma V = 0$, $V_A = 1,000 - 216 = 784$ lb. and with these values the shear diagram can be drawn.

Also from equation (1)

$$M_B = 900 - 10\,V_B = 900 - 2,160 = -1,260 \text{ lb-ft.}$$

As shown on the bending-moment diagram " by parts "

$$M_A = 20\,V_B + M_B - 6,000$$

Therefore $M_A = 4,320 - 1,260 - 6,000 = -2,940$ lb-ft.

At the load the bending moment equals

$$M_6 = M_B + 14\,V_B = -1,260 + 14 \times 216 = +1,765 \text{ lb-ft.}$$

With these values the combined bending-moment diagram can be drawn.

Example 2.   Find the location and amount of the maximum deflection of the beam in Example 1.

Solution: The position of the maximum deflection is found more easily in this example than for a simple beam.   The maximum deflection occurs where the tangent is horizontal.   Between this point and either support the area of the M diagram equals zero.   Representing the unknown distance to the right support by m, the area is

$$216\,m \times \frac{m}{2} - 1,260\,m = 0$$

$$m = \frac{1,260 \times 2}{216} = 11.67 \text{ ft. or 140 in.}$$

The maximum deflection equals the statical moment of this part of the area, with respect to either end, divided by EI.   Taking the statical moment of this area about the right-hand end the deflection is

$$y = \frac{140 \times 216 \times 70 \times \frac{2}{3} \times 140 - 1,260 \times 12 \times 140 \times 70}{30,000,000 \times 6.0} = 0.275 \text{ in.}$$

PROBLEMS

1. A 4-in., 7.7-lb. I-beam is fixed at both ends, the fixed points being 18 ft. apart. A load of 2,000 lb. is applied 6 ft. from one end.   Calculate the shear and bending moment at each end and the maximum deflection caused by the 2,000-lb. load.

$V_a = 1471.7$ $V_B = 518.3$, $Ma = 5,330 \; ft \; \#$ $M_b = 2,665 ft \#$ *Ans.* $y = 0.46$ in.

2. A steel beam has a span of 10 ft., clear, and is fixed at both ends.   A load of 6,000 lb. is uniformly distributed over the left half of the beam.   Neglecting weight of beam, draw shear and bending-moment diagrams, indicating values at significant points (including maximum bending moment). Select the lightest steel I-beam that can be used with a stress not more than 16,000 lb. per sq. in. Calculate the deflection at the center.

3. For the beam shown in Fig. 260 draw shear and bending-moment diagrams (indicating values) and select the lightest steel I-beam that can be used with stress not exceeding 16,000 lb. per sq. in. Neglect weight of beam.

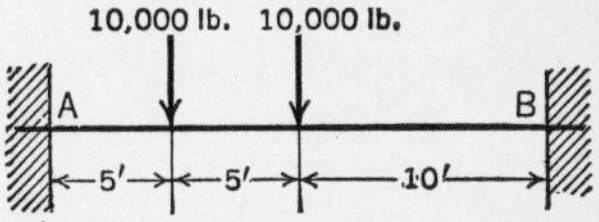

10,000 lb.   10,000 lb.

A ——————— B

5' —— 5' —— 10'

FIG. 260

Calculate deflection at center.   *Ans.* $M_B = -34,375$ lb-ft.

$y = 0.134$ $12'' I \; 40\#$ Beam

4. Calculate the size of a square timber beam required to carry the load in Problem 1. Also calculate the maximum deflection. Bending stress is not to exceed 1,200 lb. per sq. in.   Assume E to be 1,200,000 lb. per sq. in.

143. Restrained Beam Considered as Simple Beam with End Moments.

It is sometimes convenient to think of a restrained beam as being a beam simply supported at the ends and acted on not only by a load (or a system of loads) *but also by moments applied to the beam at its ends.* If these moments are of the proper amounts, they will rotate the ends of the beam until the tangents to the elastic curve are horizontal at those points.   With this the case, the beam meets all the conditions of a beam " fixed at both ends." A restrained beam, then, is simply a beam supported at the ends and acted on both by a system of loads and a system of end moments so adjusted to the loads that the tangents to the elastic curve are horizontal at the ends of the beam.

It follows from this proposition that the bending-moment diagram for a restrained beam may be shown in two parts: (1) the bending-moment diagram for a simple beam carrying the given loads, and (2) the bending-moment diagram for the beam without loads but acted on by the end moments.

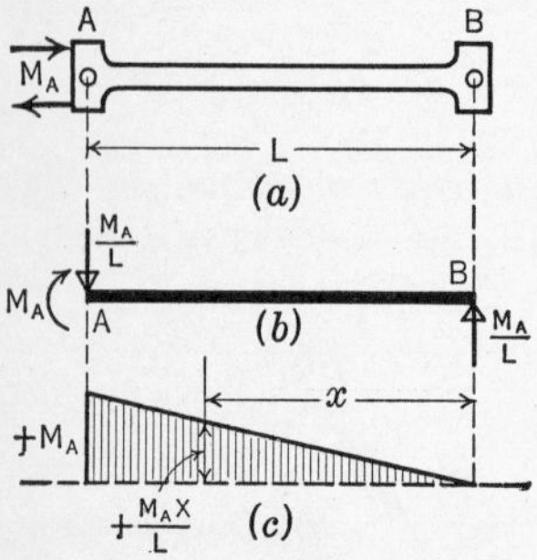

FIG. 261

Since the drawing of bending-moment diagrams for simple beams has already been discussed at length, it remains to consider the diagram which represents the bending moments caused in a beam by end moments.   This is most easily understood by considering first a beam with only one end moment, Fig. 261 (*a*). The beam is shown with supports which may exert either upward or downward reactions as may be required for equilibrium.   These supports are shown as pins passing through the ends of the beam.

Let a moment or couple M_A be applied to the beam at the A end in a clockwise direction.   Applying $\Sigma M_A = 0$, it is evident that an upward reaction of M_A/L exists at B and since $\Sigma V = 0$, there must also be a downward reaction of M_A/L at A.   Note that these two reactions constitute a counterclockwise couple which has a value of M_A.   The bending moment at a distance of x from B is $+M_A x/L$ and the bending-moment diagram is a triangle, the ordinate at A being $+M_A$ as shown in Fig. 261 (*c*).

Similarly, if instead of the moment at A, the beam is subject to a counterclockwise moment M_B at B, the bending-moment diagram is a triangle with the value of $+M_B$ at B. By the principle of summation of effects, it follows that, with couples or moments at both ends (clockwise at A and counterclockwise at B, as shown in Fig. 262), the bending-moment diagram is two triangles which form the trapezoid shown in Fig. 262 (c). The student should check the values of M for this case at a distance x from one end, using the moment and reactions as shown in Fig. 262 (b).

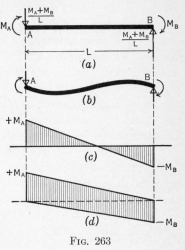

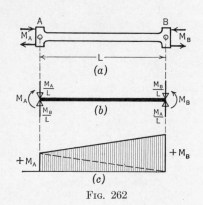

FIG. 262   FIG. 263

If the end moments or couples are both clockwise, as shown in Fig. 263, the bending-moment diagram is that shown in Fig. 263 (c), which will be observed to be the equivalent of the two triangles shown in (d).

PROBLEMS

The solution of the following problems is to be based on bending-moment diagrams drawn in two parts, as suggested in the second paragraph of this article. The area moment propositions are to be used.

1. Calculate the bending moment at the fixed end of the beam shown in Fig. 250.

2. Calculate the bending moments at the ends of the beam shown in Fig. 256.

3. Calculate the bending moments at the ends of the beam shown in Fig. 264.

4. Show that, for a beam fixed at both ends, with any symmetrical loading, the end moment equals $-A/L$, where A is the area of the moment diagram for a simple beam with the same span and loading.

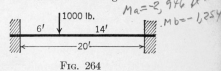

FIG. 264

5. Show that, for a beam fixed at one end and supported at the other end with any system of loads symmetrical about the midpoint, the bending moment at the fixed end equals $-\dfrac{3}{2}\dfrac{A}{L}$, in which A is the area of the moment diagram of a simple beam with the same span and loading.

GENERAL PROBLEMS

1. For a beam fixed at one end and carrying a single concentrated load not at the midpoint (Fig. 265) show that $R = \dfrac{Pb^2}{2\,L^3}\,(a + 2\,L)$.

2. Using the value of R of the preceding problem, draw shear and bending-moment diagrams for a beam in which $a = L/4$.

Fig. 265	Fig. 266

3. The beam shown in Fig. 266 is fixed at A and supported at B. $EI = 100,000,000$. Calculate the amount of R_B if the support is on the level of the tangent at A. Draw shear diagram and combined bending-moment diagram.

4. A beam L ft. long is fixed at one end and supported at the other end. A load of w lb. per ft. is uniformly distributed over the half of the beam nearest the support. Calculate the amount of the reaction.

5. A beam rests on two supports L ft. apart, and overhangs at each end a distance of $L/3$ ft. It carries a load Q at the midpoint and equal loads P at each end. What part of Q must P be in order that the elastic curve of the beam shall be horizontal at the supports? *Ans.* $P = 0.375\,Q$.

6. The principle of summation of effects shows that, in a beam fixed at one end and supported at the other end, if the end support is raised (or lowered) Δ in., the change in reaction equals the force required to produce an end deflection of Δ in. in a cantilever beam of the same length and stiffness. Show that, for such a beam uniformly loaded, if the end reaction is raised or lowered,

$$R = \frac{3}{8}\,wL \pm \frac{3\,EI\Delta}{L^3}$$

Discuss the change in the bending-moment diagram due to raising or lowering the end reaction.

7. A steel beam is fixed at one end and supported at a point 18 ft. from the fixed end. It is to carry a load of 10,000 lb. 6 ft. from the fixed end. Select the lightest steel I-beam that will carry this load with a stress not exceeding 16,000 lb. per sq. in. Neglect weight of beam.

8. Calculate the amount of the maximum deflection in a 4-in., 7.7-lb. I-beam fixed at points 20 ft. apart, caused by a load of 1,000 lb. placed 8 ft., 4 in. from one fixed point. *Ans.* $y = 0.372$ in.

9. The beam shown in Fig. 267 is a 4-in., 7.7-lb. I-beam. Calculate the maximum deflection caused by the concentrated loads. *Ans.* $y = 0.311$ in.

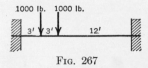

Fig. 267

10. A beam L ft. long is fixed at both ends. A load of w lb. per ft. extends from the midpoint to one fixed end. Calculate the bending moments and shears at the fixed ends.

11. A balcony is supported on an 8-in., 20.5-lb. I-beam which is fixed horizontally in a heavy masonry wall at one end and attached at the other end to two vertical 1-in.-diameter steel rods, 25 ft. long. The load on the beam is 30,000 lb., uniformly distributed. The distance from the face of the wall to the axis of the rods is 10 ft. (a) Assuming that as the load is applied to the beam there is no change in the elevation of the upper ends of the rods, what are the maximum stresses in beam and rods? (b) Assuming that the upper ends of the rods descend 0.10 in. as the load is applied, what are the stresses?

12. AA is a 4-in., 7.7-lb. I-beam fixed at both ends, 15 ft. between fixed points. BB is a 4-in., 7.7-lb. I-beam, simply supported, 10 ft. center to center of supports. AA is in an east-west direction. BB is in a north-south direction, just above AA. The two beams are just in contact at their midpoints before load is applied. (a) Calculate the reactions caused by 4,000 lb. applied at the midpoint of the upper beam. (b) What are the reactions if BB is below AA? $Ans.$ (a) $R_B = 915$ lb.

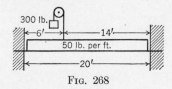

300 lb.

←6'→ ←———14'———→

50 lb. per ft.

←————20'————→

Fig. 268

13. For the beam shown in Fig. 268, calculate end shears and moments, and draw shear diagram and combined bending-moment diagram.

CHAPTER XII

DIRECT STRESS COMBINED WITH BENDING

144. Tension or Compression Member with Transverse Load.
There are many cases of members subject to forces causing tensile or compressive stress on which there are also transverse forces causing bending stresses. As a simple example consider a short vertical tension member (Fig. 269). This carries an axial load P_1 and a transverse load P_2. Between B and C the only stress on a cross-section is the tensile stress due to P_1. Above B this tensile stress exists but there are also the stresses caused by P_2, which are the same as in a cantilever beam. The resultant stress at any point in any cross-section $E-E'$, above B is the algebraic sum of the tensile stress caused by P_1 and the bending tension or compression caused by P_2.

This statement is slightly inexact. Load P_2 bends the member BD, and because of this bending the load P_1 has a small moment arm with respect to an axis through the centroid of any cross-section between B and D. There is thus a moment caused by P_1 which is subtracted from the moment caused by P_2. If P_1 were a compression load its moment would be added to the moment caused by P_2.

The deflection Δ is very much exaggerated in Fig. 269 (b). If BD is short this deflection is exceedingly small so that $P_1\Delta$ is entirely negligible compared with P_2x. For the present, only cases in which the length of the member is relatively small will be considered. In such cases the bending stresses caused by axial loads may be neglected without appreciable error. In Art. 151, however, consideration will be given to the effect which the deflection produced by the transverse load has on the stresses caused by the longitudinal load.

Example 1. In Fig. 269(a), CD is a steel bar 1 in. by 4 in. BD is 30 in., P_1 is 10,000 lb., and P_2 is 1,000 lb. Calculate the stress at both edges of the bar at D and also for a section between B and C.

Solution: The stress due to $P_1 = 10,000/4 = 2,500$ lb. per sq. in. at any point of any cross-section far enough above C so that the stress can be assumed to be uniformly distributed. Below B there is no bending stress due to P_2 and the stress is only the 2,500 lb. per sq. in., tension. At D there is bending stress caused by P_2. This is

$$S = \frac{Mc}{I} = \frac{1,000 \times 30 \times 2}{\dfrac{1 \times 4^3}{12}} = 11,250 \text{ lb. per sq. in.}$$

This is tension on the right-hand edge. At D the stress is $2,500 - 11,250 = -8,750$

lb. per sq. in., compression.   At D' the stress is $2,500 + 11,250 = 13,750$ lb. per sq. in., tension.

In general, the stress at any point in a cross-section of a member subject to direct stress and bending may be expressed thus,

$$S = \pm \frac{P}{A} \pm \frac{Mc}{I}$$

In both terms of the right-hand member the $+$ sign is commonly used to designate tensile stress and the $-$ sign compressive stress.

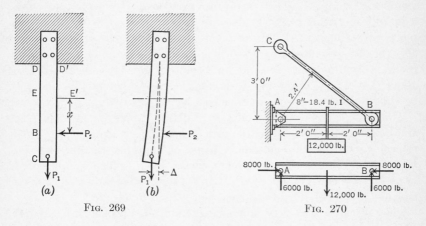

Fig. 269   Fig. 270

Example 2.   Find the maximum compressive stress in the member AB shown in Fig. 270.

Solution: By the principles of statics, the tension in BC is equal to $\dfrac{12,000 \times 2.0}{2.4} = $ 10,000 lb.   If this is resolved into horizontal and vertical components, it is seen that the force acting at B may be considered to consist of an axial compressive force of 8,000 lb. and a vertical force of 6,000 lb. AB then is a beam subjected to a concentrated force of 12,000 lb. at its midpoint and to an axial compressive force of 8,000 lb.   The maximum bending moment occurs over the load and is equal to $6,000 \times 24 = 144,000$ lb-in.   For this beam, $I/c = 14.2$ in.[3]   Therefore the maximum bending stress is $144,000/14.2 = 10,140$ lb. per sq. in.   In addition to this bending stress there is an axial compression of $8,000/A = 8,000/5.34$ sq. in. $= 1,500$ lb. per sq. in.   Therefore the maximum compressive stress in the beam is 11,640 lb. per sq. in., at the top of the beam, directly above the load.

PROBLEMS

1. What are the maximum tensile and compressive unit stresses in the vertical member of Fig. 271 at a section 1 ft. 8 in. above the pulley?   The weight of the member itself may be neglected.   (*Hint:* Resolve the pulley reaction into its horizontal and vertical components.)

2. A 6-in.-by-12-in. timber beam (Fig. 272), 10 ft. long, carries a single load of 5,000 lb. at its midpoint and is subjected to an axial pull of 10,000 lb. What are the maximum tensile and compressive stresses in the beam?

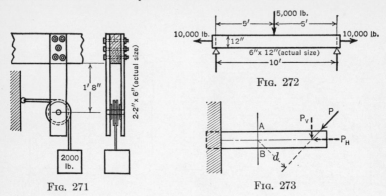

Fig. 271

Fig. 272

Fig. 273

145. Bending Forces Which Are Not Transverse.

In all the cases of bending which have been considered so far, the bending has been caused by transverse forces — that is, forces perpendicular to the longitudinal axis of the member. But transverse forces are not the only forces that may cause a member to bend. In Fig. 273, the load P evidently has a moment Pd with respect to the neutral axis of section AB, and this moment will cause bending at AB. AB may be any section between the wall and the point on the axis of the beam at which the force P cuts the axis.

The bending due to an oblique load may also conveniently be calculated by substituting for the oblique load its transverse and longitudinal components. If this substitution is made at the point where the line of action of the load intersects the neutral surface of the beam, the longitudinal component, being axial, will cause a stress uniformly distributed over the cross-section of the member. The transverse component will cause bending, just as any transverse force causes bending.

PROBLEMS

1. A 5-in., 6.7-lb. channel is used to support a large water pipe, as shown in Fig. 274, the lower end being welded to part of the steel framing of a building. If the maximum compressive stress on section AB is not to exceed 10,000 lb. per sq. in., what is the maximum load P? (Assume that the load is so applied that it does not cause twisting of the channel.)   *Ans.* $P = 610$ lb.

2. A post is to support a bracket, as shown in Fig. 275. The post is supported by loosely fitting sockets, top and bottom. The dimension a may have any value from 1 ft. to 4 ft. With the dimension a such that the greatest stress in the post results, determine the value of the load P if the post is 4-in. standard steel pipe and the stress is not to exceed 12,000 lb. per sq. in.

146. Unit Stresses Caused by Eccentric Load on a Prism. The short prism shown in Fig. 276 (*a*) rests on a rigid surface and supports a rigid plate to which loads are applied. The resultant of these loads (shown

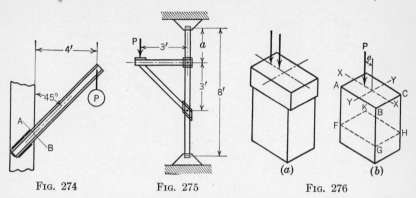

Fig. 274   Fig. 275   Fig. 276

in *b* as the load *P*) is not axial but is parallel to the axis of the prism, at a distance of *e* in. The distance *e* is called the eccentricity of the load. Only cases in which the resultant load lies on one axis of symmetry of the cross-section will be considered in this article.

Consider as a body in equilibrium the part of the prism above the plane *FG*, which represents any transverse plane. For simplicity, the side view of this part of the prism is shown in Fig. 277 and will be referred to in the following discussion.

The body *ABGF* is in equilibrium, and therefore the resultant of all the forces on the *FG* plane must be a force equal and opposite to and collinear with the load *P*. In stressing the prism, this eccentric resultant force has two effects: a direct compressive effect and a bending effect. It is convenient to evaluate these effects separately. This is easily done by

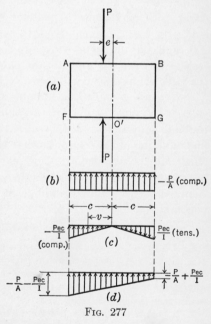

Fig. 277

noting that the eccentric force, *P*, is the resultant of an equal axial force, *P*, and a couple, or moment, *Pe*. The stress on *FG* can therefore be treated as the result of this axial load and this moment. The axial force P causes a uniformly distributed compressive stress, P/A. The moment Pe produces bending forces that vary from zero at the neutral axis of the cross-section to maximum values at the edges F and G. The intensity of the bending stress at a distance c from the neutral axis is, of course, given by $S = Mc/I$ or Pec/I since the bending moment is Pe. The total stress intensity at any distance v from the neutral axis is, $-P/A \pm Pev/I$, in which, as heretofore in this chapter, the minus sign is used to indicate compressive stress.[1]

Example. In Fig. 276(b) the length of FG is 12 in. and the length of GH is 8 in. Calculate the stresses at the ends of the cross-section if a load of 24,000 lb. is applied 3 in. from the axis Y–Y.

Solution: The stresses may both be represented by the equation $S = -\dfrac{P}{A} \pm \dfrac{Mc}{I}$.

Substituting the values in the problem

$$S = \frac{-24,000}{96} \pm \frac{24,000 \times 3 \times 6}{1,152} = -250 \pm 375 = +125 \text{ lb. per sq. in. and}$$
$$-625 \text{ lb. per sq. in.}$$

There is compressive stress along the edge FK, as was to be expected. It may seem remarkable that a " compressive " load has caused tensile stresses along the edge GH as the solution shows.

147. Maximum Eccentricity for No Tensile Stress.

It is apparent that, in the example above, for some eccentricity less than 3 in. there would be no tensile stress in the prism. The case of zero stress at one edge is of some importance, and the greatest eccentricity which will not cause tensile stresses will now be found.

When the stress at one edge is zero it is obvious that $P/A = Mc/I$. If, in Fig. 276, FG equals h and GH equals b this equation becomes

$$\frac{P}{bh} = \frac{Pe \times h/2}{\dfrac{bh^3}{12}}$$

from which $e = h/6$.

If the eccentricity exceeds $h/6$ it is evident that Mc/I becomes greater than P/A and the stress along GH is tensile.

If the prism is a solid piece of elastic material which can resist tensile stresses as well as compressive stresses this condition is not objectionable. If, on the other hand, the prism is made up of a pile of separate blocks, the tensile stress cannot exist between the separate blocks. In fact,

---

[1] Although derived for a prism of rectangular cross-section, this formula holds good for a prism of any cross-section, provided it has an axis of symmetry and that the resultant of the loads lies on this axis.

the blocks will separate from each other at each surface of contact for a short distance from the face $BCHG$ of the prism. On a masonry post or " pier," a load whose eccentricity exceeded $h/6$ would cause tensile stresses in some part of the joint and would tend to cause the joints to open. This tendency is objectionable. Hence it is an old and accepted rule that in masonry structures the resultant pressure should fall within the "middle third" if the cross-section is a rectangle.

The stress distribution in a rectangular pier loaded with the maximum eccentricity for no tensile stress is shown in Fig. 278 (a), (b), and (c).

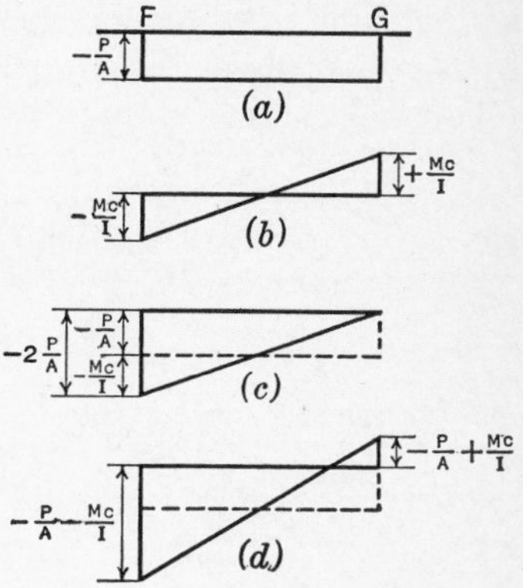

(a) is a diagram representing the constant term $-P/A$. The minus sign is used for compressive stress, which is plotted below the line FG.

(b) represents the bending stress.

(c) shows the diagram (b) superimposed on (a). This is algebraic addition. The resultant (for $e = h/6$) varies from twice P/A at F to zero at G.

FIG. 278

Fig. 278 (d) is a diagram representing a more general case in which e is greater than $h/6$ and the tensile stress $+Mc/I$ exceeds the compressive stress $-P/A$. The resulting tensile stresses are represented by the ordinates of the area above the line FG.

PROBLEMS

1. In a solid masonry pier of circular cross-section, what eccentricity of the load will cause zero stress at the side away from the load?

2. A brick pier is 6 ft. square and 10 ft. high. The masonry weighs 100 lb. per cu. ft. The pier carries a load of 30,000 lb. How far from the center of the top of the pier, on a line parallel to the sides, may the resultant of the 30,000-lb. load be placed without causing tension at the base of the pier?   *Ans.* $e = 26.4$ in.

3. With the load placed as found in Problem 2, what maximum tensile and compressive stresses occur on a horizontal section 7 ft. below the top of the pier?

4. Solve Problem 2, making the load 300,000 lb. instead of 30,000 lb.

5. A short 2-in.-by-8-in. (nominal size) plank carries an axial load which causes a compressive stress of 1,600 lb. per sq. in. If a $1\frac{1}{2}$-in.-diameter hole is bored through the plank, the center of the hole being 2 in. from the axis of the plank, how much is the maximum compressive stress increased by the hole?

148. Eccentric Load Not on Principal Axis. Consider a prism the cross-section of which has principal axes of inertia X-X and Y-Y

(Fig. 279). By the principles of mechanics it may be shown that the load P at N is equivalent to a load P at O plus a couple Pr. It may also be shown that the couple Pr in the plane ON in the figure may be resolved into two component couples Pe_1 and Pe_2 in the planes of the principal axes, respectively. The stress at any point of the cross-section $ABCD$ is the sum of (1) the stresses due to load P at O, (2) that due to the moment Pe_1 with respect to axis X–X, and (3) that due to the moment Pe_2 with respect to axis Y–Y.

Hence, $S = \dfrac{P}{A} \pm \dfrac{Pe_1y_1}{I_x} \pm \dfrac{Pe_2x_1}{I_y}$ in which x_1 and y_1 are the coordinates of the point where the stress is computed.

For the rectangular cross-section $ABCD$ of Fig. 279, the limits of the position of P in order that no tensile stress shall exist will now be found. The stress at A will be zero when

$$\frac{P}{bh} = \frac{Pe_1h/2}{\dfrac{bh^3}{12}} + \frac{Pe_2b/2}{\dfrac{hb^3}{12}}$$

Whence $\dfrac{e_1}{h/6} + \dfrac{e_2}{b/6} = 1$. This is the equation of a straight line with intercepts of $h/6$ on the Y axis and $b/6$ on the X axis. It therefore follows that there will be no tensile stress anywhere within an eccentrically loaded rectangular prism if the resultant load is compressive and if the resultant acts within the diamond-shaped area the length and width of which are $b/3$ and $h/3$ (Fig. 280). This area is called the "kern" (sometimes "kernel") of the cross-section. A kern exists for any cross-section, and its shape depends upon the shape of the cross-section.

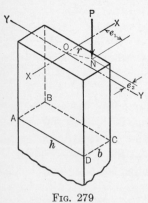

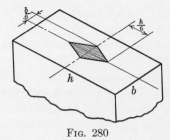

Fig. 279   Fig. 280

149. Line of Zero Stress. If a prism carries a load the resultant of which does not come within the kern, the stresses at some points of a cross-section will be compressive and those at other points will be tensile.

There must therefore be some line lying within the cross-section at every point along which the combined bending and direct stress is zero. This is called the " line of zero stress " of the cross-section.

The stresses at various points on the cross-section of the prism are proportional to the distances of those points from the line of zero stress. Using this fact, the position of the line of zero stress is easily determined. For instance, if, in Fig. 281 (a), S_b and S_c are calculated and laid off to

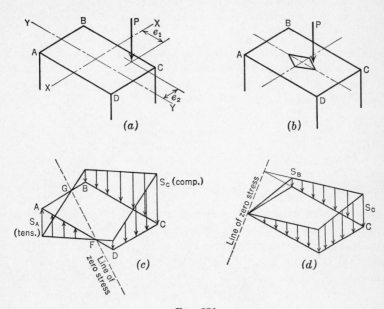

Fig. 281

scale, the point of zero stress on BC (or BC produced) is readily calculated or located graphically. Two such points of zero stress locate the line of zero stress.

If the resultant load acts at one of the boundary lines of the kern, as in Fig. 281 (b), the line of zero stress passes through the opposite corner of the prism. There is only one kind of stress in the prism, but the value of this stress decreases to zero at the corner (or along the edge of the cross-section, if the load acts through the point at which one of the principal axes cuts the kern).

Example. In Fig. 281(a) the post is 6 in. by 10 in.; $e_1 = 2.5$ in.; $e_2 = 2$ in.; $P = 10,000$ lb. P is the resultant of a load applied to the end of the post by a rigid plate or cap. Calculate the stresses at each corner of a cross-section and locate the line of zero stress.

Solution:

$$S = -\frac{P}{A} \pm \frac{M_1 c_1}{I_1} \pm \frac{M_2 c_2}{I_2} = -\frac{10{,}000}{60} \pm \frac{25{,}000}{\dfrac{6 \times 100}{6}} \pm \frac{20{,}000}{\dfrac{10 \times 36}{6}}$$

The stress at each corner is the algebraic sum of these three stresses. At the four corners the stresses are as follows (all stresses are in pounds per square inch).

S_A	S_B	S_C	S_D
+250	+250	−250	−250
+333	−333	−333	+333
−167	−167	−167	−167
+416	−250	−750	− 84

The distance from A along AD to the neutral axis is

$$AF = 10\,\frac{416}{416 + 84} = 8.33 \text{ in.}$$

Also

$$AG = 6\,\frac{416}{416 + 250} = 3.75 \text{ in.}$$

PROBLEMS

1. A 6-in.-by-8-in. post carries a load of 12,000 lb., the resultant of which is on a diagonal at a distance of 4 in. (measured on the diagonal) from the center. Calculate stresses at each corner of a cross-section, and locate the line of zero stress. A +950 B-250 C-1450 D-250 66

2. An 8-in.-by-10-in. (actual size) post carries a load of 12,000 lb., the resultant of which is 1 in. from one 8-in. edge and 1 in. from one 10-in. edge. What is the least additional axial load that will prevent tensile stress at any point in a cross-section of the post?   *Ans.* $P = 43{,}800$ lb.

150. Eccentric Loads on Machine Parts. Numerous examples of bending combined with tension or compression occur in machine frames and other parts of machines and in tools of various sorts. In many of these the eccentricity is very large, the resultant external forces being entirely outside of the cross-sections where the combined stresses occur. In such cases the bending stresses predominate and the part subjected to the combined stress is more in the nature of a beam with some loads causing direct stress. The previous examples were regarded as tension or compression members which were subject to some bending. In both cases the stresses on a cross-section are found in the same way.

Example. The cast-iron frame of a small press is shaped as shown in Fig. 282. Calculate the loads P that would cause stresses on the cross-section $A\text{--}A$ not exceeding these values: tension 3,000 lb. per sq. in.; compression 15,000 lb. per sq. in.

Solution: The eccentricity of the load is the distance from its line of action to the axis through the centroid of the cross-section $A\text{--}A$. It is therefore necessary to determine the position of the centroid and (in order to compute bending stresses) the moment of inertia with respect to the axis through the centroid. By the methods explained in Appendices A and B, the distance from the left edge to the centroid is found to be 2.59 in., and the moment of inertia of the cross-section for the centroidal axis is found to be 91.6 in.[4] The *tensile* stress due to bending will be maximum on the " fibers " nearest the load P. The maximum *compressive* stress due to bending will occur at the opposite edge. The bending moment is 12.59 P lb-in. The equation $S = \dfrac{P}{A} \pm \dfrac{Mc}{I}$ is used to determine P for each case. For tensile stress,

$$3,000 = +\frac{P}{22} + \frac{12.59\,P \times 2.59}{91.6} = 0.045\,P + 0.356\,P = 0.401\,P$$

$$P = \frac{3,000}{0.401} = 7,480 \text{ lb.}$$

A greater load than 7,480 lb. would cause the resultant tensile stress to exceed the allowable.

For compressive stress,

$$15,000 = +\frac{P}{22} - \frac{12.59\,P \times 4.41}{91.6} = +0.045\,P - 0.606\,P = -0.561\,P$$

$$P = \frac{15,000}{0.561} = 26,700 \text{ lb.}$$

Hence the maximum allowable value of the force P is 7,480 lb.

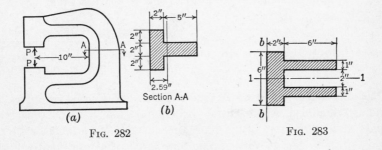

FIG. 282   FIG. 283

PROBLEMS

1. The cross-section of the cast-iron frame of a press is shown in Fig. 283. A load of 12,500 lb. is applied as in the example above, 5 in. to the left of axis $b\text{--}b$. Calculate the maximum tensile and compressive stresses.

2. A malleable-iron C-clamp has dimensions as shown in Fig. 284. When the force P exerted by the screw is 300 lb., what are the maximum tensile and compressive stresses at section $A\text{--}A$? *Ans.* $S_c = 4,340$ lb. per sq. in.

3. Find the maximum load P that the cast-iron frame shown in Fig. 285 can carry without exceeding allowable stresses of 3,000 lb. per sq. in., tension; and 15,000 lb. per sq. in., compression.   2,360

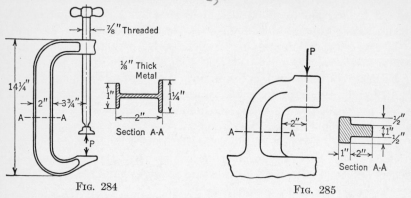

FIG. 284   FIG. 285

151. Effect Which Deflection Has on Stress.

When a member is simultaneously acted on by transverse and longitudinal loads, the deflection produced by the transverse load modifies the stresses produced by the longitudinal load. In many cases, the amount of deflection which the transverse load produces is so small that its effect on the stresses produced by the longitudinal load is negligible. In other cases, the effect on stress may be of importance.

In Example 1, Art. 144, a member subjected to transverse and longitudinal loads was discussed on the assumption that the effect of deflection could be disregarded. The same member and loading will now be reconsidered, taking into account the deflection caused by the transverse load.

Fig. 269 shows this member. Let the distance BC be 3 in. The load P_2 causes the point C to be deflected to the left a distance which can easily be determined (by the principles of Chapter X) to be 0.065 in. This deflection causes the load P_1 to have an eccentricity of 0.065 in. with respect to the centroid of the section DD'. P_1 therefore has a moment of $0.065 \times 10,000 = 650$ lb-in. with respect to the neutral axis of DD'. This moment causes a maximum fiber stress of

$$\frac{650 \times 2}{5.33} = 240 \text{ lb. per sq. in., on section } DD'.$$

This stress is tensile at D and compressive at D'.[1] The load P_1 therefore causes a stress

---

[1] It is obvious that as soon as the member is deflected by P_2, the eccentricity of P_1 will tend to straighten the beam again, or P_1 will cause a deflection in the opposite direction to that caused by P_2. Since the moment of P_1 is very much smaller than that of P_2, the deflection caused by P_1 is very much smaller than that caused by P_2. Therefore the deflection caused by P_1 may safely be disregarded, even in situations where the deflection caused by P_2 should be considered.

which equals 2,500 ± 240 and which therefore varies from +2,740 at D to +2,260 at D', instead of having the uniform value +2,500 which is obtained when the deflection caused by P_2 is disregarded. The stresses caused by P_2 remain practically unaffected by the deflection of the beam. Therefore the maximum stress on the cross-section becomes +11,250 + 2,260 = 13,510 lb., tension at D'. At D the maximum compressive stress becomes −11,250 + 2,740 = −8,510 lb. per sq. in.

Disregard of the deflection resulted (in Art. 144) in obtaining a value of 13,750 lb. per sq. in. for the maximum tensile stress, and a value of 8,750 lb. per sq. in. for the maximum compressive stress. These values are 2 and 3 per cent high, respectively.

In this case, disregard of the deflection caused by P_2 was evidently unimportant. Had the member been slenderer, the importance of deflection would have been greater, and it might have been enough to warrant its being taken into consideration.

It should be noted that disregard of the effect of deflection will lead to stress values which are too high, so long as the longitudinal load is a tensile load. If the longitudinal load is one that causes compression, the disregard of deflection produced by the transverse load will result in computed stress values that are too low. If the member is sufficiently slender and the longitudinal load sufficiently great to make the discrepancy important, however, the member will probably have to be considered as a *column* (Chapter XIII).

GENERAL PROBLEMS

1. A hollow rectangular pier is 20 in. by 16 in. in outside dimensions and has walls 4 in. thick. The resultant of a 20,000-lb. load acts on the axis through the center parallel to the 20-in. sides, at a distance of 2 in. from the center. What are the maximum and minimum compressive stresses in the pier?

Ans. Maximum S_c = 131 lb. per sq. in.

2. A piece of 2-in. standard pipe is bent into the form shown in Fig. 286. The lower end is rigidly embedded in the foundation. What is the greatest load P that can be suspended from the end of the gooseneck, if the allowable compressive stress at A is 6,000 lb. per sq. in.?

FIG. 286

3. A wall of a tank is to be built of masonry weighing 140 lb. per cu. ft. The water is to be 6 ft. deep. (*a*) If the wall is 8 ft. high and of uniform thickness, how thick must it be to avoid tension at the base of the wall? (*b*) If 3 ft. thick, how high must it be to avoid tension at the base?

Ans. (*b*) h = 10.7 ft.

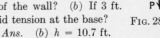

FIG. 287

4. A $\frac{1}{2}$-in.-diameter rod is bent as shown in Fig. 287. What is the allowable load P that can be applied, if the tensile unit stress is not to exceed 16,000 lb. per sq. in.?

5. A short piece of 24-in., 120-lb. I-beam is used as a strut. An axial load of 300,000 lb. is applied on the end. An additional parallel load P is to be applied so that its resultant acts on the end of the beam at the intersection of axis 2–2 with the face of one flange. What is the greatest value that P can have without causing the compressive stress to exceed 18,000 lb. per sq. in.?

6. The frame of a Brinell hardness-testing machine is shown in Fig. 288. Calculate the maximum tensile and compressive stresses on section $A–A$ resulting from the standard pressure of 3,000 kg.

Ans. Maximum S_c = 2,820 lb. per sq. in.

7. Find the maximum tensile and compressive stresses in the beam AB, Fig. 289. Neglect the weight of the beam itself.

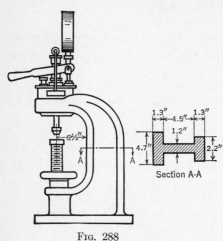

Section A-A

Fig. 288

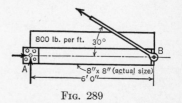

Fig. 289

8. A short post 4 in. by 6 in. in cross-section carries a load P of 1,000 lb. applied as shown in Fig. 290. Calculate the stress at each corner of a cross-section, and locate the line of zero stress.

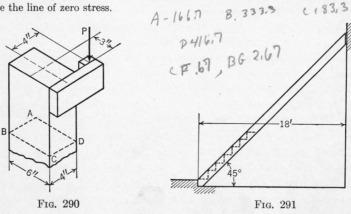

$A - 166.7$ $B. 333.3$ $C. 183.3$

$D 416.7$

$C F .67 , BG 2.67$

Fig. 290

Fig. 291

9. Stairs in a factory are supported by two 10-in., 15.3-lb. channels resting against vertical bearing plates at the top, as shown in Fig. 291. The maximum total dead load plus live load on the two channels (including their own weight) is 6,200 lb., uniformly distributed. Calculate the maximum and minimum stresses in one channel at a section at its midpoint.

CHAPTER XIII

COLUMN THEORY

152. Introduction. In the preceding chapter, a relatively short prism under an eccentric compressive load was considered and it was shown that the maximum stress produced has two components: a uniformly distributed stress P/A due to direct compression and a stress Pec/I. Because of the bending moment Pe, the axis of the prism becomes curved and the eccentricity at the midsection of the prism is increased with resulting increase in bending moment and bending stress.

In the cases which were discussed in the preceding chapter, the ratio of the length of the prism to its transverse dimensions was such that the increase in eccentricity and stress was so small as to be negligible. In this chapter compression members in which the deflection is not negligible are considered, first, when supporting axial loads and, later, when supporting eccentric loads. Chapter XIV treats of the design of actual columns and of column formulas used in practice.

153. Columns. Suppose that the length of a prism is many times the least transverse dimension as, for instance, in an ordinary yardstick. As a compressive load is applied to the ends of such a member, a large lateral deflection occurs, and the final eccentricity under some load P is much larger than the initial eccentricity with which the load P was applied. In this case, the increase in eccentricity under load cannot be disregarded in considering the stress conditions in the member, or in determining the greatest load which may safely be applied to the member. A large part of the stress in the loaded member will have resulted from the deflection of the member as the load was applied.

A compression member of such slenderness that the *increase in eccentricity due to the bending of the member* must be taken into account in determining the allowable load on the member is called a column. Generally speaking any compression member with an unsupported length more than 8 to 10 times its least transverse dimension is considered to be a column. For ratios less than this, the effect of lateral deflection due to bending of the member may usually be disregarded in stress or load computations. As the ratio increases above this range, however, the deflection of the member under load is of greater and greater importance.

Because of differences in their behavior, columns may be divided into

211

two classes, "slender" and "intermediate."[1] The action of slender columns will be discussed first, and in the light of that discussion, the distinction between slender and intermediate columns will be made clear.

IDEAL COLUMNS UNDER AXIAL LOADS

154. Round-Ended Ideal Slender Columns. Small imperfections in material and fabrication, and unavoidable accidental eccentricities of loading (of indeterminate amount) greatly affect the behavior of actual columns under load. For this reason, in approaching the study of actual columns, it is desirable first to develop the theory of column action under simpler and more definite conditions. Therefore the theoretical analysis of slender columns will assume a perfectly straight, homogeneous slender bar of round cross-section, having its ends held against any lateral movement but perfectly free to rotate. Such a bar as this, with ends in this condition, may be called a round-ended ideal column. The loading on this ideal column will be assumed perfectly axial.

The maximum axial load which can be applied to an ideal slender column depends not upon the strength (yield point) of the material, but upon its stiffness (modulus of elasticity).

For an understanding of this fact, it is necessary to consider the relation which exists, in a bent member, between the deflection of the member and the resisting moment which accompanies the deflection. It was shown in Chapter VIII, that the resisting moment in a beam is proportional to the stress in the extreme fibers. It follows from the theory of beam deflection given in Chapter X that at the midpoint of a symmetrically loaded simple beam the stress in the extreme fibers is proportional to the deflection. Therefore it follows that as such a beam is bent *the resisting moment is proportional to the deflection.* This proposition is also true if the bent member is a slender column.

Keeping this relation in mind, suppose that axial loads, P, are placed on the ends of an ideal column (Fig. 292). Let a small lateral deflection, Δ, then be caused by a lateral force, H, applied at the midpoint of the column. For any value of Δ, the bending moment at the midpoint is $P\Delta + \frac{1}{2} H \times \frac{1}{2} L$. Considering the top half of the column as a body in equilibrium, the resisting moment equals the bending moment, or

$$M_R = P\Delta + \frac{1}{4} HL$$

Now let P be increased while H is simultaneously decreased in such a way

---

[1] Using this terminology, compression members will be divided into *short compression blocks, intermediate columns,* and *slender columns.*

that the deflection remains the same.   Then, when H becomes zero, P has such a value, P', that $P'\Delta = M_R$.   The column will now hold this deflection without any side thrust.   This is true for any value of Δ that does not cause stresses above the proportional limit.   (Since M_R varies as Δ, P' is a constant in the equation $P'\Delta = M_R$, whatever the value of Δ.) If P is made greater than P', however, $P\Delta$ is greater than the resisting moment for every value of Δ and the column rapidly deflects until it fails.   On the

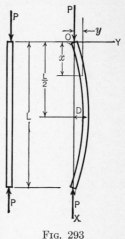

contrary, if P is less than P', $P\Delta$ is always less than the resisting moment and the column will straighten itself when the deflecting side force is removed.   The load which is just sufficient to hold the column in a bent condition is called the *critical load* for the column.   The critical load may obviously also be defined as the greatest load which the column will support.

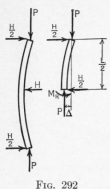

Fig. 292

Fig. 293

155. Euler's Formula for Slender Columns.   The equation which gives the value of the critical load in terms of the dimensions of the column and the modulus of elasticity of the material was first derived by Leonhard Euler, a Swiss mathematician, in 1757, and is known as Euler's formula for slender columns.

Assume an ideal slender column with both ends fixed against lateral movement but perfectly free to rotate (Fig. 293).   Let the critical load be applied to the column.   Then let the column be given the deflection d, sufficiently small so that the difference between the length of the column and the length of its projection on a vertical plane is negligible. This deflection will be maintained by the critical load, and the elastic curve of the column will be as shown.   Let the origin be taken at the upper end of the column, and let the X axis extend in the direction of the length of the column (which is consistent with the direction of axes assumed in the discussion of the elastic curve of a beam).   The equation of the elastic curve of a slightly bent member is $EI d^2y/dx^2 = M$.   In this case, the magnitude of M is Py.   Also the sign of the moment is opposite to that of the curvature.   Therefore

$$EI \frac{d^2y}{dx^2} = -Py \tag{1}$$

To integrate this expression, multiply both sides of the equation by $2\,dy$. Then

$$EI\left(2\frac{dy}{dx}\,d\frac{dy}{dx}\right) = -2\,Pydy$$

Integrating,

$$EI\left(\frac{dy}{dx}\right)^2 = -Py^2 + C_1$$

To evaluate C_1, note that, when dy/dx is 0, $y = D$. Therefore $C_1 = PD^2$, whence

$$\left(\frac{dy}{dx}\right)^2 = \frac{P}{EI}\left(D^2 - y^2\right)$$

or

$$\frac{dy}{dx} = \left(\frac{P}{EI}\right)^{\frac{1}{2}}(D^2 - y^2)^{\frac{1}{2}} \tag{2}$$

Equation (2) can be rewritten

$$\frac{dy}{\sqrt{D^2 - y^2}} = \left(\frac{P}{EI}\right)^{\frac{1}{2}}dx$$

Whence, integrating again,

$$\text{arc sin}\,\frac{y}{D} = \left(\frac{P}{EI}\right)^{\frac{1}{2}}x + C_2$$

To evaluate C_2, note that, when $x = 0$, $y = 0$; therefore $C_2 = 0$. Whence

$$\text{arc sin}\,\frac{y}{D} = \left(\frac{P}{EI}\right)^{\frac{1}{2}}x \quad\text{or}\quad y = D\sin\left(\frac{P}{EI}\right)^{\frac{1}{2}}x \tag{3}$$

This is the equation, in terms of the maximum deflection D, of the curve in which the column is maintained by the critical load, P. The column is evidently bent into a sine curve.

The usefulness of this equation is not, however, in showing the shape of the elastic curve of the column, but in permitting a determination of the value of the critical load P. To determine this value in terms other than the unknown deflection, D, note that, when $x = L/2$, $y = D$. Then

$$\sin\left(\frac{P}{EI}\right)^{\frac{1}{2}}\frac{L}{2} = 1 \quad\text{whence}\quad \left(\frac{P}{EI}\right)^{\frac{1}{2}}\frac{L}{2} = \frac{\pi}{2}$$

or $P = \pi^2EI/L^2$, for the value of the critical load.[1]

[1] The equation $\sin (P/EI)^{\frac{1}{2}} L/2 = 1$ evidently leads to the value of $\pi/2$ for $(P/EI)^{\frac{1}{2}} L/2$, as given above, or to $3\,\pi/2$, $5\,\pi/2$, etc. The correspondingly larger values of P are those required to bend the column into several nodes instead of into the single curve shown in Fig. 293. All such values of P will evidently be larger than the value corresponding to $\pi/2$, which is therefore the important value from an engineering standpoint.

PROBLEM

To determine the modulus of elasticity of a certain brass, a bar of the material $54\frac{1}{2}$ in. long and with a diameter of 0.318 in. (mean of four measurements) was tested as a slender column. The bar was placed vertically on a platform scale and load was gradually applied until the critical load was reached. With the ends of the bar supported on small hemispheres to allow freedom of rotation, the maximum scale reading was 29.5 lb. Weight of the bar was 1.2 lb., so that the maximum load on the mid cross-section was 28.9 lb. (*a*) Compute the modulus of elasticity. *17.3×10⁶* (*b*) For a check on the foregoing determination the bar was supported horizontally on rollers 52 in. apart. A load of 2 lb. applied at the midlength of the bar caused a deflection of 0.66 in. (mean of four measurements). Compute the value of *E*, and *17.65×10⁶* compare it with the value found in part (*a*).

156. Graphical Representation of Euler's Formula. Euler's formula can be written in a slightly different form. The moment of inertia, I, equals Ar^2, where A is the area of the cross-section of the column and r is its radius of gyration with respect to the centroidal axis. Making this substitution and rearranging terms, Euler's formula for a round-ended column becomes

$$\frac{P}{A} = \frac{\pi^2 E}{(L/r)^2}$$

This expression gives the *average* stress over the cross-section of the column when the critical load is being carried. This average stress under the critical load is often called the *critical stress* for the column. The ratio L/r is called the *slenderness ratio* of the column. These are terms commonly used in column discussions.

With the equation in the above form, if E is known and if various values of L/r are assumed, the corresponding values of P/A can very easily be computed. The simultaneous values of P/A and L/r can be plotted as the ordinates and the abscissas, respectively, of an "Euler curve." When such a curve has been plotted for columns of any given material (that is, for any given value of E), if the

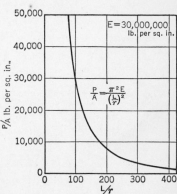

Fig. 294.   Euler curve for steel columns.

dimensions of a column are known, r and A can be determined and the critical load for the column can be computed.

Fig. 294 shows an Euler curve for round-ended columns of high-strength steel. The curve pictures very clearly the way in which the load-carrying capacity of columns decreases as their slenderness increases. A round column having a length equal to 20 diameters would have an L/r of 80, since the radius of gyration of a circle is one-fourth the diameter. Such a column, if round-ended, would have a critical stress of 44,300 lb. per sq. in. A column having a length equal to 100 diameters $(L/r = 400)$, however, would have a critical stress of only 1,770 lb. per sq. in. (one-twenty-fifth as much).

It should be noted that Euler's formula tells nothing about the *maximum* unit stress in a column carrying its critical load. The maximum stress depends on the deflection of the column. At a load just under the critical load, the maximum stress equals the average stress; but at the critical load, it may be anything between the average stress and the yield point of the column material. It should be noted, too, that the only property of the column material which enters into Euler's formula is E, which measures its stiffness. This mathematical analysis therefore confirms the physical reasoning of Art. 154 which led to the conclusion that the maximum load on a slender column is determined by the stiffness of the column material and not by its strength.

157. Limitations of Euler's Formula. As a mathematical expression, Euler's equation represents a curve which extends indefinitely both horizontally and vertically. As an expression applicable to columns of any given material, however, it holds good only for values of P/A within the proportional limit of the material to which it is applied. Derivation of the formula is based on the proportionality of unit stress and unit strain, which does not exist at stresses above the proportional limit. From Fig. 294, then, it can be seen that, for a steel having a proportional limit of 20,000 lb. per sq. in., Euler's formula applies to any axially loaded, round-ended column having a slenderness ratio of 120 or over. For a stronger steel having a proportional limit of 40,000 lb. per sq. in., the formula applies to all slendernesses in excess of 86, etc.

There is no correspondence between the elastic strength and the elastic stiffness of different materials, and therefore each different material has its particular value of L/r below which Euler's formula is inapplicable. The greater the strength in relation to the stiffness, the lower this value of L/r will be — that is, the greater the range of slendernesses over which Euler's formula will be valid. The table on page 217 shows for a number of common materials (having elastic strengths and stiffnesses as given) the values of L/r below which Euler's formula will not apply.

PROBLEM

1. Plot an " Euler curve " for each of the metals in the table on page 217, for all values of P/A less than the given proportional limit and for values of L/r up to 300. Scales: 1 in. = 8,000 lb. per sq. in.; 1 in. = L/r of 50.

IDEAL COLUMNS UNDER AXIAL LOADS

Material	Proportional Limit	Modulus of Elasticity	Least Value of L/r for Application of Euler's Formula
Nickel steel	50,000	30,000,000	77.0
Silicon steel	40,000	30,000,000	86.1
Carbon steel	28,000	30,000,000	102.7
Duralumin	28,000	10,000,000	59.4
Southern pine	7,000	1,600,000	47.5
Cypress	5,000	1,200,000	48.7

158. " Slender " Columns, " Intermediate " Columns, and " Short Compression Blocks." In all the discussion of columns up to this point, it has been specified that the column must be " slender." But what is a " slender " column?

The best definition is that it is a column that fails through lack of stiffness, by elastic instability — a column the ultimate load on which is reached while the average stress is still within the proportional limit of the column material. It is, therefore, any column for which Euler's formula is valid. Referring to the table above, we can see that any round-ended column of nickel steel of the grade there given can be considered a " slender " column if its L/r is greater than 77.0. Any round-ended column of duralumin can be considered " slender " if its L/r is greater than 59.4, etc.

A column with so small a value of L/r that the average stress on the cross-section reaches the proportional limit of the material before the " critical stress " is reached is called an " intermediate " column. A still shorter compression member for which L/r is so small as to make the effect of lateral deflection negligible may be called a " short compression block."

The maximum axial load which a short compression block can carry is determined solely by the *strength* of the material. Such a block may be considered to have " failed " when the average stress on its cross-section has reached the compression yield point of the material. As noted in a preceding paragraph, the maximum load which a *slender* column can carry is determined by the *stiffness* of the material. But what determines the strength of an intermediate column? This is a very important question, since most of the columns entering into engineering practice have slenderness ratios that place them in the intermediate column class.

The analysis down to this point makes it possible to draw graphs showing the relation between the stresses, P/A, and slenderness ratios, L/r, for short compression blocks and for slender columns (Fig. 295) under the loads that cause failure. It remains to close the gap for members in the intermediate slenderness range.

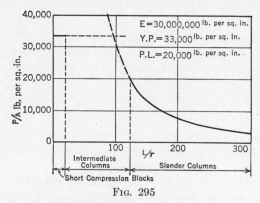

FIG. 295

159. The Load-Carrying Capacity of Intermediate Columns. The analysis of intermediate columns is much more complex than that of slender columns. The material composing a slender column is stressed below the proportional limit right up to the maximum load which the column can carry — the critical load. But long before the ultimate load on an intermediate column is reached, stresses throughout the column may have exceeded the proportional limit of the material. Therefore there is a great deal of inelastic action while an intermediate column is being loaded to failure. Whereas Euler's analysis of a slender column dates back almost two centuries, it is only within the last few decades that the problem of the intermediate column has been successfully attacked by Considère, Engesser, von Karman, and others. The intermediate column is not susceptible of as complete and exact an analysis as the slender column. Nevertheless the behavior of an ideal intermediate column is quite well understood.

If a gradually increasing axial load were to be applied to an ideal column of intermediate slenderness, the unit stress in the column would eventually just equal the proportional limit of the material. Up to this load, there would be complete recovery from any minute chance deflection that the column might suffer during the loading process. The material of the column would be elastic, and by definition of an intermediate column, the load would be insufficient to maintain the column in a bent condition. But when the load had increased past the point at which the stress in the column was equal to the proportional limit, the situation would change. The column material would now be in the plastic stress range. If any minute deflection of the column should now occur, recovery of straightness would be incomplete; a permanent set would remain. With this permanent set, however small it might be, the load would have some eccentricity with respect to all but the end cross-sections of the column. With further increase in load the column would bend more and more. Given a yield point considerably higher than the proportional limit, the load ultimately causing failure of the column might be materially greater than the load which was on the column when the first permanent deflection occurred. That is, an *intermediate column begins to bend under a load much less than the ultimate load.*

Now before the bending of the column has progressed very far, and some time before collapse of the column occurs, the addition of more load begins to have a very different effect on the material on the concave side of the column from its effect on the convex side. On the concave side increasing the load increases the compressive stress — both the direct compression and the bending compression. But on the convex side of the column, the bending of the column as the load is increased *stretches* the fibers more than the direct effect of the load shortens them. Therefore, as the amount of compressive stress in the fibers on the concave side of the column increases, the amount of compressive stress in the fibers on the convex side *decreases.*

In the *plastic* stress range, a given change in unit deformation results in much less change in unit stress than would occur if the material were still elastic (that is, the slope of the stress-strain curve is much less steep above the proportional limit). But as brought out in Art. 21, when a material stressed above its proportional limit is relieved of stress, the ratio between change in unit stress and change in unit deformation is once more equal to the modulus of elasticity of the material. Consequently, during this part of the loading of the column to failure it acts much as if it were composed of two different materials, with different moduli of elasticity. The theory which explains the action of a column of intermediate slenderness is therefore called the "double-modulus" theory.

A presentation of the double-modulus theory is beyond the scope of this book.[1] It suffices to say here that the average stress at ultimate load on an intermediate column with round ends is given by the formula $P/A = \pi^2 \bar{E}/(L/r)^2$, in which $\bar{E}$ is a " reduced modulus."   (It should be noted that this formula is the same as Euler's formula except that $\bar{E}$ takes the place of E.)   This reduced modulus $\bar{E}$ is not a constant, but is a variable the value of which depends on the shape of the cross-section of the column, the shape of the stress-strain curve of the column material,

[1] A brief presentation is given by William R. Osgood, in " Civil Engineering," Vol. 5, No. 3, March, 1935.

and the value of P/A. When P/A equals the proportional limit of the material, $\bar{E}$ equals E. When P/A is increased above the proportional limit, the value of $\bar{E}$ decreases.

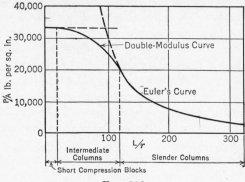

FIG. 296

As applied to steel with a yield point at 33,000 lb. per sq. in. and having a typical stress-strain curve, the double-modulus equation gives relations between P/A and L/r as shown in Fig. 296. These values close the gap shown in Fig. 295; that is, the double-modulus theory permits the determination of the buckling load on columns of intermediate slenderness.

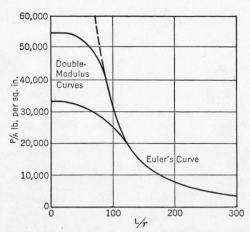

FIG. 297. Average stresses caused by maximum loads in columns of steels with yield points of 55,000 lb. per sq. in. and 33,000 lb. per sq. in.

160. The Shifting Importance of Strength and Stiffness. Double-modulus curves make it possible to consider the relative importance of strength and stiffness of the column material at different slenderness ratios.   Fig. 297 shows double-modulus-Euler curves for ideal round-ended columns of carbon and nickel steel with yield points at 33,000 and 55,000 lb. per sq. in., respectively.   For values of L/r less than about 60, the additional strength of the alloy steel is very effective in increasing the buckling load.   Thereafter the importance of strength decreases; and since both materials have the same stiffness, when the columns of both materials are " slender," there is no difference in their load-carrying capacity.   Somewhat similarly, Fig. 298 compares the strengths of ideal round-ended columns of steel and duralumin.   In this case, the " yield strength " of the duralumin (unit stress at a permanent set of 0.002) is assumed to be the same as the yield point of the steel, so that the load on short blocks of the two materials is the same.   Within the proportional limit, duralumin has only one-third the stiffness of steel, however.   Here again we see that, until L/r is in the neighborhood of 60, strength is the important characteristic of the column material.   Thereafter, however, stiffness becomes much more important than strength.

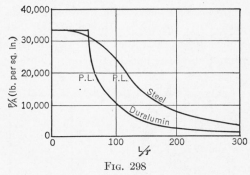

FIG. 298

PROBLEM

Fig. 297 shows double-modulus-Euler curves for columns of nickel and carbon steels, with yield points in the ratio $\frac{5}{3}$.   Using values of P/A from Fig. 297, plot a curve with values of L/r for abscissas and for ordinates the ratio of the load-carrying capacity of a nickel-steel column to the load-carrying capacity of a carbon-steel column of the same dimensions.   At about what value of L/r does the advantage of the higher yield point begin to decrease markedly?

161. Ideal Columns Having Other End Conditions.   Down to this point all discussion of columns has been based on the supposition of complete freedom of rotation of the ends of the column — the columns have been " round-ended."   But the ends of a column may be wholly fixed, so that, as the column bends under load, the tangents to the elastic curve at the ends of the unsupported length of the column retain their

original direction. Such a column as this is said to have " fixed ends "
(Fig. 299b). When a column with fixed ends bends, it can be shown
that the inflection points are at the quarter-points of the unsupported
length of the column. But since the points of contraflexure are points
of zero bending moment, they are points equivalent to the ends of a
round-ended column. Therefore the *middle half* of the unsupported
length of a column with fixed ends can be considered as equivalent to a
round-ended column. If the unsupported length of the column be
called L, then the load-carrying capacity will be the same as that of a
round-ended column with a length of $L/2$. If $L/2$ is substituted for L
in the Euler or the double-modulus equation for a round-ended column,
the equation gives correct results for the fixed-ended column.

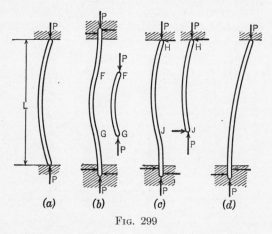

(a)   (b)   (c)   (d)

FIG. 299

Most of the columns used in actual engineering practice have end
conditions intermediate between round and fixed ends. That is, the
column bends in reversed curvature, but the inflection points are nearer
to the ends than to the midsection of the column. Any such column
can be analyzed by the formulas for a round-ended column if the distance
between inflection points is known or can be assumed satisfactorily. For
example, if the distance between inflection points is 0.80 of the unsupported length, L, then $0.80 L$ is inserted in the formula for a round-
ended column to make the formula apply to the column in question.

Columns may also have one end wholly fixed and the other end wholly
free to move laterally as well as to rotate (Fig. 299d); or one end may be
wholly fixed and the other end be fixed against lateral movement, but
wholly free to rotate (Fig. 299c). Considering column d, it is evident
that the whole unsupported length is equivalent to half the length of a
round-ended column. Therefore if the free length of column a be called

L, column d can be analyzed by means of the formulas for round-ended columns provided $2\,L$ be substituted for L in the column formula. It can be shown that the inflection point in column c is at very nearly $0.7\,L$ from the " round " end of the column. Therefore the formulas for round-ended columns can be applied to this case by substitution of $0.7\,L$ for L.

162. Effect of End Conditions on Column Strength. From the preceding article it is apparent that fixing the ends of a column will quadruple the ultimate load on a long column, or will quadruple the strength of the *column* (as distinct from the column material). Fixing the ends increases the strength of the column by increasing the stiffness of the column. Since stiffness of the column has comparatively little effect on very short columns, which fail largely by crushing of the column material rather than by bending or lateral deflection, end conditions of columns of intermediate slenderness are of less importance.

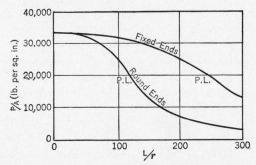

Fig. 300. Columns of same material (proportional limit, 20,000 lb. per sq. in.) but with different end conditions.

Fig. 300 shows the ultimate loads, as given by the double-modulus-Euler curves, on series of ideal columns with round ends and fixed ends respectively. On short compression blocks, the end condition is absolutely without importance, since the blocks fail entirely by crushing. As the slenderness increases and with it the importance of bending, the influence of end conditions becomes greater and greater, until at $L/r = 240$, when both the round-ended and the fixed-ended columns have become " slender " columns, the load-carrying capacity of the fixed-ended column is 4 times that of the round-ended.

PROBLEMS

1. Plot a curve having values of L/r as abscissas and having as ordinates values of the ratio of the critical load on a column with fixed ends to the critical load on a column of the same material and size, but with round ends. Plot for values of L/r from 0 to 200. Take P/A values from Fig. 300.

2. Throughout what range of slenderness ratios would doubling the cross-sectional area of a column have a greater effect on its load-carrying capacity than fixing its ends?

IDEAL COLUMNS UNDER ECCENTRIC LOADS

163. Eccentric Loads on Columns. In the actual use of columns, a load is often applied with some intentional eccentricity with respect to the column axis. In all other cases some *accidental* eccentricity of loading exists. In some kinds of columns this eccentricity may be so small as to be negligible. In a great many uses of columns, however, the designer must anticipate the existence of a sufficient amount of eccentricity of loading materially to affect the stresses in the column.[1] Since this is true, the behavior of columns under eccentric loads is, if anything, more important than the behavior of columns under axial loads.

In order to establish a foundation for the consideration of actual columns under eccentric loads, it is desirable to analyze first the behavior of an *ideal* column under such loads.

164. The Secant Formula. An ideal column loaded with an initially eccentric load acts quite differently from the same column loaded axially.

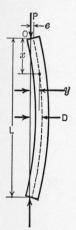

Under axial load the column does not begin to bend until (a) the critical stress is reached or (b) the average compressive stress in the column reaches the proportional limit of the material. Under an eccentric load, however, the column begins to bend just as soon as any load is applied.

Moreover, the maximum deflection (at the midlength) of an eccentrically loaded column is definite for any given load and initial eccentricity. This deflection can be computed if the dimensions of the column and the stiffness of the column material are known. With the deflection known, the moment arm of the load with respect to the centroid of the mid cross-section can be determined and the maximum compressive stress in the column can be found. The equation expressing the relationship between the eccentric load and the maximum stress it causes in the column is called the "secant formula." It is derived as follows:

Fig. 301

Suppose a column with ends perfectly free to rotate (round-ended column) to be acted on by a load, P, having an eccentricity, e, with

---

[1] This eccentricity may result from lack of initial straightness of the column, from lack of homogeneity of the column material, from discrepancies between the actual cross-section and the nominal cross-section, from failure to plane the ends of the column exactly at right angles to the axis or to locate pin holes with absolute accuracy, as well as from inequalities of loading.

respect to the centroid of the end cross-section of the column (Fig. 301). Let y be the deflection of the column at a distance x from the end, the origin and axes being taken as shown. Then, as in the case of a slender column under its critical axial load, the equation of the elastic curve of this column can be written $EI d^2y/dx^2 = -Py$. Multiplying through by $2\, dy$, this becomes

$$2\, EI \frac{dy}{dx} d\frac{dy}{dx} = -2\, Py\, dy$$

Integrating,
$$EI \left(\frac{dy}{dx}\right)^2 = -Py^2 + C_1$$

To evaluate C_1, note that, when $dy/dx = 0$, y equals the maximum deflection D. Therefore $C_1 = PD^2$. Whence

$$\frac{dy}{dx} = \left(\frac{P}{EI}\right)^{\frac{1}{2}} (D^2 - y^2)^{\frac{1}{2}}$$

Or
$$\frac{dy}{(D^2 - y^2)^{\frac{1}{2}}} = \left(\frac{P}{EI}\right)^{\frac{1}{2}} dx$$

Integrating again,

$$x = \left(\frac{EI}{P}\right)^{\frac{1}{2}} \left(\sin^{-1}\frac{y}{D} + C_2\right)$$

(It may be noted that to this point the derivation of the secant formula is identical with the derivation of Euler's formula.) To evaluate C_2, note that, when $x = 0$, $y = e$. Therefore $C_2 = -\sin^{-1}(e/D)$. Whence

$$x = \left(\frac{EI}{P}\right)^{\frac{1}{2}} \left(\sin^{-1}\frac{y}{D} - \sin^{-1}\frac{e}{D}\right)$$

To evaluate $\sin^{-1}(e/D)$, note that, when $x = L/2$, $y = D$. Then

$$\frac{L}{2} = \left(\frac{EI}{P}\right)^{\frac{1}{2}} \left(\sin^{-1}1 - \sin^{-1}\frac{e}{D}\right)$$

Whence
$$\sin^{-1}\frac{e}{D} = \frac{\pi}{2} - \left(\frac{PL^2}{4\, EI}\right)^{\frac{1}{2}}$$

Therefore
$$e = D \sin\left(\frac{1}{2}\pi - \left(\frac{PL^2}{4\, EI}\right)^{\frac{1}{2}}\right) = D \cos\left(\frac{PL^2}{4\, EI}\right)^{\frac{1}{2}}$$

Whence
$$D = e \sec\left(\frac{PL^2}{4\, EI}\right)^{\frac{1}{2}}$$

As shown in Chapter XII, the maximum stress, S, equals $P/A +$ Mc/I. The maximum bending moment occurs where the deflection equals D and is PD or $Pe \sec (PL^2/4 EI)^{\frac{1}{2}}$. Inserting this value, substituting Ar^2 for I and factoring,

$$S = \frac{P}{A}\left(1 + \frac{ec}{r^2} \sec \frac{L}{r}\left(\frac{P}{4\ EA}\right)^{\frac{1}{2}}\right) \quad \text{or} \quad \frac{P}{A} = \frac{S}{1 + \left(\dfrac{ec}{r^2}\right)\sec \dfrac{L}{r}\sqrt{\dfrac{P/A}{4\ E}}}$$

This equation, the *secant formula,* gives the maximum stress, S, caused by a load P having an eccentricity e with respect to the centroid of the end section of a round-ended column with length L, area of cross-section A, radius of gyration r, distance from the neutral axis to the most remote fiber c, and modulus of elasticity E.

The foregoing derivation is rational. For small deflections (such as are encountered in practice), and for stresses within the proportional limit, it gives results that are theoretically correct. Moreover, careful measurements of the deflections of columns loaded with a measured end-eccentricity have checked the theory satisfactorily, not only as applied to small, nearly " ideal " columns, but for full-sized structural columns as well.[1] This makes the secant formula a very valuable foundation for practical column analysis and design.

It may be noted that, when L/r approaches zero in the secant formula, S approaches P/A $(1 + ec/r^2)$ or $P/A + Pec/I$, which is the stress in a short, eccentrically loaded compression block. The quantity ec/r^2 therefore expresses the limiting ratio of the bending stress (caused by the eccentricity) to the direct compressive stress, as the slenderness of the column decreases. The quantity ec/r^2 is often called the " eccentricity ratio."

PROBLEMS

1. A round steel bar, 1 in. in diameter and 50 in. long, carries a load of 5,000 lb. applied with an eccentricity of $\frac{1}{16}$ in. at each end. The ends of the bar are free to rotate. Calculate the maximum deflection $(D - e)$ which the midpoint of the axis undergoes as the load is applied. *0.4895 in*

2. Using the equation $S = P/A + PDc/I$, find the maximum stress which the 5,000-lb. load causes in the column of Problem 1.

Ans. $S = 34,150$ lb. per sq. in.

3. Use the secant formula as given in this article to check the value obtained for S in Problem 2.

165. Curves Representing the Secant Formula.
The secant equation can be used to determine the maximum stress in a given column when

[1] See Final Report of Special Committee on Steel Column Research, *Trans., Am. Soc. C. E.,* Vol. 98, p. 1460, Conclusion 1.

acted on by a given load with a given eccentricity. S will then be the only unknown and can be conveniently solved for. As for columns under axial loads, however, it is convenient to plot a graph that will show the average stress, P/A, accompanying any maximum stress, S, for a series of columns of all slenderness ratios, the eccentricity e having some arbitrarily chosen value.

Such a graph can be most conveniently plotted as follows: The secant equation is put in the form

$$\frac{L}{r} = \frac{\sec^{-1} \dfrac{S - P/A}{(ec/r^2)P/A}}{\sqrt{\dfrac{P/A}{4\,E}}}$$

Now if the arbitrarily chosen eccentricity for which the curve is to be plotted is expressed in terms of the diameter of the round column, the expression ec/r^2 reduces to a numerical coefficient of P/A. The value of S for which the curve is to be plotted is also arbitrarily selected. A value for P/A is then assumed, and the corresponding value of L/r is

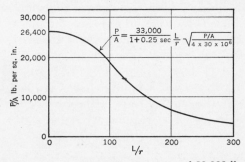

FIG. 302. Average stresses causing maximum stress of 33,000 lb. per sq. in. when eccentricity of load is about 3 per cent of diameter.

computed. These simultaneous values of P/A and L/r are then plotted as a point on the curve. This process is repeated for as many values of P/A as may be needed. The curve shown in Fig. 302 represents the secant formula for $ec/r^2 = 0.25$, $s = 33,000$ lb. per sq. in., and $E = 30,000,000$ lb. per sq. in.

PROBLEM

Check the value of L/r corresponding to a value of 15,000 lb. per sq. in. for P/A in the curve of Fig. 302. $L/r = 121.2$

166. Effect of Initial Eccentricity on Load-Carrying Capacity of Columns. The secant curves of Fig. 303 show strikingly how greatly initial eccentricity of loading decreases the load which will cause a given maximum stress in a relatively short column. On a very slender column, initial eccentricity has less effect. In engineering work, however, the usual practice calls for values of L/r sufficiently small to make eccentricity of loading very important.

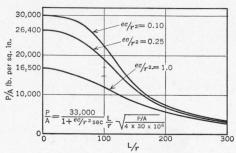

Fig. 303. Columns of structural steel with three different eccentricities of load.

PROBLEMS

1. Calculate the values of e in terms of the column diameter d when $ec/r^2 = 0.25$, 0.10 and 1.0.

2. In much engineering practice it is assumed that nominally axial loads on columns may actually have eccentricity enough to make ec/r^2 equal 0.25. Taking values of P/A from Figs. 296 and 302, plot a curve having values of L/r for abscissas, and for ordinates the ratio of the ultimate load on an axially loaded column to the ultimate load on a column of the same size but so loaded that $ec/r^2 = 0.25$. How great must L/r be for this amount of eccentricity to cause a reduction of 10 per cent in the ultimate load? $\frac{L}{R} = 270$

167. Importance of Strength and Stiffness of Column Material.

In the discussion of the ideal column under axial loads it was shown that strength is the important property of the material of columns having small slenderness ratios, but that for slender columns, stiffness is the important property. Under axial loading, it was noted that strength begins to decrease in importance and stiffness to increase at a slenderness ratio in the neighborhood of 60 (for most ordinary materials).

Under eccentric loading, the same relationships between strength and stiffness exist, with the difference that stiffness begins to be important at still lower values of L/r. This difference is reasonable, since under eccentric loads bending effects are more important and direct crushing effects are less important than under axial loads. Conversely, strength of the material retains some importance in eccentrically loaded columns at greater values of L/r than was found to be the case for axially loaded columns. These relationships are illustrated by Fig. 304.

168. Relation between Increase in Load and Increase in Maximum Stress. In an eccentrically loaded column with a relatively small value of L/r, there is little lateral deflection of the column under load, and consequently the maximum stress in the column does not increase much more rapidly than the load increases. But if the slenderness ratio of the column is large, this is not the case. Each increment of load causes a considerable bending of the column; the maximum stress is increased

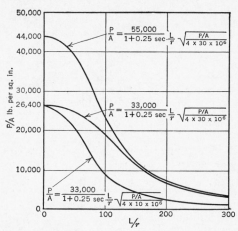

FIG. 304. Columns of three materials but with same eccentricity of load.
Upper: high-strength steel.
Middle: structural steel.
Lower: Aluminum alloy of same strength as structural steel.

not only by the greater load but by the greater moment arm. Consequently, in a slender column the maximum stress increases *much more rapidly* than the load increases. This is especially true after the load on the column has become fairly large. The following table shows the relation between increase in load and increase in stress for a round-

P/A lb. per sq. in.	Per cent of first P/A Value	Maximum Unit Stress, S			
		$L/r = 50$		$L/r = 150$	
		lb. per sq. in.	Per cent of first stress value	lb. per sq. in.	Per cent of first stress value
4,000	100	5,050	100	5,550	100
8,000	200	10,180	202	13,900	250
12,000	300	15,420	306	54,500	982

ended ideal steel column with an L/r of 50 and a second column with an L/r of 150.   In both cases the eccentricity ratio is 0.25.

PROBLEM

For a column with each of the above slenderness ratios, plot a curve having for its abscissas values of P/A, and for its ordinates values of S.   Also plot such a curve for a " short compression block " loaded with an eccentricity ratio of 0.25.

169. Eccentric Loads on Columns with Other End Conditions.   Up to this point the columns considered in connection with eccentric loads have all been round-ended.   In Art. 161, the fact was developed that a column with its lower end wholly fixed and its upper end wholly free can be treated as if it were the upper half of a round-ended column. Therefore if such a column carries an eccentric load the secant formula can be made applicable to it by using *twice* the unsupported length of the column as the value of L in the secant formula.   Similarly, a column with one end wholly fixed and the other end free to rotate but not to move laterally can be analyzed without great error by using 0.7 of the unsupported length of the column for L in the secant formula.

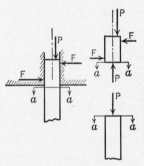

Fig. 305

However, a column with both ends wholly fixed against rotation, if the column is initially straight, must act as if the load were applied axially, no matter how the load may really be applied.   Applying the load eccentrically merely increases the forces F, F (Fig. 305).   The force exerted on the end a–a of the unsupported length of the column is an axial force until the column begins to bend either under the critical load or the load which raises the average stress above the proportional limit. If the ends of a column are wholly fixed, the distinctive characteristic of eccentric loading — bending of the column under any load, no matter how small — is not present.

when 0.7 L
one end fixed

L for column having end moments =
, length between inflection pts = $\frac{L}{2}$

CHAPTER XIV

THE DESIGN OF COLUMNS

170. Introduction. Columns can be divided into two main use classifications: structural columns (as used in buildings and bridges) and machine columns. The two classifications overlap, since columns are used structurally in the frames of many machines. The booms of steel erection derricks and the frames of airplanes are examples. But there is obviously a great difference between the conditions of use of a locomotive side rod, moving with great accelerations and with loads transmitted to it through lubricated pins, and a stationary column in the compression chord of a bridge or in a building.

171. Structural Steel Columns. The ideal column discussed in the foregoing chapters was a perfectly straight prismatical bar, with ends so arranged that the amount of restraint offered to rotation was definitely known, and with loads either perfectly axial or with definitely known eccentricity.

This perfection of material, fabrication, and loading is impossible to attain in practice. Specifications of the American Institute of Steel Construction, for example, permit an initial bend of 1/1,000 of the length. This means that a column 25 ft. long may have a crookedness of almost $\frac{1}{3}$ in. Most columns fall well within the specification, but crookedness must be considered in design since enough may be present to affect materially the stresses in the loaded column.

Another uncertain condition in structural columns is the amount of restraint at the ends. In a building frame, each of the floor systems provides restraint against lateral movement, so that the unsupported length, L, of the column is usually taken as the distance from center to center of beam connections for successive stories. But while the floors may be considered to prevent any lateral movement of the column axis, they do not wholly prevent its rotation. The end condition is intermediate between complete fixation and complete freedom to rotate.[1] The same situation exists in trusses, whether riveted or pinned. In a riveted truss, deformation of the truss as a whole permits some

[1] For columns of the proportions ordinarily used in practice the rotation of the ends of a round-ended column as it is gradually loaded to nearly the buckling load is very small — often only 20 or 30 minutes of arc.

rotation of the joints. On the other hand, in a pinned truss, friction between the pin and the column offers a considerable amount of restraint so that the condition is not comparable to that of a round-ended column. Fig. 306 shows a column with a " pinned " end and a column with the end at least quite largely " fixed."

Fig. 306.   Pin-ended column and fixed-ended column.   Both columns are in railroad viaducts.

A third uncertainty in structural columns is eccentricity of load. In loading a column, the load is, of course, not applied directly to the axis of the column. The load may be applied through plates covering the ends of the column, or through pins, or through rivets. When a column is said to be " axially loaded " it is meant that the line of action of the resultant of the loads is *intended* to coincide with the axis of the unbent column. It is reasonable to believe, however, that this condition is rarely attained.

In considering the design of structural columns, therefore, it must be kept in mind that, because of lack of straightness of the column and of loading conditions, the loading is practically always eccentric. In the column formulas first used in practical design, that fact was not directly taken into consideration, but was usually allowed for in ways that will be mentioned later. More recent column formulas are based on the secant analysis in which an assumed " equivalent eccentricity of loading " is used to provide for lack of initial straightness, uncertainties in load application, as well as other conditions which distinguish the actual from the ideal case.

172. Cross-Sections of Actual Columns. For simplicity the ideal column of the preceding chapter was made round. Solid round columns are rarely encountered in practice, however, because of the small radius of gyration of a circle and because of the difficulty of connecting beams and other members to round columns. These and other considerations have led to the adoption of many different column cross-sections.

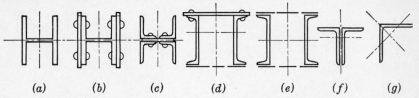

(a)   (b)   (c)   (d)   (e)   (f)   (g)

FIG. 307. Some common cross-sections of structural columns.

Some of those which are extensively used at the present time are shown in Fig. 307:

(a) The " H-column " rolled out of a single piece of material — now widely used, especially in buildings but also in bridges.

(b) The H-column with cover plates riveted to the flanges to provide a larger cross-section.

(c) The " built-up " H-column, made by riveting together a " web " plate and four angles. This section may also have cover plates added.

(d) The plate and channel column — frequently used in bridge chords. The open side is generally " latticed " with diagonal flat steel bars to stiffen the lower flanges of the channels. (This latticing is not considered a part of the column cross-section.)

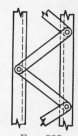

(e) The channel column latticed on both sides. (See Fig. 308 for side view.) This type of column is often used for truss diagonals and verticals.

(f) Two angles, back to back, either in contact or separated by the thickness of a gusset plate — often used for compression members in roof trusses.

FIG. 308

(g) A single angle — sometimes used for columns carrying small loads.

Still other types of cross-section are used, compression members in large bridge trusses often being very elaborate. A *hollow* round section makes a very effective column. Until the introduction of welded connections round columns were difficult to attach to other members, but steel tubing and pipe are now coming into more general use for columns.

173. Least Radius of Gyration. Any area which does not have the same value of I with respect to every centroidal axis will have one centroidal axis with respect to which the moment of inertia is greater than for any other.   Perpendicular to this will be the centroidal axis for which the moment of inertia is least.   These axes are called the "principal axes" of the cross-section.   In the cross-sections shown in Fig. 307 the principal axes are parallel to the sides of the cross-sections except for the single angle.

A column under a nominally axial load will bend about that axis for which the moment of inertia is least.   That is, it will bend in the direction of the *least radius of gyration* of the cross-section, as may easily be demonstrated with a slender bar of rectangular cross-section, such as a yardstick.   Consequently the *least* radius of gyration is the radius of gyration to be used in figuring the slenderness ratio of a column.

Illustrative Example 1. A 12-in., 65-lb. wide-flange section is used as a column with a length of 16 ft.   Find its slenderness ratio.

Solution: From Table III, the least r of this section (with respect to axis 2–2) is 3.02 in.   Therefore the slenderness ratio is $16 \times 12/3.02 = 63.6$.

Illustrative Example 2. Find the slenderness ratio of a single 4-in. $\times$ 4-in. $\times \frac{3}{8}$-in. angle if used as a column with a length of 6 ft. 2 in.

Solution: For this column, $L = 74$ in. and the least radius of gyration is that with respect to the axis 3–3 and is 0.79 in. (Table V).   Therefore $L/r = 74/0.79 = 93.7$.

PROBLEMS

1. A column is made by riveting a 1-in.-by-16-in. plate to each flange of a 14-in., 48-lb. wide-flange steel shape.   What is the slenderness ratio if the column is 20 ft. long? $R = 60.2$

2. A 5-in. $\times$ 5-in. $\times$ 1-in. angle has almost exactly the same cross-sectional area as two 5-in. $\times$ 3$\frac{1}{2}$-in. $\times \frac{9}{16}$-in. angles.   For any given length, compare the slenderness ratio of a column consisting of a single 5-in. $\times$ 5-in. $\times$ 1-in. angle with that of a column made by riveting two 5-in. $\times$ 3$\frac{1}{2}$-in. $\times \frac{9}{16}$-in. angles "back to back," (*a*) if the 5-in. legs are riveted together, (*b*) if the 3-in. legs are riveted together.

3. An 8-in., 19-lb. wide-flange beam has almost exactly the same cross-sectional area as a 6-in. standard steel pipe.   Find the ratio of the slenderness ratios of columns having the respective cross-sections and equal lengths.

4. A column is made of one 20-in.-by-$\frac{1}{2}$-in. plate and two 10-in., 15.3-lb. channels, arranged as shown in Fig. 307 (*d*).   The length of the columns is 14 ft. 4 in.   The distance back to back of channels is 14$\frac{3}{4}$ in.   Find the slenderness ratio. 46.1

174. Euler's Formula Applied to Design.   The general form of Euler's

equation for the critical load P_c is $\dfrac{P_c}{A} = \dfrac{\pi^2 E}{(kL/r)^2}$.   Here kL represents the length of the column between inflection points, the value of k being 1 for a column without end restraint, 0.5 for a column with fully fixed ends, etc. (Art. 161).   To convert this equation into a design formula giving the average allowable stress, P/A, the right-hand side of the equation is divided by any desired factor of safety, f.   The formula then

Know (handwritten)

becomes $\dfrac{P}{A} = \dfrac{\pi^2 E}{f(kL/r)^2}$. This formula is not applicable to columns of the slendernesses commonly used in building frames and roof and bridge trusses. It has been employed considerably in airplane design, particularly with high-strength steels and with wood and aluminum alloys. For all these materials, it is applicable to lower ratios of L/r than for structural steel. In such use, k is taken as unity except in very rigid frames where it may be taken as $\frac{7}{8}$ or, in exceptional cases, $\frac{3}{4}$.

When structural steel columns first came into use Euler's was the only theoretical analysis of column action that had been achieved. For the design of intermediate columns to which Euler's formula was inapplicable, various semi-rational or frankly empirical formulas were used. Some of these formulas have become so well established that they are still used and doubtless will be for a long time.

PROBLEMS

1. Part of a mechanism for opening and closing a ventilating transom is to be a round brass bar ($E = 14,000,000$ lb. per sq. in.) 24 in. long. The maximum force that can act on the bar is to be taken as 40 lb. At its ends the bar is to be supported on lubricated pins; it is to be treated as a round-ended column. A factor of safety of 2 is considered sufficient. What is the required bar diameter?

2. For a derrick mast 25 ft. long it is proposed to use a standard steel pipe. The maximum load which the mast is designed to withstand is 7 tons. The factor of safety is to be 3. Connections at the ends of the mast are such that loads may be assumed axial. Consider the mast to be a round-ended column and determine whether a 4-in. or a 5-in. pipe should be used. *5" pipe* (handwritten)

3. If a 10-in.-by-10-in. (nominal size) Douglas fir stick ($E = 1,600,000$ lb. per sq. in.) is substituted for the steel pipe of Problem 2, what will the factor of safety become? *F.S. = 8.5* (handwritten)

175. Rankine's Formula. Rankine's formula, which has been very widely used in this country, was perfected between 1856 and 1860 by a Scotch engineer, Rankine, from an earlier formula derived by another Scotchman, Gordon. For this reason it is sometimes called the Rankine-Gordon formula.

Rankine's formula is derived as follows: Let S be the allowable stress in a column at the point of maximum stress. Let P be the nominally axial load which causes this allowable stress, and let D be the maximum deflection which the column has under the load P. Then

$$S = \frac{P}{A} + \frac{PDc}{I}$$

which may be rewritten

$$S = \frac{P}{A} + \frac{PDc}{Ar^2}$$

where r is the least radius of gyration. From this

$$S = \frac{P}{A}\left(1 + \frac{Dc}{r^2}\right) \quad \text{or} \quad \frac{P}{A} = \frac{S}{1 + Dc/r^2}$$

So far this is correct and rational but not usable because D is not known and cannot be determined. It is assumed in the derivation of the Rankine formula that D will vary as L^2/c in columns of a given material and all loaded to the same maximum stress. This assumption is not exact, but it is reasonably near the truth. If this assumption is admitted, then $D = qL^2/c$, where q is the constant relating D and L^2/c. Substituting this value for D in the equation above, it becomes

$$\frac{P}{A} = \frac{S}{1 + q(L/r)^2}$$

which is Rankine's formula.[1]

Rankine's formula has been used with many different values of S and q, depending on the material, the end conditions, and the purpose

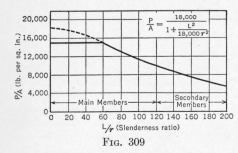

$$\frac{P}{A} = \frac{18{,}000}{1 + \dfrac{L^2}{18{,}000\,r^2}}$$

Main Members — Secondary Members

L/r (Slenderness ratio)

Fig. 309

of the column. A formula of the Rankine type which has been and still is very widely used in design of columns in frames of buildings was first given in the 1923 Specifications (for buildings) of the American Institute of Steel Construction, and will be referred to hereafter as the A.I.S.C. Rankine formula.[2] It is plotted in Fig. 309. The steel specified for this use was of such strength that 18,000 lb. per sq. in. was taken as the basic stress in tension and compression. Therefore this value was used for S in the formula. The value of 1/18,000 was given to q, the formula

---

[1] After the approximation that D varies as L^2/c has been made, it is no longer permissible to regard S as the maximum stress actually present in a column carrying the load P which the formula gives. For if so, S must vary as P, which contradicts the very idea of column action (see Art. 168). Therefore in the Rankine formula $P/A = S/[1 + q(L/r)^2]$, S is definable only as the allowable direct compressive stress in the column material. It has no other meaning.

[2] The 1936 A.I.S.C. Specifications restrict the use of this formula to columns with values of L/r greater than 120 and not above 200 which are classified as " bracing and other secondary members in compression." For main compression members a " parabolic " formula is specified as stated in Art. 179. The A.I.S.C. Rankine formula is specified in many building codes (including New York City, 1938) for main columns as well as bracing.

therefore becoming

$$\frac{P}{A} = \frac{18,000}{1 + \dfrac{1}{18,000}(L/r)^2}$$

In addition to giving this formula, the specifications also stipulate that under no circumstances shall P/A be allowed to exceed 15,000 lb. per sq. in. This value is given by the formula when L/r equals 60. For all lower slendernesses, therefore, the value of P/A given by the formula must be disregarded. Also it is specified that L/r is not to exceed 120 for main compression members or 200 for bracing.

The use of this " flat " stress for all slenderness ratios to and including 60 is based on column tests. Such tests have indicated that, for all slenderness ratios up to somewhere in the neighborhood of 60, slenderness of the column has no pronounced effect on the value of P/A at which failure occurs.[1]

The A.I.S.C. Rankine formula makes no provision for variation in end conditions, and this has been true of most of the other Rankine type formulas used in recent years. The value given q in the A.I.S.C. formula implies a condition between round and fixed ends.

176. Investigation and Design of Columns by Rankine's Formula. In using Rankine's formula to determine the allowable load on a given column, the procedure is as shown in the following example:

Example. A latticed channel column is made up of two 7-in., 12.25-lb. channels, 5 in., back to back (Fig. 307e). Its length is 14 ft., 6 in. What is the maximum load allowed on the column by the A.I.S.C. Rankine formula?

Solution: Referring to Table IV, the cross-sectional area of this column is seen to be $2 \times 3.58 = 7.16$ sq. in. The table gives r_{1-1} for this channel as 2.59 in. and this is evidently the value of r_{1-1} for the built-up column also. With respect to axis 2–2, $r_{2-2} = \sqrt{(0.58)^2 + (2.5 + 0.53)^2}$. This is evidently greater than 2.59, so 2.59 is the value of least r. Therefore the slenderness ratio is $14.5 \times 12/2.59 = 67.2$.

Inserting this value, $\dfrac{P}{A} = \dfrac{18,000}{1 + \dfrac{(67.2)^2}{18,000}} = 14,400$ lb. per sq. in., and the allowable

value of P therefore is $14,400 \times 7.16 = 103,200$ lb.

[1] This fact is consistent with the secant curve, which is relatively flat for low values of L/r (see Fig. 302). For small slenderness ratios, initial eccentricities of loading are much more important than eccentricities developed by bending of the column as load is applied. Rankine's formula makes no allowance for initial eccentricity. Use of the " flat " stress for small slendernesses may be considered as a rather crude device for compensating for this deficiency.

" Designing " a column usually means determining a suitable cross-section for a column of specified length to carry a given load in accordance with some design formula. This is a more difficult problem than investigation. Neither A nor L/r can be known in advance. Moreover, there is no fixed relationship between A and r for column sections such as are ordinarily used, whether the sections be rolled or " built-up." Therefore the Rankine formula has too many unknowns in it for a direct solution, and resort must be had to a process of selection and trial.

In making such a selection, it is convenient to remember that the majority of columns have slenderness ratios which give values of P/A between about 12,000 and 14,000 lb. per sq. in.

Example. Select the lightest wide-flanged steel section to carry a load of 550,000 lb. in accordance with the A.I.S.C. Rankine formula, if the column length is 20 ft.

Solution: As a guide to the selection of a trial section, assume that $P/A = 13,000$ lb. per sq. in. This will necessitate a cross-section of 42.3 sq. in. Referring to Table III, sections with approximately this area are the 12-in., 147-lb., and the 14-in., 142-lb. Of these the latter has the larger least r ($r_{2-2} = 3.97$ in.) and would therefore be the more efficient column section. Investigating this section, $L/r = 240/3.97 = 60.4$. This is so close to 60 that the allowable value of P/A may be taken as 15,000 lb. per sq. in. Therefore the allowable load on this column is 15,000 × 41.85 = 627,000. Since this is considerably in excess of the load to be carried, it is probable that a lighter column can be found.

Investigating the 14-in., 136-lb. section, $A = 39.98$ sq. in. and least $r = 3.77$ in. Therefore $L/r = 63.7$. The corresponding value of P/A is found to be 14,700 lb. per sq. in. This multiplied by 39.98 gives an allowable load of 588,000 lb. This column will evidently be acceptable.

A quick investigation can be made of the next lighter (127-lb.) section. Since it has substantially the same least r, the value of P/A for it will also be 14,700 lb. per sq. in. The allowable load on it would therefore be 37.33 × 14,700 = 548,000 lb. This section comes so close to fulfilling the requirements that it would probably be regarded as acceptable.

PROBLEMS

1. Using the A.I.S.C. Rankine formula, find the allowable axial load on each of the following wide-flange steel sections:

Column Section	Length	Column Section	Length
(a) 18.69-in., 426-lb.	30 ft., 0 in.	(d) 14-in., 74-lb.	28 ft., 0 in.
(b) 14-in., 150-lb.	16 ft., 0 in.	(e) 12-in., 72-lb.	28 ft., 0 in.
(c) 14-in., 53-lb.	16 ft., 0 in.	*Ans.* (c) $P = 180,000$ lb.	

2. The Rankine formula $\dfrac{P}{A} = \dfrac{16,000}{1 + \dfrac{1}{13,500}(L/r)^2}$ has been extensively used in bridge design. What load does it permit on the column of Problem 4, Art. 173?

3. Using the A.I.S.C. Rankine formula, select the lightest wide-flange section to serve as a column 14 ft. long, carrying a load of 500,000 lb.

4. Solve Problem 3 if the length is 18 ft. and the load 300,000 lb.
5. Solve Problem 3 if the length is 24 ft. and the load 270,000 lb.

177. Straight-Line Formulas. Rankine's formula came into wide use during the years following its publication. During these same years, however, the experimental testing of columns was greatly extended. As a mass of data on actual column tests accumulated, it was observed that, for the lower slenderness ratios particularly, these test results when plotted did not lie along any *line* but covered a wide band.[1] From this fact, T. H. Johnson, in 1884, drew the conclusion that in the existing state of column theory (at that time neither the secant analysis nor the double-modulus analysis were known) the load-carrying capacity of columns of varying slenderness ratios could be as well expressed by a graph consisting of Euler's curve for large slenderness ratios and a *straight line* tangent to Euler's curve for small ratios as well as by any more complex curve. The particular formulas which Johnson proposed did not come into wide use, but other " straight-line " formulas were widely adopted and extensively used for many years.

One of the most widely used of these is $P/A = 16,000 - 70 \ L/r$ with a " flat " maximum stress of 14,000 lb. per sq. in. Where this formula was specified, it was also generally specified that main members designed in accordance with it should not have slenderness ratios greater than 120. This formula was proposed and principally used at a time when steel was manufactured with a lower yield point than that now generally specified and when 16,000 lb. per sq. in. was considered the proper allowable stress in flexure and in direct compression.

The investigation and design of columns in accordance with any straight-line formula follows the procedure described in Art. 176.

PROBLEMS

1. The American Railway Engineering Association (1929) specifications for buildings specify the following equation for column design: $P/A = 18,000 - 60 \ L/r$. Using this equation, select a suitable wide-flange section of the column in (a) Problem 3, Art. 176; (b) Problem 5, Art. 176.

2. What is the maximum length that a 6-in., 12.5-lb. American Standard I-beam may have if it is to carry a load of 40,000 lb. in accordance with the formula $P/A = 16,000 - 70 \ L/r$? If the column is braced at the midpoint and at each of the quarter-points, the bracing being in the plane of the axis 1–1, what may the length be? *Ans.* $L = 4.22$ ft.

[1] This might have been expected since in the different tests steels with a wide variation in yield point were used, and since in many tests there were undoubtedly uncertainties and errors in loading. The importance of these factors was not recognized at the time, however. See " Report of the Special Committee on Steel Column Research," *Trans., Am. Soc. C. E.*, Vol. 98, 1933.

178. Applicability of the Secant Formula to Column Design. While formulas of the types discussed in the preceding articles were in use, the secant analysis showing the effect of an eccentric load on an ideal column was being worked out. This analysis was not immediately applied to column design, but in 1912, Professor O. H. Basquin suggested that most of the defects in the fabrication and loading of an · actual column could be considered as an " equivalent eccentricity of loading." He proposed that a reasonable value for this equivalent eccentricity be derived from a careful study of column tests and then be inserted in the secant formula for use in the design of structural columns. Subsequently a Special Committee on Steel Column Research was appointed by the American Society of Civil Engineers, and over a period of years this Committee did make a very careful study of existing column test data, which it supplemented by elaborate additional tests. The result of this investigation was the recommendation by the Committee (in 1933) that the equation

$$\frac{P}{A} = \frac{\text{Yield point of material}}{1 + 0.25 \sec \dfrac{kL}{r} \sqrt{\dfrac{P/A}{4\,E}}}$$

be accepted as a basis for the design of structural columns.[1]

This general form of the secant equation is applicable to a column with any end condition when a value of k consistent with the end condition has been introduced.   (That is, the part of the column length between inflection points acts as a round-ended column, and this part of the length is represented by kL.)   From its study of column tests, the Committee recommended that, in pinned structures, k be taken as $\frac{7}{8}$ and in riveted structures as $\frac{3}{4}$.[2]

[1] Since the secant equation is derived from the *elastic curve* of a column, and since the yield point is decidedly above the proportional limit, use of the yield-point stress in the secant equation is not theoretically correct.   Art. 158 shows that, for values of P/A approaching the yield point, the buckling load on an axially loaded column is much less than that given by Euler's equation.   The same thing is true of an eccentrically loaded column when the eccentricity is very small.   The actual buckling load may then be expected to be much less than that calculated by means of the secant equation with the yield-point stress.   With larger eccentricity of loading, however, the resulting error is much less since the buckling load is reached while stresses on a large part of the cross-section are still within the proportional limit. For an eccentricity ratio as large as 0.25, the error resulting from use of the yield-point stress was found not to be serious.

[2] In Art. 169 it was noted that, with the ends of a column *wholly* fixed against rotation, there is no possibility of loading the unsupported length of an ideal column eccentrically.   It does not follow, however, that there can be no eccentric loading of a column having ends only partially restrained, and having some initial crookedness.

In the secant formula as just given, P/A represents the average stress on the cross-section when the ultimate or *buckling* load is on the column. It is not permissible to convert the buckling load formula into a formula for *allowable* load simply by replacing the yield-point stress with the allowable compressive stress. The reason for this is that, for a column of any marked slenderness, a given percentage increase in *load* results in a much greater increase in *maximum stress*. To convert the given equation into a working formula, therefore, let the buckling load, P, be replaced by the allowable load, P' times the desired factor of safety, f. Then P/A becomes $P'f/A$, and the equation becomes

$$\frac{P'f}{A} = \frac{\text{Yield point of material}}{1 + 0.25 \sec \dfrac{kL}{r} \sqrt{\dfrac{P'f/A}{4\,E}}}$$

This can be written

$$\frac{P'}{A} = \frac{1/f \;(\text{Yield point of material})}{1 + 0.25 \sec \dfrac{kL}{r} \sqrt{\dfrac{P'/A}{4\,E/f}}}$$

It is seen therefore, that the factor of safety must be applied both to the ultimate strength of the material (in a column the yield point establishes the ultimate strength) and to its stiffness. This is consistent with the fact that the load-carrying capacity of a short column is determined by the strength of the column material, whereas that of a slender column is determined by the stiffness.

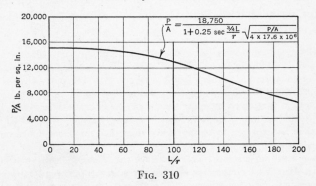

Fig. 310

The Committee recommended the use of 32,000 lb. per sq. in. for the yield point and a factor of safety such as to reduce the average stress in a short compression block to 15,000 lb. per sq. in. (the same value as prescribed by the A.I.S.C. Rankine formula). With the 0.25 eccentricity ratio, this makes the maximum stress $1.25 \times 15,000 = 18,750$ lb. per sq. in. The factor of safety which will make this reduction is $32,000/18,750 = 1.71$. Making these substitutions and assuming a value of 30,000,000 for E, the equation for riveted-ended columns becomes

$$\frac{P'}{A} = \frac{18,750}{1 + 0.25 \sec \frac{\frac{3}{4} L}{r} \sqrt{\frac{P'/A}{4 \times 17.6 \times 10^6}}}$$

This curve is plotted in Fig. 310.

179. Parabolic Formulas Based on the Secant Formula. The secant formula, though correct and widely applicable, is of very inconvenient form to use. For this reason, the Committee on Steel Column Research proposed the use of working formulas of more convenient form based on parabolic curves that have nearly the same shape as the secant curve for values of L/r up to 160. For ordinary carbon steel, the Committee proposed:

$$P/A = 15,000 - \tfrac{1}{4}(L/r)^2 \qquad \text{for riveted ends}$$
$$P/A = 15,000 - \tfrac{1}{3}(L/r)^2 \qquad \text{for pinned ends}$$

These formulas are purely arbitrary, merely fulfilling two conditions: they give the same value for P/A when $L/r = 0$ that the recommended secant curve gives; and curves plotted from them lie close to the secant curve throughout the slenderness range they are designed to cover (Fig. 311).

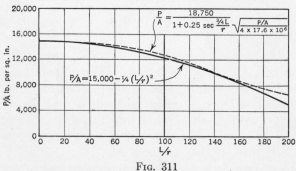

Fig. 311

These formulas have been incorporated in the specifications for Street Railway Bridges of the American Railway Engineering Association (1935), with the proviso that main compression members shall not have a slenderness ratio in excess of 100. The American Association of State Highway Officials also adopted these formulas in their 1935 specifications, with 120 as the maximum L/r for main members. These formulas are therefore widely used in present American bridge design. The "basic" stress in both of these specifications is 18,000 lb. per sq. in. The 1936 specifications of the American Institute of Steel Construction, based on an allowable stress in direct compression of 20,000 lb. per sq. in., include a parabolic column formula $P/A = 17,000 - 0.485(L/r)^2$. The 17,000-lb. value reflects the higher basic stress. The larger coefficient of $(L/r)^2$ reflects the fact that this higher stress is unimportant in a slender column. The A.I.S.C. specifications permit main compression members to have slenderness ratios not exceeding 120. Secondary members are allowed to have a slenderness ratio not exceeding 200, and if L/r exceeds 120 are to be designed in accordance with the A.I.S.C. Rankine formula given in Art. 175.

PROBLEMS

1. Draw graphs similar to those of Fig. 311 for steel columns with pinned ends.

2. Solve Problem 1, Art. 176, using (a) $P/A = 15,000 - \frac{1}{4}(L/r)^2$; (b) $P/A = 15,000 - \frac{1}{3}(L/r)^2$.

3. Solve Problem 5, Art. 176, using (a) $P/A = 15,000 - \frac{1}{4}(L/r)^2$; (b) $P/A = 17,000 - 0.485(L/r)^2$.

4. In repairs made on the Washington Monument in 1934, a scaffold of steel pipe was erected around the shaft. (See *Engineering News-Record*, December 20, 1934.) The corner posts in the lowest tier of this scaffold were 3-in. extra heavy steel pipe (diameters, 3.50 in. outside, 2.30 in. inside) with a length of 6 ft. 6 in. between lateral supports. The design load on each of these posts was 50,000 lb. How does this load compare with the load allowed on the column by the equation $P/A = 15,000 - \frac{1}{3}(L/r)^2$? Is this an appropriate formula for use?

5. An elevated bin, which with its contents weighs 280,000 lb., is to be carried on four 6-in.-by-6-in. angles 10 ft. long. Determine the necessary thickness of the angles if they are to be designed in accordance with the equation $P/A = 15,000 - \frac{1}{4}(L/r)^2$.

180. Columns of High-Strength Steel.

The column formulas which have been given are for ordinary carbon or "structural" steel. Comparable formulas for stronger nickel and silicon steels have also been incorporated in specifications. Such formulas take into consideration the higher strength of the alloy steels, and also the fact that they have no greater stiffness than ordinary carbon steel.

The Rankine type formula is made applicable to stronger steels by increasing the coefficient of $(L/r)^2$ in the same ratio that the basic allowable stress, S, is increased. The American Society of Civil Engineers specifications for railway and highway bridges (1922) stipulate use of the Rankine formula $\dfrac{P}{A} = \dfrac{16,000}{1 + \dfrac{1}{13,500}(L/r)^2}$, with the added specification that for stronger steels the numerator may be increased in the ratio which specified yield point of the stronger steel bears to 30,000 lb. per sq. in., provided the coefficient of $(L/r)^2$ is increased in the same ratio. For a steel with a yield point of 45,000 lb. per sq. in., this specification results in the formula $\dfrac{P}{A} = \dfrac{24,000}{1 + \dfrac{1}{9,000}\,(L/r)^2}$, and this formula has been used in the design of several large bridges. Certain compression members of the George Washington Bridge were fabricated of silicon steel with a specified yield point of 55,000 lb. per sq. in. and were designed in accordance with the straight-line formula $P/A = 27,000 - 80\ L/r$, with a maximum P/A of 23,000 lb. per sq. in.

The specifications of the American Railway Engineering Association (1935) provide for the use of silicon steel with a yield point of 45,000 lb. per sq. in. and nickel steel with a yield point of 50,000 lb. per sq. in., in addition to carbon steel (which has a specified yield point of 33,000 lb. per sq. in.). Columns made of these alloy steels are to be proportioned in accordance with the following equations:

	Riveted Ends	Pinned Ends
Silicon steel......	$P/A = 20,000 - 0.46(L/r)^2$	$P/A = 20,000 - 0.61(L/r)^2$
Nickel steel	$P/A = 22,500 - 0.57(L/r)^2$	$P/A = 22,500 - 0.76(L/r)^2$

PROBLEM

1. Plot on the same axes curves showing values of P/A for values of L/r from 0 to 100, for pinned-ended columns of carbon, silicon, and nickel steels, using the A.R.E.A. formulas for pinned ends. For values of L/r of 0, 20, 40, 60, 80, and 100, find the ratio of (a) allowable load on nickel-steel column to allowable load on carbon-steel column, (b) allowable load on silicon-steel column to allowable load on carbon-steel column. Tabulate these ratios.

181. Cast-Iron Columns. Cast-iron columns were extensively used in the nineteenth century but are no longer used in large and important structures. This is largely because of the likelihood of defects in the castings and because of the brittleness of the material, both of which make the column unreliable. Cast-iron columns in building work are nearly always circular in cross-section and hollow, though occasionally hollow and square.

The Building Code Committee of the United States Bureau of Standards recommends

$$\frac{P}{A} = 9,000 - 40\frac{L}{r}$$

with a maximum L/r of 90. The 1938 New York City Code uses the same equation but limits the maximum slenderness ratio to 70.

PROBLEMS

1. What load would be allowed by the New York Building Code on a cast-iron column 8 ft. long with an outside diameter of 5 in. and an inside diameter of 4 in.?

$Ans.$ $P = 46,600$ lb.

2. Assuming a cross-sectional area of 20 sq. in. in each case, and that the wall thickness must not be less than 1 in., compare the allowable loads on cast-iron columns of (a) hollow round cross-section, (b) hollow square cross-section, if the length is such as to make $L/r = 70$ for the round column. (Use the New York Code formula.)

182. Aluminum-Alloy Columns. Because of low weight in comparison with strength, columns made of various aluminum alloys are gradually coming into structural use, particularly in the frames of aircraft, in movable cranes, etc. There are many different aluminum alloys, with widely varying characteristics, and the processes of fabrication (tempering, cold working, etc.) also greatly affect the properties of the different alloys. The " strong " alloys produced by the Aluminum Company of America are 17S (aluminum alloyed with copper, manganese, and magnesium) and 25S (aluminum alloyed with copper, manganese, and silicon). When heat-treated and properly aged to bring out their best qualities, these alloys are designated as 17ST and 25ST. Both 17ST and 25ST are specified to have " yield points " at 35,000 lb. per sq. in. in tension and compression.[1] Their modulus of elasticity is taken as 10,000,000 lb. per sq. in.

For the design of *round-ended* columns of these materials, the Aluminum Company of America recommends the following formulas:

For average stresses greater than 5,000 lb. per sq. in. (L/r up to 81)

$$\frac{P}{A} = 15,000 - 123\frac{L}{r}$$

For average stresses less than 5,000 lb. per sq. in. (L/r over 81)

$$\frac{P}{A} = \frac{33,000,000}{(L/r)^2}$$

---

[1] Unlike mild steel, the aluminum alloys do not have a definite yield point at which there is an increase in deformation with no increase in load. Their " yield point " is arbitrarily set at the stress at which the stress-strain curve shows a departure of 0.002 unit of strain from the initial modulus line produced. See " Structural Aluminum Handbook," published by the Aluminum Company of America, 1930, page 15.

These two formulas evidently give a straight line tangent to and followed by a Euler extension, as originally proposed by T. H. Johnson, and are plotted in Fig. 312, curve a. The juncture of the straight line with Euler's curve occurs at 5,000 lb. per sq. in. because of the fact (discovered by Johnson) that any tangent to Euler's curve has an ordi-

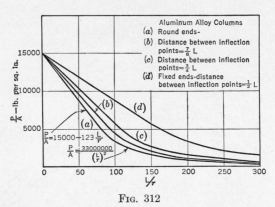

Aluminum Alloy Columns
(a) Round ends-
(b) Distance between inflection points=$\frac{7}{8}$ L
(c) Distance between inflection points=$\frac{3}{4}$ L
(d) Fixed ends-distance between inflection points=$\frac{1}{2}$ L

$$\frac{P}{A}=15000-123\frac{L}{r}$$

$$\frac{P}{A}=\frac{33000000}{\left(\frac{L}{r}\right)^2}$$

FIG. 312

nate for $L/r = 0$ that is three times the ordinate of the point of tangency. This Euler curve is the curve for critical stresses divided by a factor of safety of 3.

For columns of aluminum or other elastic materials it is logical to follow the recommendations which the Special Committee on Steel Column Research made with respect to the assumed distances between inflection points; namely, that, in truss columns with riveted and pinned ends, the distances between inflection points can be taken as $\frac{3}{4} L$ and $\frac{7}{8} L$, respectively. Fig. 312 shows the curves based on the above formulas for columns where the distance between inflection points is L, $\frac{7}{8} L$, $\frac{3}{4} L$, and $\frac{1}{2} L$.

PROBLEMS

1. In a riveted aluminum alloy truss, one member consists of two 3-in.-by-2½-in.-by-¼-in. angles placed as shown in Fig. 313. The length of the column is 5 ft. 6 in., and the distance between inflection points may be considered to be $\frac{3}{4}$ of the length. What load is allowed on the column by the formulas of this article?

2. A column 10 ft. 6 in. long is made up of two 8-in. channels and two 10-in. plates. The area of the cross-section is 11.72 sq. in., and the least radius of gyration is 3.08 in. Compare the allowable loads on it if it is (a) of steel, and conforms to the A.R.E.A. Specifications for a column with riveted ends, (b) of aluminum alloy, with the middle $\frac{3}{4}$ of the length considered to be a "round-ended" column.

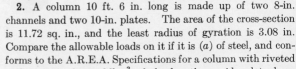

FIG. 313

183. Timber Columns. Timber columns nearly always have solid rectangular cross-sections. It is customary to specify allowable average stresses in terms of L/d instead of L/r (d is the least dimension of the cross-section).

A formula which has been extensively used for the design of wood columns is $P/A = C - 20\,L/d$, where C is the allowable compressive unit stress on the end of a short block. L/d must not exceed 40. Values of C given for the following woods are:

Southern longleaf yellow pine and Douglas fir............... 1,175
Red and white oak... 1,000
Spruce... 800

On the assumption that the cross-sections of timber columns are solid rectangles, which is nearly always the case, an equivalent formula in terms of L/r is easily found. The radius of gyration of a rectangle of which d is the length of the side is $d\sqrt{1/12}$ or 0.29 d. $P/A = 1{,}175 - 20\,L/d$ may be written $P/A = 1{,}175 - 20 \times 0.29\dfrac{L}{0.29\,d}$. Whence

$$\frac{P}{A} = 1{,}175 - 5.8\frac{L}{r}$$

This is equivalent to the original formula but is not restricted to solid rectangular cross-sections.

The Forest Products Laboratory of the Department of Agriculture has proposed a column formula for wood columns which is based on a large number of tests. The formula is

$$\frac{P}{A} = c\left[1 - \frac{1}{3}\left(\frac{L}{Kd}\right)^4\right]$$

Values of c and K for this formula are given below for a few of the commoner woods, when used under shelter in dry locations. All values are for select grades.

	c	K	E
Douglas fir (western Washington and Oregon)........................	1,175	23.7	1,600,000
Hemlock (western)...................	900	25.3	1,400,000
Oak, commercial red and white.........	1,000	24.8	1,500,000
Pine, southern yellow.................	1,175	23.7	1,600,000
Pine, southern yellow, dense...........	1,290	22.6	1,600,000
Spruce (red, white, Sitka)	800	24.8	1,200,000

If L/d is 11 or less, the allowable stress c may be used without reduction.

If L/d exceeds the number given for K, the column is a " long column " and the above formula does not apply; Euler's formula should be used instead. With a factor of safety of 3, and in terms of d instead of the least radius of gyration, the Euler formula for a round-ended column is

$$\frac{P}{A} = \frac{0.274\,E}{(L/d)^2}$$

and this is specified. The Forest Products Laboratory formulas have been included in the specifications for highway bridges of the American Association of State Highway Officials and in other specifications.

PROBLEMS

1. Plot the Forest Products Laboratory formula for dense southern yellow pine, from $L/d = 0$ to $L/d = 40$. Scales: 1 in. = 200 lb. per sq. in.; 1 in. = 8 L/d.

2. A column 15 ft. long is to be made by spiking together four planks each 2 in. by 8 in. (actual dimensions) in cross-section. Using the Forest Products Laboratory equation, find the allowable load on the column (a) if the planks are placed side by side to give an 8-in.-by-8-in. solid cross-section, (b) if the planks are arranged so as to form a hollow square 10 in. on a side. The wood is Douglas Fir.

3. What size Douglas fir timber would you purchase for use as a column 18 ft. long to carry a load of 70,000 lb.? Use the straight-line formula given in this article. *Ans.* Use 10 in. × 12 in.

4. Determine the required size if the timber is spruce.

184. Columns with Intentionally Eccentric Loads. Many columns are designed to carry loads which are definitely and intentionally eccentric. These loads cause bending stresses because of the known eccentricity in addition to the bending stresses resulting from " column action."

Using the Rankine type formula, eccentric loads are usually provided for as follows: The formula for nominally axial loads

$$\frac{P}{A} = \frac{S}{1 + q(L/r)^2}$$

may be written $P/A + (P/A)q(L/r)^2 = S$. In this equation P/A represents the direct stress and $(P/A)q(L/r)^2$ represents the stress due to " column action."

Now suppose that P is applied on one of the principal axes, but with an intentional eccentricity e with respect to the other axis. This eccentricity will cause additional stress equal to Pec/I, where I is the moment of inertia with respect to the axis about which the intentional eccentricity of P causes the column to bend, and where c is the distance from this axis to the extreme fibers. In a column with eccentric loading this additional stress must be added to the other two stresses and the sum of the three stresses must not exceed the basic stress, S. Hence a formula for columns with eccentric loading is

$$\frac{P}{A} + \frac{P}{A} q(L/r)^2 + \frac{Pec}{I} = S$$

This may be written

$$\frac{P}{A} = \frac{S}{1 + q(L/r)^2 + ec/r'^2} \qquad \textit{Know}$$

In these formulas it should be noted that r is the *least* radius of gyration but that r' is the radius of gyration with respect to the axis from which the intentional eccentricity e is measured. Therefore, depending on the loading of the column, r' may be the least radius of gyration or it may be the other principal radius of gyration.

If a column carries two loads, one nominally axial, one intentionally eccentric, before the procedure just outlined is carried out it is necessary to determine the line of action of the *resultant* of the two loads and use the resultant in the above formulas.

A straight-line formula can be modified somewhat similarly to make it applicable to eccentric loading. When this is done, it becomes $P/A + Pec/I = S - qL/r$, which may be stated: The direct stress plus the bending stress due to the eccentric load must not exceed the average stress for axial loading permitted by the straight-line column formula on a column of the given slenderness ratio.

The methods outlined above are not exact but they are widely used and give results that are safe and economical for columns with slenderness ratios within the limits permitted by common structural specifications.

The A.R.E.A. Specifications (1935) provide that for columns with known eccentricity of loading the following secant formula shall be used

$$\frac{P}{A} = \frac{1/f \text{ (Yield point of material)}}{1 + (ec/r^2 + 0.001 \, L/r) \sec \dfrac{kL}{r} \sqrt{\dfrac{P/A}{4 \, E/f}}}$$

In this formula e is the intentional eccentricity of loading, r is the least radius of gyration of the cross-section in question, and c is the distance of the most remote point on that cross-section from the axis with respect to which r is least.[1] The value of k is $\frac{3}{4}$ for columns with riveted ends and

---

[1] If the intentional eccentricity is at right angles to the least radius of gyration, this is not a logical procedure, but any error to which it leads is on the " safe " side.

$\frac{7}{8}$ for columns with pinned ends; f is 1.76 for carbon steel with a yield point of 33,000 lb. per sq. in. The term $0.001\ L/r$ provides for chance eccentricity due to crookedness of the column, etc., which exists in addition to the intended eccentricity.

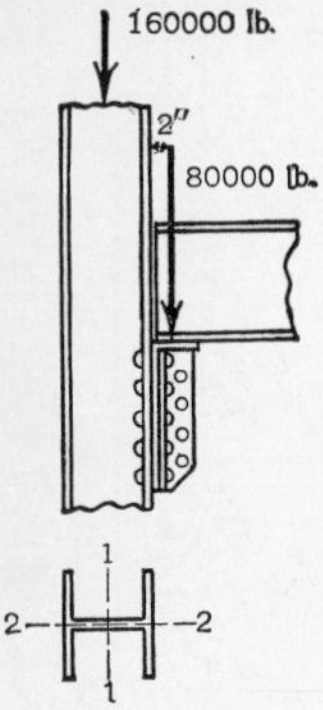

When a column carrying both nominally axial and intentionally eccentric loads is to be investigated or designed by means of the secant formula, the two loads are replaced by their resultant as described in connection with Rankine's formula.

Fig. 314

Illustrative Example. A steel column 21 ft. long is to carry an axial load of 160,000 lb. and an eccentric load of 80,000 lb. applied 2 in. from the face of the flange, as shown in Fig. 314. Select a wide-flange section to carry the loads in accordance with the A.I.S.C. Rankine formula as modified in this article.

Solution: Assume use of a 12-in., 99-lb. section. $A = 29.09$ sq. in.; $r_{1-1} = 5.43$ in.; $r_{2-2} = 3.09$ in.; depth of section = 12.75 in., from which the eccentricity of the 80,000-lb. load is

$$\frac{12.75}{2} + 2 = 8.38 \text{ in.} \quad c = \frac{12.75}{2} = 6.38 \text{ in.}$$

The resultant of the two loads is 240,000 lb. acting with an eccentricity

$$e = \frac{80,000}{240,000} \times 8.38 = 2.79 \text{ in.}$$

$$\frac{P}{A} = \frac{240,000}{29.09} = 8,250 \text{ lb. per sq. in.} \quad \frac{L}{r_{2-2}} = \frac{252}{3.09} = 81.5$$

Therefore

$$S = 8,250 \left(1 + \frac{(81.5)^2}{18,000} + \frac{2.79 \times 6.38}{(5.43)^2} \right)$$

$$= 8,250 \ (1 + 0.37 + 0.60)$$

$$= 8,250 \times 1.97 = 16,300 \text{ lb. per sq. in.}$$

It is possible that the next lighter section will be adequate. The dimensions differ so slightly that the variation in A is all that need be considered. The area of the 12-in., 92-lb. section is 27.06 sq. in., which gives $P/A = 8,870$ lb. per sq. in. Multiplying this by 1.97, $S = 17,500$ lb. per sq. in. Since this is slightly less than 18,000 lb. per sq. in., this column will be satisfactory.

PROBLEMS

1. A column 24 ft. long supports the load from a column above, and also a crane reaction, as shown in Fig. 315. Select a steel wide-flanged section to carry the load in accordance with the A.I.S.C. Rankine formula as modified in this article.

Ans. Use 14 in., 84 lb.

2. Assume that the column of Problem 1 is braced laterally at each third-point, in the plane of the axis about which its moment of inertia is greatest, and select a suitable wide-flange section.

3. Assuming the column braced as in Problem 2, select a suitable wide-flange section to carry the load in accordance with the A.R.E.A. formula given in this article. Let the yield point be 33,000 lb. per sq. in. $f = 1.76$, $k = \frac{3}{4}$.

4. A transformer unit weighs 800 lb. and is carried on a southern yellow pine post as shown in Fig. 316. Will a 10-in.-by-10-in. (nominal size) post suffice? (*Hint:* Use the appropriate Forest Products Laboratory column formula to determine the allowable value of P/A for an axial load. Consider the length of the column to be 30 ft. The sum of the direct compression and the bending due to the intentional eccentricity should not exceed the value of P/A given by the column formula.)

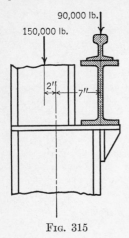

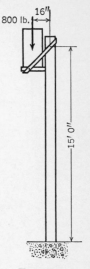

185. Columns in Machines.

Structural columns in machine frames can be designed in accordance with formulas of the types already given, using constants appropriate to the material, fabrication, use, etc.

Columns, in addition to being used in the *frames* of machines, often form part of the mechanism itself. Such columns are sometimes of complex (non-prismatical) form, and are subject to accelerations which result in a complicated loading due to both longitudinal and transverse forces. It is often impractical to design such members by the procedures which have been described. Some machine columns are prismatical, however, and move with low accelerations or are stationary, and can be designed much as structural columns are.

A column of this sort often has its ends supported on lubricated pins. These pins develop so little friction that the ends of the column are practically unrestrained against rotating in the plane perpendicular to the axes of the pins. In the plane of the pins, however, the closeness of fit and the rigidity of the end fastenings may afford a considerable degree of restraint against rotation of the column ends, so that a fixed-ended condition is frequently assumed (although complete fixation exists only in exceptional cases).

If the cross-section of a column with ends as just described is round or square or of other shape that has equal moments of inertia with respect to all centroidal axes, evidently the column should be designed simply as a round-ended column. But often the difference in the stiffness of the end connections in the two perpendicular planes is taken into account and the column is given an unsymmetrical cross-section, such as a

FIG. 315

FIG. 316

rectangle, having its smaller dimension parallel to the plane of the pins.

A column with such end conditions may bend in *single* curvature in the plane perpendicular to the axes of the pins; or it may bend in *reversed* curvature in the plane containing the axes of the pins (Fig. 317). In the first case, the distance between inflection points is the full unsupported length of the column. In the second, it is less than the unsupported length. If the ends are fully fixed, it is $\frac{1}{2} L$. A member designed so as to take this difference in end rigidity into account is given a cross-section such that $L/r_1 = kL/r_2$, at least approximately. Then the column offers approximately equal resistance to buckling in either of the two planes.

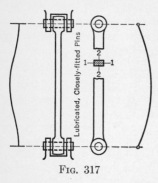

FIG. 317

For many years Rankine's formula has been applied to the design of columns in machines with a value of q equal to $4/25{,}000$ for the " pinned-end " condition. Rankine's formula then becomes

$$\frac{P}{A} = \frac{S}{1 + \dfrac{4}{25{,}000}\,(L/r_1)^2}$$

for bending as a pinned column and

$$\frac{P}{A} = \frac{S}{1 + \dfrac{4}{25{,}000}\,(\frac{1}{2} L/r_2)^2} \quad \text{or} \quad \frac{P}{A} = \frac{S}{1 + \dfrac{1}{25{,}000}\,(L/r_2)^2}$$

for bending as a column with ends fully fixed. The allowable unit stress is made consistent with the yield point of the material and the conditions of use.[1]

A more logical procedure for the design of machine columns would be to use the secant formula,

$$\frac{P}{A} = \frac{(1/f)\ (\text{Yield point of material})}{1 + ec/r^2 \sec \dfrac{kL}{r}\sqrt{\dfrac{P/A}{4\,E/f}}}$$

---

[1] In Art. 175 it was noted that the coefficient of $(L/r)^2$ in Rankine's formula should be made proportional to the yield point of the column material. The above coefficients cannot logically be accepted as applicable to all grades of steel, although they have been used for grades with strengths covering a fairly wide spread.

using values of yield point, and of f, ec/r^2, k, and E appropriate to each situation. Eccentricity in the plane perpendicular to the pins would be small, and 0.10 might be used for ec/r^2. In the plane of the pins, the eccentricity might be considerably greater, however, and a greater eccentricity ratio might well be used. For r_1 (measured perpendicular to the pins) k should equal 1. For r_2 (measured in the plane of the pins) k would lie between 1 and $\frac{1}{2}$, depending on the amount of restraint assumed to be present.

This formula would be applicable to any elastic material used with any factor of safety. Up to the present time, however, the secant formula has not been extensively applied to the design of machine columns.

PROBLEM

A steel bar has a rectangular cross-section 4 in. by 2 in. It is used as a pin-ended column, the pins being perpendicular to the broad faces (Fig. 317). The distance from center to center of pins is 6 ft. The pins are well lubricated and offer negligible resistance to rotation of the ends of the column in a plane perpendicular to the axis of the pins. They may be considered, however, to fix the ends of the column against rotation in the plane of the axis of the pins. Using the Rankine formulas given in this article, find the maximum allowable compressive load on the member if the maximum compressive stress S is not to exceed 8,000 lb. per sq. in.

$Ans.$ $P = 39,500$ lb.

GENERAL PROBLEMS

1. A built-up H-section is formed of a 14-in.-by-$\frac{1}{2}$-in. web and four 6-in.-by-6-in.-by-$\frac{1}{2}$-in. angles. Depth of the column, back to back of angles, is $14\frac{1}{2}$ in. If the length is 20 ft., what nominally axial load is allowed by (a) the A.I.S.C. (1934) specifications, (b) the A.I.S.C. (1936) specifications?

2. If two 14-in.-by-$\frac{3}{4}$-in cover plates are added to the column section of Problem 1, what is the allowable load in accordance with each of the formulas?

3. The A.R.E.A. formulas are based on the supposition that 0.25 is a reasonable value for ec/r^2. For each of the columns having the following cross-sections, what eccentricity does the A.R.E.A. formula imply: (a) a 14-in., 142-lb. wide-flange section, (b) 8-in. standard pipe, (c) two $5 \times 3\frac{1}{2} \times \frac{3}{8}$-in. angles with 5-in. legs parallel and $\frac{1}{2}$-in. apart?

4. A light derrick mast 40 ft. long is made of four steel angles 3 in. by 3 in. by $\frac{5}{16}$ in., forming a square as shown in Fig. 318. The angles are latticed together so that they act together as a column. What central load is permitted on this column by the $P/A = 15{,}000 - \frac{1}{3}(L/r)^2$? Would this be a suitable column formula to use? (The lattice bars are assumed not to carry any of the load.)

5. Four 3-in. $\times$ 3-in. $\times \frac{5}{16}$-in. angles are riveted back to back as shown in Fig. 319 to form a column 12 ft. 6 in. long. What load is permitted on it by the A.I.S.C. parabolic formula? $Ans.$ $P = 72{,}500$ lb.

6. If a steel pipe (Table VIII) is substituted for the timber column of Problem 4, Art. 184, what size pipe will be required, using the secant formula as given in

Art. 184, with the following values: $e = 14$ in., Yield point $= 30,000$ lb. per sq. in., $f = 2$, $k = 2$, $L = 15$ ft.

(*Hint:* For a trial section, assume that $\dfrac{P}{A} + \dfrac{P \times 14 \times c}{I}$ may equal 15,000 lb. per sq. in.)

7. A sand bin which weighs 100 tons when full is to be supported by four square timber columns 20 ft. long. What size southern pine timbers should be bought to comply with the straight-line formula of Art. 183? *Ans.* Use 10 in. × 10 in.

8. What load does the Forest Products Laboratory formula allow on each of the columns of Problem 7?

9. An 8-in., 17-lb. wide-flange section is used as a column 9 ft. 6 in. long. It carries a load the resultant of which acts on the axis 1–1 and 1 in. from the axis 2–2. What may the load be in accordance with the secant equation of the A.R.E.A. specifications? The yield point equals 33,000 lb. per sq. in., $f = 1.76$, $K = \frac{3}{4}$.

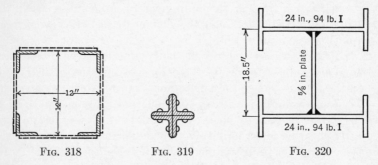

FIG. 318   FIG. 319   FIG. 320

10. The A.I.S.C. (1936) specifications provide that eccentricity of load on a column be taken into consideration by finding the allowable value of P/A for an axial load and equating that to $\dfrac{P'}{A} + \dfrac{P'ec}{I}$, where P' is the eccentric load. Following this procedure and using the equation $P/A = 17,000 - 0.485\ (L/r)^2$, find the allowable load on the column of Problem 9.

11. A column in a welded bridge in Europe is made of two wide-flange beams and a web plate. Fig. 320 shows the type of column but with American sections. If the length of this column is 47 ft., what load is allowed by the formula $P/A = 15,000 - \frac{1}{4}(L/r)^2$? *Ans.* $P = 930,000$ lb.

CHAPTER XV

COMBINED STRESSES — ELEMENTARY APPLICATIONS

186. Introduction. In a beam the tensile stress on a vertical plane at a point y in. from the neutral axis is given by the formula $S = My/I$, and the shearing stress on horizontal and vertical planes through the same point is given by $S_s = VQ/Ib$. It will be shown in this chapter that, at any point in the cross-section of a beam where there are both tensile and shearing stresses, there are greater tensile stresses than the stress found by $S = My/I$. Does this greater tensile stress ever exceed the tension in the extreme fibers?

In a shaft, such as a vertical turbine shaft, subject to axial compressive forces, and also subject to torque, there are shearing stresses at the surface (on the transverse and on longitudinal planes) which are given by $S_s = Tc/J$ and compressive stresses on transverse planes equal to P/A. It will be shown that, at any point where both these stresses occur, there are greater shearing and compressive stresses than those given by the formulas. Can these be disregarded in the design of the shaft?

At a point in the shell of a boiler subject to steam pressure it was found that tensile stresses exist in two directions, the circumferential tension being twice the longitudinal tension. Do still greater stresses on some oblique plane result from the combination of these calculated stresses? These questions and many similar questions can be intelligently answered only if the relationships between given stresses and the resulting maximum stresses are understood. If stresses exist greater than those commonly calculated and regarded as maximum stresses, then they cannot be ignored if designing is to be done intelligently.

The term "combined stresses" is commonly used to designate the stresses calculated by combining other stresses. In this chapter are derived relationships which exist between given combinations of stress on certain planes at a point (such as the combinations mentioned above) and the stresses that exist on other planes through the same point. Only "two-dimensional" stresses (all forces and stresses being parallel to one plane) will be considered in this chapter.

187. Representation of a State of Stress in a Body. The state of stress existing at a point in a stressed body is conveniently represented by showing the unit stresses acting on the faces of a small rectangular solid at the point in the body. If the stresses in the body are uniformly

255

distributed (that is, do not vary in intensity from point to point) the rectangular solid may be of any size. However if, as is common, the stresses vary from point to point (as in a beam) the solid is taken of infinitesimal size so that the stresses may without error be regarded as uniform over its faces.

It is evidently possible to represent the same state of stress in a body in different ways. As an example, consider a prism with axial tensile loading causing a tensile stress of 10,000 lb. per sq. in. on all transverse planes. This condition of stress may be represented by an infinite number of different combinations of shearing and tensile stresses on differently inclined planes. Three of these are shown in Fig. 322. Inspection of the stresses shown in (d) does not indicate the identity of this state of stress with that shown in (b), but if the " principal stresses " (defined later) for (d) are calculated they are found to be the stresses shown in (b).[1]

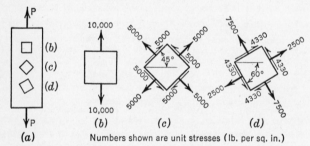

(a)   (b)   (c)   (d)

Numbers shown are unit stresses (lb. per sq. in.)

FIG. 322.   The same state of stress represented in three ways.

It is important to keep in mind that stress at a certain point cannot be considered quantitatively without considering a plane (passing through the point) on which the stress acts. On different planes through a given point in a stressed body the stresses differ.

In the following discussion the term *normal stress* will be used to denote either tensile unit stress or compressive unit stress as distinguished from shearing unit stress. Tensile and compressive stresses are " normal " inasmuch as they result from forces acting perpendicular to the plane of stress, whereas shearing stresses result from forces parallel to the plane on which the shearing stresses act. Shearing stresses are sometimes called " tangential " stresses.

188. Calculation of Stresses on an Oblique Plane. When known stresses act on mutually perpendicular planes, the stresses on any in-

---

[1] The principal stresses shown in (b) are no more the " true stresses " than are those shown in (c) or (d) which represent the same state of stress at the given point in the body but show the stresses that exist on other planes.

clined plane are found by applying the conditions of equilibrium to a wedge-shaped solid two faces of which coincide with the planes of known stress and one face of which is in the direction of the inclined plane.

Example. A steel rod, 1 in. in diameter, fixed at the upper end, is used as a tension member to carry a load of 12,560 lb. and at the same time is subject to a torque of 1,570 lb-in. applied at the lower end as shown diagrammatically in Fig. 323(a). The tensile stress resulting from this load is 16,000 lb. per sq. in. over all transverse sections. Shearing stresses at the surface caused by the torque are 8,000 lb. per sq. in. Calculate the stresses which exist at a point on the surface of the rod on a plane making an angle of 60° with the element of the surface through that point.

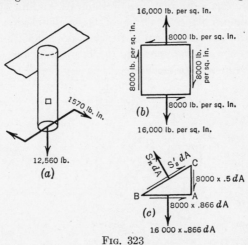

Fig. 323

Solution: The given tensile and shearing stresses are shown on a cube in Fig. 323(b).[1] In (c) is shown a wedge cut from the cube by a plane making an angle of 60° with an element of the cylinder or 30° with the horizontal. This wedge is a particle in equilibrium, and the forces holding it in equilibrium result from the given unit stresses and the unknown unit stresses. Equating the sum of the components parallel to BC to zero,

$$S'_s dA - 16,000 \times 0.866 \, dA \times 0.5 + 8,000 \times 0.866 \, dA \times 0.866 - 8,000 \times 0.5 \, dA \times 0.5 = 0$$

$$S'_s = +6,930 - 6,000 + 2,000 = +2,930 \text{ lb. per sq. in.}$$

The plus sign indicates that the stress on the face BC of the wedge is in the direction assumed when writing the equation.

Equating the sum of the components normal to BC to zero,

$$S'_n dA - 16,000 \times 0.866 \, dA \times 0.866 - 8,000 \times 0.866 \, dA \times 0.5 - 8,000 \times 0.5 \, dA \times 0.866 = 0$$

$$S'_n = 12,000 + 3,460 + 3,460 = +18,920 \text{ lb. per sq. in.}$$

The plus sign indicates that the normal stress on BC is tensile, as assumed in writing the equation.

[1] The same intensity of shearing stress that acts on the horizontal surfaces of the cube must also act on the vertical surfaces. See Art. 35.

PROBLEMS

1. By the method used in this article, calculate the shearing and normal stresses on a 45° plane which result from the stresses shown in Fig. 323(b).

2. Same as Problem 1 except that plane is inclined 135° with horizontal.

189. Shearing and Normal Stresses Resulting from One Normal Stress Combined with Shearing Stresses.

In the example solved in the preceding article, a known normal stress and a known shearing stress existed on a given plane, and an equal shearing stress existed on a plane at right angles. Numerical values were calculated for the normal and shearing stresses on a plane having a known inclination to the planes of known stress. In this article the same type of stress condition will be considered, and a general expression for the shearing and normal stresses on an inclined plane will be derived.

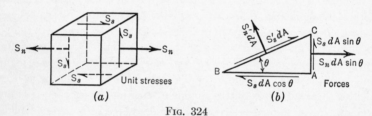

(a)   (b)

Fig. 324

Fig. 324 shows an elementary cube with faces parallel to and perpendicular to the given stresses, and (b) shows a wedge cut from this cube, the inclined face making an angle θ with the direction of the normal stress. On the faces of the cube the given unit stresses are shown, but on the faces of the wedge the *forces* due to these unit stresses are indicated. The forces on the BC face are expressed in terms of the unknown normal unit stress S_n' and the unknown shearing unit stress S_s', expressions for both of which are desired. If the area of the BC face of the wedge is dA, that of the AC face is $dA \sin \theta$ and that of the AB face is $dA \cos \theta$.

Summing up all components parallel to BC and placing the sum equal to zero,

$$S_s'dA + S_ndA \sin \theta \cos \theta + S_sdA \sin^2 \theta - S_sdA \cos^2 \theta = 0$$

Whence

$$S_s' = -S_n \sin \theta \cos \theta + S_s(\cos^2 \theta - \sin^2 \theta)$$

or

$$S_s' = -\frac{S_n}{2} \sin 2\theta + S_s \cos 2\theta \tag{1}$$

which gives the value of the resultant shearing stress on a plane inclined at an angle θ to the direction of the given normal stress.

Summing up all components normal to BC and placing the sum equal to zero,

$$S_n'dA - S_n \sin^2 \theta dA + S_s \sin \theta \cos \theta dA + S_s \sin \theta \cos \theta dA = 0$$

$$S_n' = S_n \sin^2 \theta - 2 S_s \sin \theta \cos \theta = S_n \frac{1 - \cos 2\theta}{2} - S_s \sin 2\theta$$

or

$$S_n' = \frac{S_n}{2} - \frac{S_n}{2} \cos 2\theta - S_s \sin 2\theta \tag{2}$$

which gives the value of the resultant normal stress on a plane inclined at an angle θ with the direction of the given normal stress.

The signs in equations (1) and (2) result from the assumption that S_n is plus if tension and minus if compression, and that S_s is plus if the shearing forces act as shown in Fig. 324 (a) and minus if they act oppositely. This system of signs should be followed in determining numerical values of the shearing and normal stresses on the inclined plane by equations (1) and (2).[1] If this is done a plus value for S_s' indicates shearing stress on the inclined plane acting up the plane and a plus value for S_n' indicates that the normal stress on the inclined plane is tension. It should be kept in mind that $\cos 2\theta$ is a minus quantity for values of θ between 45° and 90°.

PROBLEM

By means of the formulas derived in this article, calculate the resultant shearing and normal stresses found in the previous example (Art. 188).

190. Maximum Shearing Stress Resulting from One Normal Stress Combined with Shearing Stresses. The value of θ for the plane upon which the resultant shearing stress will be a maximum is found from equation (1) by putting the derivative of S_s' with respect to θ equal to zero.

$$\frac{dS_s'}{d\theta} = -S_n \cos 2\theta - 2 S_s \sin 2\theta = 0$$

[1] For example, if S_n represents a compressive stress of 12,000 lb. per sq. in. and S_s represents shearing stresses of 5,000 lb. per sq. in., in directions opposite to those shown in Fig. 324, equation (2) would be written

$$S_n' = \frac{(-12,000)}{2} - \frac{(-12,000)}{2} \cos 2\theta - (-5,000) \sin 2\theta, \text{etc.}$$

from which

$$\tan 2\,\theta_s = -\,\frac{S_n}{2\,S_s} \tag{3}$$

where θ_s is that value of θ which gives maximum S_s. There are two values of $2\,\theta_s$, 180° apart, for any given value of $\tan 2\,\theta_s$; and consequently there are two values of θ_s which differ by 90°. This result is consistent with the fact, previously demonstrated, that equal shearing stresses exist on mutually perpendicular planes at a point. The value of $\tan 2\,\theta_s$ is negative as given in formula (3) if both S_n and S_s are positive, or both negative; if one is positive and the other negative the sign of $\tan 2\,\theta_s$ will be plus. If $\tan 2\,\theta_s$ is minus, the smaller value of θ will be between 45° and 90°; if $\tan 2\,\theta_s$ is plus, the smaller value of θ will be between 0° and 45°.

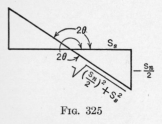

The maximum value of S_s' is found by substituting in equation (1) the values of $\sin 2\,\theta$ and $\cos 2\,\theta$ corresponding to $\tan 2\,\theta = -\,\dfrac{S_n}{2\,S_s}$. The values of these functions

FIG. 325

are conveniently found by constructing right triangles as shown in Fig. 325, in which it is evident that

$$\tan 2\,\theta = -\,\frac{S_n}{2\,S_s}$$

From this triangle

$$\sin 2\,\theta = -\,\frac{S_n}{2\sqrt{\left(\dfrac{S_n}{2}\right)^2 + S_s^2}} \quad\text{and}\quad \cos 2\,\theta = \frac{S_s}{\sqrt{\left(\dfrac{S_n}{2}\right)^2 + S_s^2}}$$

Substituting these values in equation (1),

$$\text{max. } S_s' = +\,\frac{S_n}{2}\times\frac{S_n}{2\sqrt{\left(\dfrac{S_n}{2}\right)^2 + S_s^2}} + S_s \times \frac{S_s}{\sqrt{\left(\dfrac{S_n}{2}\right)^2 + S_s^2}}$$

$$= \sqrt{\left(\dfrac{S_n}{2}\right)^2 + S_s^2} \tag{4}$$

Inspection of this equation shows that, if S_n is small compared with S_s, the maximum S_s' is only slightly greater than S_s. When S_n is large compared with S_s, the maximum S_s' is only slightly greater than $S_n/2$. Also the value of the maximum S_s' is independent of the signs of S_s and

S_n. However, the planes on which S'_s is maximum are different for different combinations of signs of S_s and S_n.

Example. At a point A in a certain beam shearing stresses of 7,000 lb. per sq. in. exist on horizontal and vertical planes and tensile stress of 12,000 lb. per sq. in. acts on vertical planes as shown in Fig. 326(b). Determine the maximum shearing stress and the directions of the plane of maximum shearing stress. The maximum shearing stress is:

Solution:

$$\text{max. } S'_s = \sqrt{\left(\frac{S_n}{2}\right)^2 + S_s^2} = \sqrt{6{,}000^2 + 7{,}000^2} = 9{,}220 \text{ lb. per sq. in.}$$

The planes of maximum shearing stress are found thus:

$$\tan 2\,\theta = -\frac{S_n}{2\,S_s} = -\frac{12{,}000}{14{,}000} = -0.857$$

Whence $2\,\theta = 139°\,24'$ and $319°\,24'$ and $\theta = 69°\,42'$ and $159°\,42'$ with the direction of normal stress.

The directions of the maximum shearing stresses are shown in Fig. 326(c).

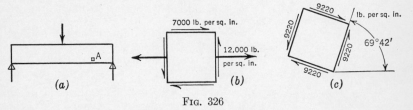

(a) (b) (c)

Fig. 326

PROBLEM

Verify the maximum shearing stresses and the direction of the stresses by taking a wedge as a body in equilibrium. (Two cases may be considered: (a) the inclined plane sloping upward to the right $69°\,42'$ above the horizontal; (b) the inclined plane sloping upward to the left $20°\,18'$ above the horizontal.)

191. Principal Stresses. The maximum and minimum normal stresses at a point in a stressed body are called the *principal stresses* at that point, and the planes on which the principal stresses act are called the *principal planes* at that point. It will be shown that the two principal planes at a point are mutually perpendicular and that on the principal planes there are no shearing stresses.

In Art. 189 it was shown that, for a case of one given normal stress combined with shearing stresses, the resulting normal stress on a plane making an angle of θ with the direction of the given normal stress is given by

$$S'_n = \frac{S_n}{2} - \frac{S_n}{2}\cos 2\,\theta - S_s \sin 2\,\theta \tag{2}$$

The maximum value of S_n' will occur on a plane so inclined that

$$\frac{dS_n'}{d\theta} = 0 + S_n \sin 2\,\theta - 2\,S_s \cos 2\,\theta = 0$$

from which $\tan 2\,\theta_n = 2\,S_s/S_n$ where θ_n is the value of θ for which S_n is maximum. Since, for maximum shearing stresses, $\tan 2\,\theta_s = -S_n/2\,S_s$, it is seen that $2\,\theta_s$ for maximum shearing stress and $2\,\theta_n$ for maximum normal stress differ by 90° and consequently the planes on which shearing stresses are maximum make angles of 45° with the principal planes.

There is no shearing stress upon the principal planes. This is easily shown as follows: The equation for shearing stress along any plane making an angle θ with the horizontal is

$$S_s' = -\frac{S_n}{2}\sin 2\,\theta + S_s \cos 2\,\theta$$

If this is equated to zero and solved for θ, it is seen that

$$\tan 2\,\theta = \frac{2\,S_s}{S_n}$$

which gives the same value for θ for planes of zero shearing stress as was found for the planes of maximum and minimum normal stress.

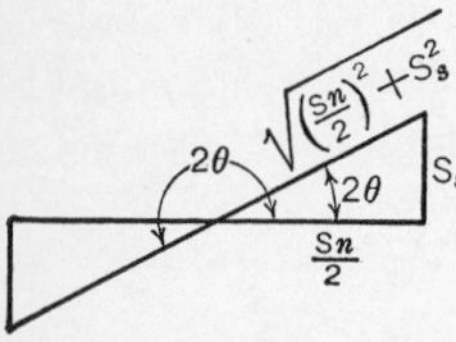

FIG. 327

The maximum and minimum values of S_n' are found by substituting in equation (2) the values for $\sin 2\,\theta$ and $\cos 2\,\theta$ corresponding to $\tan 2\,\theta_n = 2\,S_s/S_n$. By constructing the right triangles (Fig. 327) with one leg equal to S_s and one leg equal to $S_n/2$ (making $\tan 2\theta = 2\,S_s/S_n$) the following values are obtained

$$\sin 2\,\theta_n = \pm \frac{S_s}{\sqrt{\left(\dfrac{S_n}{2}\right)^2 + S_s^2}} \quad \text{and} \quad \cos 2\,\theta_n = \pm \frac{\dfrac{S_n}{2}}{\sqrt{\left(\dfrac{S_n}{2}\right)^2 + S_s^2}}$$

Putting these values in equation (2)

$$\text{max. } S_n' = \frac{S_n}{2} \mp \frac{\left(\dfrac{S_n}{2}\right)^2}{\sqrt{\left(\dfrac{S_n}{2}\right)^2 + S_s}} \mp \frac{S_s^2}{\sqrt{\left(\dfrac{S_n}{2}\right)^2 + S_s}}$$

$$= \frac{S_n}{2} \mp \sqrt{\left(\frac{S_n}{2}\right)^2 + S_s^2} \tag{5}$$

Since $\sqrt{\left(\dfrac{S_n}{2}\right)^2 + S_s^2}$ is the maximum shearing stress, as found in Art. 190, this equation states that the principal stresses equal one-half the given normal stress plus and minus, respectively, the maximum shearing stress.

Unless S_s is zero, $\sqrt{\left(\dfrac{S_n}{2}\right)^2 + S_s^2}$ is always greater than $S_n/2$. It follows that one principal stress will be plus or tension and the other principal stress will be minus or compression. Also the greater principal stress will be of the same kind as the given normal stress.

The principal stress determined by the upper $(-)$ sign before the radical in equation (5) occurs on the plane determined by the *upper sign* (which is the same as the sign of S_s) for sin 2 θ_n. This relation is sufficient to determine on which of the two perpendicular planes each of the principal stresses acts. However, if any doubt exists as to the correctness of the angle computed for the plane on which the maximum principal stress exists, it may be easily verified by taking a wedge-shaped particle with the inclined face parallel to the direction found for the principal plane. The forces on the three faces should be calculated, assuming the area of the inclined face to be unity. If the angle is correct, the sum of all components normal to the inclined face is equal to the calculated principal stress and the sum of the components parallel to the inclined face equals zero (there being no shearing stress upon a principal plane).

Example. At four different points in a certain beam a normal stress of 12,000 lb. per sq. in. acts upon a vertical plane and shearing stresses of 7,000 lb. per sq. in. act on horizontal and vertical planes. For each of the four possible combinations shown in Fig. 328, determine the principal stresses and the planes on which the principal stresses act.

Case (a). $S_n = +12,000$ lb. per sq. in., $S_s = +7,000$ lb. per sq. in.

$$\text{max. } S_n' = \frac{S_n}{2} \mp \sqrt{\left(\frac{S_n}{2}\right)^2 + S_s^2} = +6,000 \mp \sqrt{6,000^2 + 7,000^2} = +6,000 \mp 9,220$$

$$= -3,220 \text{ lb. per sq. in. (compression), or}$$
$$+15,220 \text{ lb. per sq. in. (tension)}$$

The angle with the direction of the normal stress (horizontal) is found from

$$\tan 2\,\theta = \frac{2\,S_s}{S_n} = \frac{+14,000}{+12,000} = \frac{7}{6}\,, \text{ hence}$$

$$2\,\theta = 49°\,24' \text{ or } 229°\,24' \text{ and } \theta = .24°\,42' \text{ and } 114°\,42'$$

The upper sign for sin 2 θ is $+$ since the shearing stress is $+$ and sin 2 θ is $+$ for 2 $\theta = 49°\,24'$, consequently the principal stress (determined by the upper sign) of 3,220 lb. per sq. in. compression acts on the plane making the angle of 24° 42' with the horizontal. The principal stresses are those shown in Fig. 329.

The stress on the plane sloping 24° 42′ with the horizontal may be verified by taking a wedge and calculating the equilibrant normal to the inclined face. If this plane is a principal plane the shearing stress on it is zero. Fig. 330 shows this wedge. The area of the inclined face is taken as unity. Consequently the unit

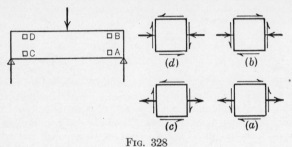

FIG. 328

stress on the inclined face has the same value as the force. Sin 24° 42′ = 0.4179, cos 24° 42′ = 0.9085. The normal and shearing forces on the vertical and horizontal faces are

12,000 × 0.4179 = 5,014 lb., 7,000 × 0.4179 = 2,925 lb., 7,000 × 0.9085 = 6,359 lb.

The normal and parallel components are found from these and are as shown. Note that the resultant of the normal components is 3,220 lb. which is upward and to the left. Consequently the normal force on the inclined face is 3,220 lb. downward and to the right. The normal stress is therefore 3,220 lb. per sq. in. compression. The resultant of the components parallel to the inclined plane is zero, and consequently there is no shearing stress on the inclined plane as must be the case if it is a principal plane.

If the given stresses act as shown in Fig. 328(b), S_s is plus and S_n is minus, and tan 2 θ = −7/6 and θ = 65° 18′ or 155° 18′.

The principal stresses are

−6,000 ∓ 9,220 = −15,220 lb. per sq. in. or +3,220 lb. per sq. in.

The compressive stress (−15,220 lb. per sq. in.) occurs on the plane for which sin 2 θ is + which is the plane for which θ = 65° 18′.

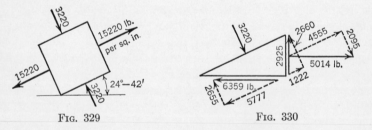

FIG. 329   FIG. 330

For the case illustrated in Fig. 328(c), S_s is minus and S_n is plus, and tan 2 θ = −7/6 and θ = 65° 18′ or 155° 18′. The principal stresses are +6,000 ∓ 9,220 = −3,220 lb. per sq. in. and +15,220 lb. per sq. in. The compressive stress of 3,220 lb. per sq. in. occurs on the plane for which sin 2 θ is minus, which is the plane for which θ = 155° 18′.

With the given stresses as shown in Fig. 328(d), both S_s and S_n are negative and tan $2\ \theta = +7/6$ and $\theta = 24°\ 42'$ and $114°\ 42'$. The principal stresses are

$$-6,000 \mp 9,220 = -15,220 \text{ lb. per sq. in. and } +3,220 \text{ lb. per sq. in.}$$

The compressive stress of 15,220 lb. per sq. in. occurs on planes for which sin $2\ \theta$ is minus and for which θ equals $114°\ 42'$.[1]

PROBLEMS

1. Verify, by considering a wedge in equilibrium, the results found for cases illustrated in Fig. 328(b), (c), and (d).

2. For values of S_s/S_n of 0, 0.1, 0.5, 1.0 and 2.0, calculate values of the principal stresses in terms of the given normal stress. Show the results in the form of a curve.

3. In a boiler shell, subject to internal pressure, longitudinal tensile stress exists, and also circumferential stress which is twice the longitudinal stress. Do stresses greater than the circumferential stress exist? If so, on what planes? If not, why not? Discuss fully.

192. Principal Stresses in a Body Subjected to Pure Shear. It is possible for a body to be loaded in such a way that at certain points there are planes on which nothing but shearing stresses exist. This is true of a shaft subjected to torsion only. In that case, there is a shearing stress on transverse planes and on axial planes, but no normal stresses exist on either transverse or axial planes. As another illustration, at a cross-section of an overhanging beam where there is an inflection point ($M = 0$) there are longitudinal and transverse shearing stresses but no normal (flexural) stresses. At any point where this stress condition occurs, the material is said to be in a state of " pure shear."

In this case the maximum normal stresses become $\pm S_s$ and the angle $2\ \theta$ becomes 90°. Evidently, then, in a body at a point where only shearing stresses exist on two mutually perpendicular planes, there are resulting tensile and compressive principal stresses of the same magnitude as the shearing stresses, on planes making angles of 45° with the planes of shearing stress. This result can be obtained directly by equating the forces normal to the inclined planes to zero.

An example of the effect of such stresses is afforded by the failure, under torsional loads, of a cylinder made of some material having a tensile strength less than its shearing strength. A common chalk crayon, twisted until it fractures, illustrates this. The tensile fracture of a round cast-iron rod tested in torsion is shown in Fig. 331.

The existence of these tensile and compressive stresses resulting from shear may be visualized by considering the corresponding deformations.

[1] Maximum stresses in a steel wide-flange beam are calculated and their importance discussed in Art. 252. That article can be studied at this point, if desired.

Fig. 332 represents a cylinder subject to torsion. Upon the surface of this cylinder, before the torsional forces were applied, two parallel lines

FIG. 331. Tensile failure of a cast-iron torsion specimen.

(elements of the cylindrical surface) were drawn and two lines were drawn around the cylinder. The included area, $ABCD$, was rectangular

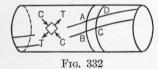

FIG. 332

before the torsional deformation occurred, but during the deformation the diagonal BD lengthens and AC shortens. These deformations are in the directions of the tensile stress and the compressive stress respectively.

193. Bending Combined with Torsion in a Circular Shaft. The transverse loads due to belt tensions, weights of pulleys, etc., and of the shafting itself cause bending stresses which in many instances are not negligible compared with the shearing stresses due to torsion.

The formulas derived in Arts. 190 and 191 may be applied to these cases to find the maximum resultant shearing stresses and the maximum resultant tension or compression. However, for circular shafts the solution may be expressed in more convenient formulas.

The shearing stress in the extreme fibers of a circular shaft, as given by the common torsion formula, is $S_s = Tc/J$, and the bending stress is $S_b = Mc/I$. In these two formulas, $J = 2I$ for either a solid or hollow circular shaft. The maximum resultant shearing stress is

$$\text{max. } S_s' = \sqrt{\left(\frac{S_b}{2}\right)^2 + S_s^2} = \sqrt{\frac{M^2c^2}{J^2} + \frac{T^2c^2}{J^2}} = \frac{c}{J}\sqrt{M^2 + T^2}$$

or

$$\frac{S_s'J}{c} = \sqrt{M^2 + T^2}$$

In the case of a shaft so supported or loaded that no bending moment acts on it, this reduces to $\dfrac{S_sJ}{c} = T$, as it should.

The maximum resultant tensile or compressive stress is

$$\text{max. } S' = \frac{S_b}{2} + \sqrt{\left(\frac{S_b}{2}\right)^2 + S_s^2} = \frac{Mc}{2\,I} + \frac{c}{2\,I}\sqrt{M^2 + T^2}$$

$$= \frac{M + \sqrt{M^2 + T^2}}{2} \times \frac{c}{I}$$

This obviously reduces to the flexure formula, $S = Mc/I$, when the torsional moment is reduced to zero.

If, for a given material used as shafting, allowable shearing, tensile, and compressive stresses are specified, the *resultant* maximum shearing and normal stresses as given by the above formulas should not exceed the respective specified allowable stresses.

The form of the equation $\dfrac{S_s'J}{c} = \sqrt{M^2 + T^2}$ indicates that a curve may easily be constructed from which may be read the amount of torque and bending moment which together will cause a given maximum shearing stress in a shaft of a given size. The curve is a circular arc, the radius being equal to the resisting torque $S_s J/c$. The center of the circle is the origin, and M and T are respectively ordinates and abscissas to any point on the arc.

The equation

$$\frac{SI}{c} = \frac{M + \sqrt{M^2 + T^2}}{2}$$

may also be represented by a curve for a given allowable S and for a given diameter of shaft. In Fig. 333, curves are drawn for an allowable

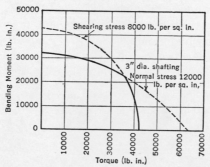

Fig. 333.   The ordinate and abscissa of a point on the curve are the allowable simultaneous bending moment and torque, respectively.

normal stress of 12,000 lb. per sq. in. and allowable shearing stress of 8,000 lb. per sq. in., both curves for 3-in.-diameter shafting. For these allowable stresses the curves show that, for torques less than 37,000 lb-in., the normal stress limits the torque and bending moment while for greater torques the shearing stress limits the torque and bending moment.

PROBLEMS

1. A handbook gives for shafting subject to bending moment and torque this formula for determining the diameter:

$$d = \sqrt[3]{\frac{5.1}{S}\left(M + \sqrt{M^2 + T^2} \right)}$$

and adds that for ductile materials it is well to check the value of d by means of

$$d = \sqrt[3]{\frac{5.1}{S} \sqrt{M^2 + T^2}}$$

In these formulas S is defined as the " fiber stress in pounds per square inch." Are these formulas rational? Do they apply to hollow shafting? Should S be the same in the two formulas? Discuss fully.

2. Plot curves representing the combined allowable bending moment and torsional moment for 2-in.-diameter shafting. One curve is for values as limited by maximum normal stress of 12,000 lb. per sq. in., and the other curve as limited by maximum resultant shearing stress of 8,000 lb. per sq. in. Ordinates of curves are to be bending moments, and abscissas are to be torsional moments, both in pound-inches. Both curves are to be plotted on the same set of axes.

3. If S_s and S_t are the allowable shearing and tensile stresses, what is the greatest ratio of S_s to S_t in order that the allowable torque and bending moment will be determined by S_s for all allowable combinations of T and M? *Ans.* $S_s = 0.5\,S_t$.

4. In the derivation of the formulas of this article no consideration was given to shearing stresses which exist because of beam action although in cantilever shafts the maximum shear and maximum bending moment may occur at the same section. Is the ignoring of shear due to beam action justified, and if so why?

GENERAL PROBLEMS

1. At a point in the web of an I-beam the bending stress is compression and equals 16,250 lb. per sq. in. The shearing stress is 11,400 lb. per sq. in. and is the result of negative total shear. Calculate the maximum shearing stresses at this point and the inclinations of the planes on which they exist.

2. For the condition stated in Problem 1, calculate the principal stresses and the inclinations of the principal planes. Check the results by considering the equilibrium of two wedges, each having an inclined face in the direction of one of the principal planes.

3. A 3-in.-diameter solid shaft is subjected to a torque of 42,400 lb-in. and a bending moment of 28,000 lb-in. (*a*) Calculate the maximum shearing stress and the inclinations of the planes of maximum shearing stress. (*b*) Calculate the principal stresses and the inclinations of the principal planes. Draw a diagram illustrating these stresses.   *Ans.* (*a*) S'_s = 9,600 lb. per. sq. in.

4. The load P in Fig. 334 is 4,800 lb. The cross-section at AB is rectangular, 2.5 in. by 1 in. Calculate the principal stresses at a point on the cross-section AB which is 0.5 in. from B. (Note that the shearing stress due to P is not uniform over AB.)

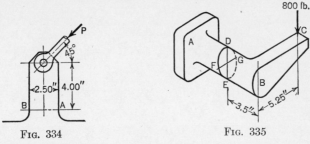

FIG. 334   FIG. 335

5. The longitudinal stress in a boiler shell is 5,000 lb. per sq. in. and the circumferential stress 10,000 lb. per sq. in. If Poisson's ratio is 0.25, what tensile stress acting alone would produce the same maximum unit elongation?

6. The bracket shown in Fig. 335 supports a load of 800 lb. as shown. The diameter of AB is 2.0 in. Calculate the principal stresses and the maximum shearing stresses at D, and the inclinations of the planes on which the stresses act.

$Ans.$ $S_s' = 3,215$ lb. per sq. in.

7. Calculate the principal stresses and the maximum shearing stresses at F or G (whichever has the larger shearing stresses) in the bracket shown in Fig. 335. Note that at F and at G there are shearing stresses due to the action of AB as a cantilever beam.

8. A rivet joining two plates is subject to a shearing stress in one plane of 12,000 lb. per sq. in. and to tensile stress due to cooling of 10,000 lb. per sq. in. Calculate the maximum shearing stress and the principal stresses and the inclination of the planes on which the maximum stresses occur.

CHAPTER XVI

COMBINED STRESSES (continued)

(The principles developed in this chapter are not referred to in subsequent chapters of this book. This chapter may therefore be omitted.)

194. Introduction. The case of two given normal stresses combined with given shearing stresses is considered and formulas are derived for maximum shearing stress and for the principal stresses. Relationships between principal stresses and the "resultant total stress" on planes inclined to the principal planes are derived and the "ellipse of stress" is discussed. The relationship between E and E_s in terms of Poisson's ratio is derived and, finally, "theories of failure" are considered.

195. Normal Stresses in Two Directions Combined with Shearing Stresses. At points where loads are applied to beams it is apparent that normal stresses are introduced in a direction perpendicular to the normal stresses due to bending. Other examples of the occurrence of this stress condition are found in structures and in machine parts. However, the greatest importance of this case is in connection with the design of massive structures subject to constraint in several directions. Dams, arches, etc., are of this sort.

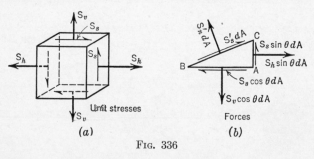

Unit stresses

(a)

Forces

(b)

Fig. 336

An infinitesimal cube taken from a point in a stressed body is shown in Fig. 336 (a), and the arrows indicate the unit stresses. The first problem is to determine, as was done (Art. 190) for a single normal stress, the amount of the resultant maximum shearing stress and the direction of the plane on which it acts. Fig. 336 (b) shows the forces which these stresses cause on the three faces of a wedge the inclined face of which makes an angle θ with the direction of the stress S_h. As with a

270

single given normal stress, the signs of the given normal stresses are to be regarded as plus if tension and minus if compression, and the given shearing stress is plus if as shown in Fig. 336 (a).   If this convention is followed throughout the computations, the signs of the final results will be consistent; that is, plus and minus will mean tension and compression respectively.

Placing the sum of all forces parallel to BC equal to zero and solving for S_s, the following equation is obtained:

$$S_s' = S_v \sin \theta \cos \theta - S_h \sin \theta \cos \theta + S_s (\cos^2 \theta - \sin^2 \theta)$$

$$= -\frac{S_h - S_v}{2} \sin 2\theta + S_s \cos 2\theta$$

Placing the derivative of S_s' with respect to θ equal to zero, it is found that, for the plane of maximum resultant shearing stress, $\tan 2\theta = -\frac{S_h - S_v}{2 S_s}$.   Substituting the values for $\sin 2\theta$ and $\cos 2\theta$ corresponding to this value for $\tan 2\theta$, the maximum shearing stress becomes:

$$\text{max. } S_s' = \sqrt{\left(\frac{S_h - S_v}{2}\right)^2 + S_s^2}$$

The equation for normal stress is derived by placing the sum of all normal components equal to zero.   Note that $S_v dA \cos^2 \theta$ may be written $S_v dA \left(\frac{1 + \cos 2\theta}{2}\right)$.   Solving for the normal stress on the plane making an angle θ with S_n:

$$S_n' = S_h \left(\frac{1 - \cos 2\theta}{2}\right) + S_v \left(\frac{1 + \cos 2\theta}{2}\right) - S_s \sin 2\theta$$

$$= \frac{S_v + S_h}{2} + \frac{S_v - S_h}{2} \cos 2\theta - S_s \sin 2\theta$$

This gives for the direction of the planes of maximum normal stresses or principal planes

$$\tan 2\theta = -\frac{2 S_s}{S_v - S_h}$$

The two principal stresses are given by the equation

$$\text{max. } S_n' = \frac{S_h + S_v}{2} \pm \sqrt{\left(\frac{S_v - S_h}{2}\right)^2 + S_s^2}$$

The value found by using the same sign for both terms is the maximum principal stress, that found by using opposite signs being the minimum principal stress. Note that the principal stresses are equal to half the algebraic sum of the given normal stresses plus and minus respectively the maximum shearing stress which results from the same given stresses. It may be shown that the planes of zero shearing stress are also given by $\tan 2\,\theta = -\dfrac{2\,S_s}{S_v - S_h}$, and it consequently follows that along the planes of maximum and minimum normal stress there is no shearing stress.

It will also be observed that the value of $\tan 2\,\theta_s$ for the planes of maximum shearing stress is the reciprocal of the value of $\tan 2\,\theta$ for maximum normal stress.   Consequently the planes of maximum shearing stress are at 45° with the plane of maximum normal stress.

It should be noted that the stress condition discussed in the foregoing chapter (one normal stress combined with shearing stresses) is merely a special case of this more general stress condition, and that, if S_v (or S_h) is made equal to zero, all the equations of this article reduce to those of the foregoing chapter.

PROBLEMS

1. Calculate the principal stresses which exist at a point where the shearing and normal stresses on 30° and 60° planes are those shown in Fig. 322(d). Also calculate the maximum shearing stresses.

2. A short piece of 2-in. standard pipe with ends sealed is shown in Fig. 337. A force P of 5,400 lb. is applied to the ends, and two forces F apply a torque of 3,200 lb-in. to the upper end, the lower end being fixed to prevent rotation.   An internal pressure of 800 lb. per sq. in. exists. Calculate the principal stresses and the inclination of the principal planes at a point in the outer surface.   Also calculate the maximum shearing stress at the same point.

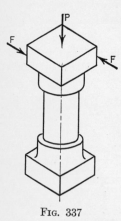

FIG. 337

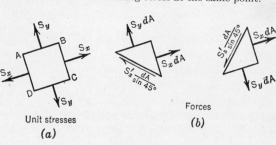

Unit stresses

(a)

Forces

(b)

FIG. 338

196. Maximum Shearing Stress in Terms of Principal Stresses. A simple expression for the maximum shearing stress at a given point in a stressed body is easily obtained in terms of the principal stresses at that point. Fig. 338 (a) represents a cube of infinitesimal size with faces

taken parallel to the principal planes of stress. S_x and S_y are the principal stresses. As was shown in previous articles, the diagonal planes AC and BD (Fig. 338 b) are planes of maximum shearing stress. The intensity of this shearing stress equals

$$S_s' = \frac{S_x dA \sin 45° - S_y dA \sin 45°}{\dfrac{dA}{\sin 45°}} = (S_x - S_y) \sin^2 45° = \frac{S_x - S_y}{2}$$

In words, the maximum shearing stress at a given point equals half of the difference between the principal stresses. Note that larger shears result if the principal stresses are of opposite kinds.

This result may also be reached by the principle of " summation of effects " or " superposition," noting that each principal stress causes a maximum shearing stress of one-half its intensity on the 45° plane. If both principal stresses are of the same character the shearing stress due to one is opposite in direction to that due to the other. In photoelastic stress analysis a transparent loaded model is viewed by transmitted polarized monochromatic light. Alternate light and dark bands appear. Each of these is a contour line at all points of which there is a constant difference between the two principal stresses. Since, as was shown above, the maximum shearing stress at any point equals $\dfrac{S_x - S_y}{2}$, it follows that any dark or light band is a contour of constant intensity of maximum shearing stress.

PROBLEM

At a given point in a body the principal stresses are 3,000 lb. per sq. in. and 7,000 lb. per sq. in. Calculate the maximum shearing stresses: (a) if both stresses are tension; (b) if the larger stress is tension and the smaller stress is compression.

197. Resultant of Stresses on Different Planes at a Point, Ellipse of Stress. If axes of reference are chosen which have the directions of the principal stresses, simple expressions for the resultant of the stresses on any inclined plane may be found, since there are no shearing stresses in the directions of the axes. If, in the wedge shown in Fig. 339, the area of the plane AB is unity, the areas of other planes are, respectively, $\sin \theta$ and $\cos \theta$. If x and y are the respective components of the resultant total stress on AB, then $x = S_x' \sin \theta$ and $y = S_y' \cos \theta$, which are parametric

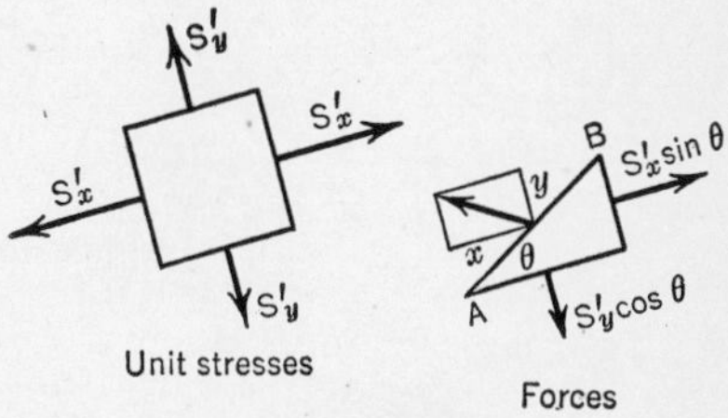

Unit stresses

Forces

Fig. 339

equations of an ellipse.[1] It follows that the " resultant total stresses " on all planes, if laid off from a point, form the semi-diameters of an ellipse called the " ellipse of stress," the major axis of which is the maximum principal stress and the minor axis of which is the minimum principal stress. It is frequently not realized that this " resultant total stress " is not in a direction normal to the plane (except for the two planes parallel to the principal stresses) and, consequently, it is not a stress in the commonly accepted meaning of that term, being neither tension, compression, nor shear. It is a force divided by an area, but the force is oblique to the area.

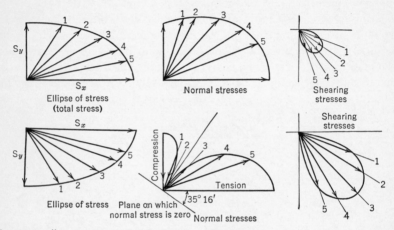

FIG. 340. " Total stress," normal stress, and shearing stress on principal planes and planes inclined to horizontal (1) 160°, (2) 150°, (3) 135°, (4) 120°, (5) 110°. Horizontal principal stresses are twice the vertical. Upper group, principal stresses both tension. Lower group, horizontal stress, tension; vertical stress, compression.

Fig. 340 shows, for two cases of principal stresses and for planes making angles in the second quadrant, the " total resultant stress " and the corresponding part of the ellipse of stress. The radii of a second set of curves show the normal stresses in amount and direction. The radii of a third set show the variation in shearing stress.

[1] By eliminating θ from these two equations the standard equation for the ellipse results:

$$\sin \theta = \frac{x}{S'_x} \quad \text{and} \quad \cos \theta = \frac{y}{S'_y}$$

But $\sin^2 \theta + \cos^2 \theta = 1$; hence

$$\frac{x^2}{S'^2_x} + \frac{y^2}{S'^2_y} = 1$$

which is the equation for an ellipse having semi-major axes S'_x and S'_y.

PROBLEMS

1. By considering the equilibrium of a wedge-shaped particle, determine the amount and inclination of the " total stress " (the radius of the ellipse of stress) corresponding to a plane making an angle of 30° with the greater stress for a point in a body where the principal stresses are 12,000 lb. per sq. in. and 5,000 lb. per sq. in., both tension.

2. Solve Problem 1 if the 5,000 lb. per sq. in. is compression.

198. E and E_s in Terms of Poisson's Ratio. It is shown in Art. 192 that, if shearing stresses alone act on two mutually perpendicular planes, principal stresses of the same intensity as the shearing stresses, and of opposite kinds from one another, act on planes at 45° with the planes of shearing stress. Using this fact there may be derived a relation between the modulus of elasticity E and the shearing modulus of elasticity E_s, in terms of Poisson's ratio, m. Consider a point in a stressed body (such as a point on the surface of a shaft) where only shearing stresses S_s exist on mutually perpendicular planes (Fig. 341a). Now suppose at this

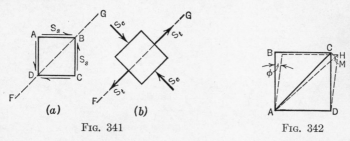

(a)   (b)

Fig. 341   Fig. 342

same point, O, a cube (Fig. 341b) is taken with sides at 45° to those of the previous cube. It has already been shown that on the faces of this cube there will be no shearing stresses and that the tensile and compressive unit stresses will equal the shearing unit stresses at 45°, or in other words S_s, S_t, and S_c are numerically equal. Now in this stressed body a certain *unit* deformation (elongation) occurs along the line FG^1. Obviously this may be regarded either as resulting from the stresses S_s in (a) or from the stresses S_c and S_t in (b).

The unit elongation in the diagonal direction due to S_s is equal to $S_s/2 E_s$. This may be shown as follows: In Fig. 342 the total elongation is MH and the unit elongation $= MH/AM$ since the angle is very small.

But $MH = CH \cos 45° = CD \times \dfrac{S_s}{E_s} \cos 45°$ and $AC = \dfrac{CD}{\cos 45°}$. Hence

---

[1] It must be kept in mind that at point O a certain state of stress exists and this state of stress is accompanied by deformations, the deformation along FG being the only one considered here. Fig. 341a and b represent in two different ways the state of stress that results in the deformation which exists along FG.

the unit elongation along AC due to S_s is

$$\delta = \frac{MH}{AC} = \frac{CD\dfrac{S_s}{E_s}\cos 45°}{\dfrac{CD}{\cos 45°}} = \frac{1}{2}\frac{S_s}{E_s}$$

The unit elongation along FG due to S_t and S_c is

$$\delta = \frac{S_t}{E} + m\frac{S_c}{E} = \frac{S_s}{E} + m\frac{S_s}{E}$$

since $S_s = S_t = S_c$. Equating these two different values for the same unit elongation,

$$\frac{1}{2}\frac{S_s}{E_s} = \frac{S_s}{E} + m\frac{S_s}{E}$$

whence

$$E_s = \frac{E}{2(1 + m)}$$

If $m = \frac{1}{4}$, as is commonly assumed for steel, $E_s = \frac{2}{5}E$.

PROBLEM

Calculate E_s for the following metals:

Aluminum alloy; $E = 10,000,000$ lb. per sq. in., $m = 0.36$
Brass; $E = 16,000,000$ lb. per sq. in., $m = 0.33$
Monel metal; $E = 25,000,000$ lb. per sq. in., $m = 0.26$

199. Theories of Failure. As the forces or loads acting on an elastic body are gradually increased, stresses and deformations also increase until, at some point in the body where unit stresses are high and unit deformations are large, failure occurs. Failure as here used means either one of two things. Failure or " elastic breakdown " of a ductile material begins when its elastic behavior ends and permanent set begins. Failure of a brittle material occurs when rupture occurs, which, for a perfectly brittle material, is also when its elastic behavior ends. The body or member as a whole may not have failed, but at some point " elastic breakdown " of the material has begun.

The elastic strength of a material is commonly determined by tests of axially loaded prisms, and in such prisms only a single principal stress exists. The same material used in a member of a machine or structure is, in general, subjected to a much more complicated state of stress. Is it rational to base the design of members subjected to very complex states of stress on the allowable stresses determined from tests involving a much simpler stress? Obviously the answer to this question depends upon a knowledge of the true causes of failure. The conclusions of investigators have been presented as " theories of failure," and a number of these have been proposed. Four of the best known ones are presented and discussed here.[1]

200. The Maximum Stress Theory. According to this theory, failure or elastic breakdown occurs when the maximum principal stress becomes equal to the corresponding yield point (or ultimate strength, if the material is brittle). This is the oldest and simplest of the various theories (and is sometimes called Rankine's theory of failure). It assumes that the effect of the maximum principal stress is not modified by the presence of the principal stress at right angles. The theory, in the form stated above, will not in general apply to materials having a shearing elastic limit considerably below the tensile (or compressive) elastic limit, for the reasons given below. With two principal stresses of opposite sorts (one tension, one compression), the maximum shearing stress equals half the numerical sum of the two principal stresses. Therefore for a case of loading such as to cause two nearly equal principal stresses of opposite character the shearing stress will nearly equal the principal stress. Therefore failure could not occur in the manner specified by the theory unless the material has a shearing elastic limit nearly equal to its tensile and compressive elastic limits. This seems improbable for many materials. The theory is sometimes stated in the form given below, which considerably widens its possible application.

Failure will occur when the maximum principal stress equals the corresponding elastic limit or when the maximum shearing stress equals the shearing elastic limit. This theory is the basis of most structural design as commonly carried out.

201. Maximum Shear Theory. According to this theory (generally attributed to J. J. Guest) elastic breakdown occurs (yielding begins) when the maximum shearing stress in a loaded member becomes equal to the maximum shearing stress that exists in a tensile specimen of the same material when stressed to the elastic limit. The maximum shear theory assumes that failure, both in the tensile test specimen and in the member with more complex loading, results from shearing stress.

For the case of principal stresses in two directions the maximum shearing stress is $\dfrac{S_x - S_y}{2}$, and for a tensile specimen the maximum shearing stress at the tensile elastic limit is Elastic limit/2. The theory is there-

[1] For extended discussions, see J. Marin, *Trans. Am. Soc. of Civil Engineers*, Vol. 101, 1936, p. 1162, and H. M. Westergaard, *Journal of Franklin Inst.*, Vol. 189, 1920, p. 627.

fore expressed by the equation

$$\frac{S_x - S_y}{2} = \frac{\text{Elastic limit in tension}}{2}$$

If this theory were strictly correct, all tensile specimens should fail on 45° planes. In many ductile materials failure appears to have begun on such planes, and the initial yielding may in fact have occurred on such planes even though the final rupture does not follow these planes. On the other hand, the rupture of a cylinder made of a brittle material in pure torsion indicates failure in tension and in no way resembles a shear failure notwithstanding the fact that shearing stresses are equal to the tensile stresses (Fig. 331). Also the failure of cast iron and other brittle materials under tensile loading does not suggest a shear failure (Fig. 27).

It is rather widely believed that the maximum shear theory applies more or less well to ductile materials but not at all to brittle materials.

202. The Maximum Strain Theory. This theory is attributed to the French elastician, St. Venant. It states that elastic breakdown in a stressed body occurs when the maximum *unit elongation* becomes equal to the maximum unit elongation existing in a tensile test specimen at the elastic limit or when the maximum unit shortening becomes equal to the maximum unit shortening in a compression member at the elastic limit.

In a stressed body the unit deformation in the direction of the maximum principal stress is $\delta = \dfrac{S_{\text{max.}}}{E} \pm m\,\dfrac{S_{\text{min.}}}{E}$ in which m is Poisson's ratio.

It follows that, if both principal stresses are tensile stresses, failure will not occur until the larger principal stress *exceeds* the tensile elastic limit of the material. On the other hand, if the larger principal stress is tension and the lesser compression, failure will occur even if the larger principal stress is somewhat less than the tensile elastic limit.

The maximum strain theory may be expressed by the following equation:

$$\frac{S'_{\text{max.}}}{E} \pm m\,\frac{S'_{\text{min.}}}{E} = \frac{\text{Elastic limit}}{E}$$

203. The Maximum Energy or Maximum Resilience Theory. According to this theory elastic breakdown occurs when, at some point in a loaded member, the energy of deformation per unit of volume has become equal to the maximum energy of deformation per unit of volume in a prism of the same material when stressed to the yield point.

The four theories of failure mentioned are the best known of a number that have been proposed. It is certain none of them can be accepted as a true " theory of failure " for all types of material and of loading.

It is desirable that engineering design should proceed steadily towards the substitution of rational for empirical processes, as rapidly as correct rational processes can be established.   For this reason it is desirable to know exactly what are the conditions of stress and deformation that lead to failure of an elastic material.   At the same time, theories of failure must be based on the assumptions of a perfect and homogeneous material.   It seems probable that failure may actually begin at some microscopic flaw (cavity, particle of foreign matter, etc.) in the material where stress conditions differ materially from those calculated by accepted methods.   Furthermore, even in the absence of flaws, actual stresses generally differ from calculated stresses because of initial stresses which result from methods of fabrication, and which are present even in the unloaded body.

CHAPTER XVII

ELASTIC ENERGY — STRESSES PRODUCED BY MOVING BODIES

204. Elastic Energy. An elastic body that is deformed by external force has energy stored within it. This energy is sometimes called " potential energy of deformation." Other names in common use are " internal work," " strain energy," and " elastic energy." The property of a material which makes it capable of storing elastic energy is called resilience.

The ability of a member to store elastic energy is frequently of great importance in situations where the member is called upon to resist moving bodies. In many such cases most of the kinetic energy of the moving body must be transformed into elastic energy of the resisting member. As will become apparent, the design of members called upon to resist moving bodies may be quite different from the design of members which must resist only static or gradually applied loads.

205. Forces Exerted on or by a Moving Body. When a moving body is brought to rest by forces acting upon the body, *work* (equal to the kinetic energy of the body) is done by the forces. Work is the product of a force and a distance. The greater the distance in which the velocity is reduced to zero, the less is the force required. Therefore the stresses produced are inversely proportional to the distance the body moves while it is being brought to rest.

As an illustration, at the end of a railroad track a " car bumper " (frequently consisting of a large block of reinforced concrete) is ordinarily placed to stop cars. If this relatively rigid block and the relatively rigid frame of the car, were allowed to come into sudden direct contact, the velocity of the car would be destroyed in such a short distance that a very large force would be exerted between car and bumper and injuriously large stresses would be produced in each. To prevent this, a set of coil springs is used to cushion the impact. These springs cause a gradually increasing force to be exerted on the bumper and on the car frame, and permit the car to travel a much greater distance in being brought to rest. The forces and stresses produced are therefore much less than if the car frame came into direct contact with the bumper.

280

In the design of energy-absorbing members (such as the foregoing spring) it is frequently important that the production of the allowable stress should be accompanied by a large amount of total deformation of the member.

206. Elastic Energy of a Prism under Axial Loads. Let a right prism of cross-section A and length L be acted on by axial forces that produce a unit stress of S lb. per sq. in. at all points of any cross-section. Then the unit deformation is S/E (provided the proportional limit of the material is not exceeded) and the total deformation is SL/E. If the body was initially unstressed and if the stress increases proportionally with the deformation, the average unit stress is $S/2$ and the average force exerted on the prism is $SA/2$. Let U be the work done on the prism (or the elastic energy stored in it). Then $U = SA/2 \times SL/E$ or $S^2AL/2\,E$, which equals $S^2/2\,E$ times the volume of the prism. This shows that the energy which can be absorbed by a prism without exceeding a given unit stress is independent of the relative dimensions of the prism, but is a function of the amount of material in it.

207. Modulus of Resilience. The amount of energy *per unit of volume* that a given material stores when stressed to the elastic limit is called the *modulus of resilience* of that material.[1] The modulus of resilience evidently equals $S_e^2/2\,E$, where S_e is the elastic limit. Since the modulus of resilience is proportional to the square of the elastic limit and inversely proportional to E, it follows that a material with a high elastic limit and a low modulus of elasticity is capable of storing a large amount of elastic energy, or of absorbing a large amount of shock without being damaged thereby.

Example. Compare the moduli of resilience of two steels with elastic limits of (a) 30,000 and (b) 150,000 lb. per sq. in., respectively, and (c) an aluminum alloy having an elastic limit of 30,000 lb. per sq. in.

Solution: (a) $\dfrac{S_e^2}{2\,E} = \dfrac{30,000^2}{2 \times 30,000,000} = 15.0$ in-lb. per cu. in.

(b) $\dfrac{S_e^2}{2\,E} = \dfrac{150,000^2}{2 \times 30,000,000} = 375$ in-lb. per cu. in.

(c) $\dfrac{S_e^2}{2\,E} = \dfrac{30,000^2}{2 \times 10,000,000} = 45$ in-lb. per cu. in.

The stronger steel, because of its higher elastic limit, has 25 times the resilience of the weaker; the aluminum alloy, although no stronger than the weaker steel, because of its less stiffness, has three times the resilience.

---

[1] In this chapter it is assumed that the proportional limit and the elastic limit of a material have the same value, as is usual.

PROBLEM

Calculate the modulus of resilience of each of the following materials having the physical properties as given (pounds per square inch):

	E	Proportional Limit
Gray cast iron (tension)	12,000,000	8,000
Gray cast iron (compression)	14,000,000	30,000
Malleable iron	22,000,000	15,000
Hickory	1,800,000	4,000
Spruce	1,200,000	2,500

208. Design of Members to Resist Axial Dynamic Loads. The design of a member which is to resist axial dynamic or moving loads differs in several important ways from the design of a member to receive static loads only. In the first place, Art. 206 shows that the amount of energy which a member can store at a given stress is inversely proportional to the modulus of elasticity of the member. If a choice of materials for a member which is to resist dynamic loads is available, the material with the lowest E may be the most desirable on that account. There is no corresponding consideration in the design of members that resist static loads only.

In the second place, while the maximum unit stress in a prismatic member resisting an axial static load is determined by the size of the *cross-section* of the member, the maximum stress in a prismatic member resisting axial dynamic loads is determined not by the cross-section but by the *volume* of the member. In the static load member, the only way to reduce the maximum stress is to increase the cross-section. In the member resisting dynamic loads, it is just as effective to increase the *length*. The same amount of energy can be absorbed by a small average force F (Fig. 343a) coupled with a large total deformation Δ as by a much larger average force F' coupled with a correspondingly smaller total deformation Δ'. A long member decelerates the moving load less rapidly and therefore absorbs its energy with the exertion of smaller forces on it and therefore with smaller unit stresses. It is sometimes possible to increase the length of a bolt, for example, and thereby materially to decrease the stresses set up in it by a tensile impact load. In Fig. 344a, a cover, which is subject to dynamic loads, is held to a flange by means of bolts. Most of the energy delivered to these bolts must be absorbed in a length l. By the simple expedient of placing a thick washer under the head and nut of each bolt, as shown at b, the length of the bolt material which absorbs most of the energy is increased to l' and materially lower stresses result.

In yet a third way the design of a member to resist dynamic loads differs from design of the static load member. In both members the maximum stress occurs on the minimum cross-section. In the static load member, however, it is only the *minimum* cross-section that determines the maximum stress. Other cross-sections may have *any* (larger) size, and the maximum stress is unaffected. In a member

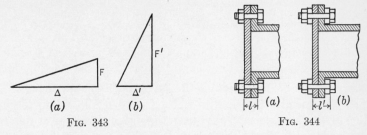

(a)   (b)

FIG. 343

(a)   (b)

FIG. 344

resisting dynamic loads, however, it is very important that there be *no excess of material* but that the cross-sections throughout the greater part of the length of the member *be not materially greater than the minimum cross-section.* The following example illustrates this fact:

Example. Compare the maximum stresses produced in the two cylindrical bodies shown in Fig. 345 by the absorption of U in-lb. of energy.

Solution: For the first body (a) the relationship derived in Art. 206 is

$$U = \frac{S^2}{2E} \times AL, \quad \text{or} \quad S^2 = \frac{2EU}{AL}$$

The second body (b) can be considered to be composed of two cylinders, one with cross-section A and length $0.2 L$ and the other with cross-section $4A$ and length $0.8 L$. For simplicity assume a uniform stress distribution over all cross-sections of each cylinder. Then if the unit stress on cross-section A is S', the unit stress on the cross-section with area $4A$ will be $\frac{1}{4} S'$. Therefore the total energy U stored in the two cylinders is

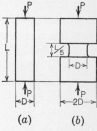

(a)   (b)

FIG. 345

$$U = \frac{S'^2}{2E} \times A \times 0.2 L + \frac{(\frac{1}{4} S')^2}{2E} \times 4A \times 0.8 L = \frac{S'^2 AL}{10 E} + \frac{S'^2 AL}{10 E} = \frac{S'^2 AL}{5 E}$$

whence $S'^2 = \frac{5 EU}{AL}$. Therefore $\frac{S'^2}{S^2} = \frac{5}{2}$, whence $S' = 1.58 S$.

It is very interesting to note that though these two bodies have the same net section, under a dynamic load possessing a given amount of energy the member with the *more* material in it receives 58 per cent higher stress than the member with the less material. The extra material is not only wasted, it is *definitely disadvantageous.* The reason is, of course, that the part of body (b) with the larger cross-section receives so small a unit stress and therefore so small a unit deformation that the energy stored in it is very small. Most of the energy absorbed by (b) is stored in the small cylinder which, though it comprises but one-seventeenth of the total volume of (b), absorbs one-half of the energy. The same amount of material in the prism (a) absorbs only 20 per cent of the energy and is therefore much less highly stressed. It is quite important that members which are to resist dynamic loads should have, so far as practicable, the same amount of material at every cross-section. Therefore bolts which may have to resist energy loads are often turned down so that their diameter through the greater part of their length is equal to the diameter at the root of the thread; or sometimes a hole is drilled through the head of the bolt extending down almost to the beginning of the thread and of such size that the cross-section of the remaining body of the bolt equals the cross-section at the root of the thread (Fig. 346).

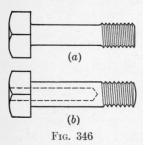

(a)

(b)

Fig. 346

The shorter the length of the part of a tensile or compressive member which has a reduced cross-section, the more severe is the effect in raising the stress under shock loads. A tensile member punched or drilled at the ends for rivets or bolts may be stressed very highly at the reduced cross-sections when subjected to dynamic loading even though its total length is so great that it could absorb a considerable amount of energy with low stress, had it a uniform cross-section throughout. Serious failures have sometimes resulted from disregard of this fact.

PROBLEMS

1. In the example above, what would be the ratio of maximum stresses in bodies (a) and (b) if one-half of the length of the larger cylinder were turned down to diameter d?

2. A machine part is required to resist variable forces causing a certain amount of energy load in each cycle of operation of the machine. Two possible designs are shown in Fig. 347(a) and (b). If the factor of safety of design (a) is 5, what is the factor of safety of design (b)? How do the weights compare?

3. What must be the length of a carbon-steel rod, 1 in. in diameter, if, owing to the application of an axial tensile load, it is to absorb 565 in-lb. of energy without exceeding the proportional limit of 30,000 lb. per sq. in? *Ans.* L = 48 in.

What diameter must a nickel-steel bar of the same length have to absorb the same amount of energy without being stressed above the proportional limit of 50,000 lb. per sq. in.?

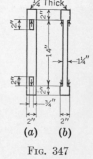

(a)   (b)

Fig. 347

209. Elastic Energy of Bodies Uniformly Stressed in Shear. For a body uniformly stressed in shear it may be shown (in exactly the same way as for tensile or compressive stress) that for stresses below the elastic limit the elastic energy is $U = \dfrac{S_s^2}{2\,E_s} \times$ Volume.   This expression is in the same form as that for the elastic energy of tension or compression. It should be kept in mind, however, that, for equal stresses and a given material, the elastic energy for shear is greater per unit volume since E_s is less than E.   On the other hand, the elastic limit in shear is generally less than that in tension or compression.

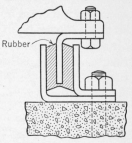

FIG. 348

A good example of the absorption of energy through shearing deformation is furnished by the rubber spring or " sandwich " shown in Fig. 348.   An energy load applied to the central plate is absorbed by the layers of rubber.[1]

210. Elastic Energy of Torsion; Helical Springs.   When a bar is subjected to a torque, a twisting deformation results.   The work done on the bar by the applied torque equals the elastic energy stored in the bar, if the stresses produced do not exceed the elastic limit of the material.

Let U be the number of inch-pounds of work done by a gradually applied external torque whose maximum value is T, acting through an angle θ and acting on a cylindrical bar with polar moment of inertia J, length L, and modulus of rigidity E_s.   Then $U = T\theta/2$, since $T/2$ is the average torque twisting the bar.   But $\theta = TL/E_sJ$.   Therefore $U = T^2L/2\,E_sJ$.

The relationship between the elastic energy stored in the bar, its dimensions and torsional stiffness, and the maximum stress in it is found by substituting the value S_sJ/c for T.   This gives

$$U = S_s^2 JL/2\,E_s c^2 \tag{1}$$

Since J for a solid bar equals $\pi c^4/2 = c^2 A/2$, the above equation becomes

$$U = \frac{S_s^2}{2\,E_s} \times \tfrac{1}{2}\,\text{Volume} \tag{2}$$

For the absorption of energy loads, helical springs are often used.   The above equations apply to such springs, which are bars subjected to torsional stress.   Equation (2) shows that the capacity of a helical spring to store energy at a given stress is directly proportional to the volume of the spring.   The relative values of length, cross-section, and

[1] For an interesting discussion of the use of rubber in absorbing shocks and vibration, see Walter C. Keys, " Rubber Springs," *Mechanical Engineering*, May, 1937.

radius of coil, however, determine the amount of deformation which will accompany the storing of any given amount of energy at a given stress.

The deformation of a helical spring is given by the equation $\Delta = PR^2L/E_sJ$ (Art. 67), where R is the mean radius of the helix and P is the load causing the deformation. But the work done in deforming the spring is $U = P\Delta/2$. Therefore $\Delta^2 = 2\ UR^2L/E_sJ$, or, for a solid circular wire,

$$\Delta^2 = 4\ UR^2L/\pi E_s c^4 \tag{3}$$

Eliminating L between equations (1) and (3),

$$c^3 = \frac{4\ UR}{\pi\Delta S_s} \quad \text{or} \quad c = \sqrt[3]{\frac{4\ UR}{\pi\Delta S_s}} \tag{4}$$

This equation can be used to determine the necessary radius of wire for a spring to absorb any given amount of energy with a given maximum stress and deformation, the radius of the helix being known. After the diameter of the wire has been determined, the length which it must have is found from equation (2). If the spring is to absorb tensile loads, it will probably be " close-coiled," and the length will be $2\ \pi RN$ (very closely), where N is the number of coils. If the spring is to absorb compressive loads, it must be " open-coiled." In this case, the length will be $2\ \pi RN/\cos\phi$, where ϕ is the pitch angle of the helix.

Example. A helical spring, made of a round bar of spring steel, is to have a mean radius of 5 in. and is to absorb 6,000 ft-lb. of energy, given it by compressive forces. The allowable stress is 60,000 lb. per sq. in., and the allowable deformation is to be approximately 8 in. Determine the required radius of the bar, the number of coils required, and the " pitch " of the helix.

Solution: Since $c = \sqrt[3]{\dfrac{4\ UR}{\pi\Delta S_s}}$

$$c = \sqrt[3]{\frac{4 \times (6,000 \times 12) \times 5}{\pi \times 8 \times 60,000}} = \sqrt[3]{0.955} = 0.986 \text{ in.}$$

Let the diameter of the bar be 2 in. From Equation (2), the necessary volume of the bar must be $\dfrac{4\ UE_s}{S_s^2}$, and this must also equal $\pi c^2 L$. Therefore

$$L = \frac{4\ UE_s}{\pi c^2 S_s^2} = \frac{4 \times 72,000 \times 12,000,000}{\pi \times 1 \times 60,000 \times 60,000} = 306 \text{ in.}$$

Although this must be an open-coiled spring, the pitch of the helix will be small and no material error will result from considering the length of the spring to be $2\ \pi RN$. Therefore $N = \dfrac{306}{2\ \pi \times 5} = 9.74$ turns. Say 10 turns. The spring must be capable of compressing 8 in. in 10 turns, or 0.8 in. per turn. Therefore the pitch of the helix must be 2.8 in., and the helix will be 28 in. long.

Since neither the bar diameter nor the number of coils is exactly what the equations call for, the spring will not be stressed to exactly 60,000 lb. per sq. in. when it absorbs 6,000 ft-lb. of energy, nor will it be compressed exactly 8 in.[1]

PROBLEMS

  1. Calculate the torsional stress and deformation in the spring of the above example when it has 6,000 ft-lb. of energy stored in it.

$$Ans. \quad S_s = 59,100 \text{ lb. per sq. in.}$$

  2. Calculate the torsional stress in the above spring when it is compressed 8 in. How much energy of torsion will be stored in it?

  3. The above spring is made with a space of 1 in. between coils. What is the torsional stress in it when it is closed " solid "? How much energy of torsion is stored?

211. Elastic Energy of Bending. The amount of elastic energy of bending[2] that is stored in a beam in equilibrium under an applied load is determined as follows: A slice of a beam between two transverse planes a distance dx apart is considered. This is shown in Fig. 349. The bending moment at the point in the beam where the slice is taken is M and may be regarded as constant throughout the length dx. Consider a " fiber " extending from one plane to the other. Let dA be its cross-sectional area and y its distance from the neutral surface. On this fiber the unit stress is My/I and the total force is $MydA/I$. The change in length due to the bending stress is $Mydx/EI$. As the moment at this section has increased from zero to M, the force on the ends of the fiber has varied from zero to $MydA/I$. The work done on the fiber is

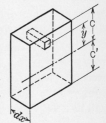

Fig. 349

$$\frac{MydA}{2\,I} \times \frac{Mydx}{EI} = \frac{M^2 dx y^2 dA}{2\,EI^2}$$

[1] This discussion has not taken into account the " direct " shearing stress in the helical spring. The direct shearing stress is generally small in comparison with the torsional stress, and in practice is almost always disregarded. In this example, it can be shown that the maximum force exerted on the spring is 18,600 lb. when 6,000 ft-lb. of energy are stored as energy of torsion. This results in a direct shearing stress of 5,900 lb. per sq. in., on the assumption of uniform distribution of that stress. But this direct shearing stress has also stored energy in the spring, so that actually 6,000 ft-lb. of energy are stored when the force on the spring is somewhat less than 18,600 lb. Taking into account both torsional and direct shear, and the energy stored by each, it can be shown that the maximum stress in the helix when it has 6,000 ft-lb. of energy stored in it is about 64,000 lb. per sq. in. Disregard of the direct shearing stress in this case leads to an error of 7 per cent.

[2] Usually there is an additional amount of elastic energy of shearing deformation in the beam. In Art. 255 it is stated that shearing deflections of beams are ordinarily small in comparison with deflections caused by bending. The same thing is true of the energies stored by shearing and bending deformations.

$$\int y^2 dA = I$$

On the entire slice the work done is

$$\frac{M^2 dx}{2\,EI^2}\int_{-c}^{c} y^2 dA = \frac{M^2 dx}{2\,EI}$$

For the entire beam,

$$U = \int_0^L \frac{M^2 dx}{2\,EI}$$

To evaluate this for a given beam it is necessary to express M as a function of x (assuming E and I to be constant).

Example. Calculate the elastic energy of bending stored in a cantilever beam by a load P at the end.

Solution: $M = Px$ at a distance x from the load.

$$U = \int_0^L \frac{M^2 dx}{2\,EI} = \int_0^L \frac{P^2 x^2 dx}{2\,EI} = \frac{P^2}{2\,EI}\frac{x^3}{3}\Big]_0^L = \frac{P^2 L^3}{6\,EI}$$

The maximum stress $= PLc/I$. Therefore

$$U = \frac{S^2 LI}{6\,Ec^2}$$

Also the maximum stress in this beam is

$$S = \sqrt{\frac{6\,Ec^2 U}{LI}}$$

For a cantilever beam of *rectangular* cross-section with a load P at the end

$$U = \frac{S^2 L\left(\dfrac{bh^3}{12}\right)}{6\,E\left(\dfrac{h^2}{4}\right)} = \frac{S^2}{2\,E} \times \frac{\text{Volume}}{9}$$

indicating that in this case the energy stored for a given maximum stress is $\frac{1}{9}$ of that stored in a tension or compression member of the same volume and with stress equal to the maximum in the beam.

PROBLEMS

1. Derive an expression for the elastic energy of bending in a uniformly loaded cantilever beam, the load being w lb. per in.

$$\text{Ans.}\quad U = \frac{w^2 L^5}{40\,EI}.$$

2. Calculate the amount of elastic energy of bending stored in a prismatic beam of rectangular cross-section resting on two supports with a concentrated load P at the midpoint.

3. Using the same processes of reasoning followed in the example above, show that the energy of shearing deformation stored in a prismatic cantilever beam of rectangular cross-section by a load P at the end is $3\,P^2L/5\,E_sA$ or $(S_s^2/2\,E_s)\times(\frac{8}{15})$ volume.

212. Calculation of Beam Deflections by Energy Relations. In Art. 211 it was shown that the elastic energy of bending stored in a prismatic cantilever beam with a load P at the end is $P^2L^3/6\,EI$. This must equal the work done by the load, as the end of the beam moves through the distance Δ, the deflection due to bending. The force exerted on the end of the beam has increased from 0 to the value P and has an average value of $P/2$. Therefore the work done on the beam by the load is $P\Delta/2$. Equating the work and energy, $P\Delta/2 = P^2L^3/6\,EI$, whence $\Delta = PL^3/3\,EI$, the same value as was obtained for this beam and loading by the double-integration and area moment methods. In a similar way to this, expressions for the bending deflections of prismatic beams with other loadings can be obtained.

PROBLEM

Using the expression of Prob. 3, Art 211, for elastic energy of shearing deformation show that the shearing deflection of a prismatic cantilever beam of rectangular cross-section due to a load P at the end is $6\,PL/5\,E_sA$.

213. Beams of Constant Strength. If I/c for every cross-section of a beam is proportional to the bending moment at that section, evidently $\dfrac{M}{I/c}$ will be a constant. That is, a beam having its section modulus varied in this way would have the same maximum fiber stress at every cross-section. Such a beam is called a beam of constant strength.

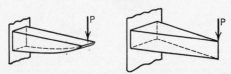

Fig. 350.   Cantilever beams of constant strength.

Consider a cantilever beam with a concentrated load P at the end. Then $M = Px$. If this beam is to have constant strength, the I/c of any cross-section must be proportional to the distance of that section from the free end of the beam. If the successive cross-sections are rectangular, for each, $I/c = bd^2/6$. Therefore bd^2 must vary as x. This can be accomplished by varying either the width or the depth of the sections. If the depth is made constant, it is evident that the width must vary as x; that is, the plan view of the beam will be a triangle. If the width is made constant, the d^2 must vary as x, or $d^2 = qx$, where q is a constant. The depth must therefore vary as the ordinates of a parabola (Fig. 350).

For any type of beam and loading, uniformity of strength is accomplished by setting up the equation $I/c = M/S$, regarding S as constant, and making I/c vary as M.

Beams with exactly constant strength are impractical. For example, in the case of the cantilever with a concentrated load at the end, an infinitely short distance away from the end there is an infinitely small bending moment, and therefore an infinitely small area is required to resist bending stresses. But there is a vertical shear at this section equal to the load, and there must be enough material at this section to resist the shearing stress. The beam cannot be allowed to taper to an actual edge. In the case of forged and cast beams, however, it is practical to vary the cross-section so as roughly to *approximate* a beam of uniform strength. Where such beams are used under conditions that make it necessary for the beam to absorb shock loads (axles, etc.), the cross-section is often varied in such a way as to diminish the differences between the maximum bending stresses on different cross-sections.

214. Elastic Energy of Beams of Constant Strength. Since at every cross-section of a beam of constant strength the maximum fiber stress is the same, it follows that, for a given maximum stress and a given volume of material, a beam of constant strength will store more elastic energy than a prismatic beam. Fig. 351 represents a thin elementary length of a beam included between transverse planes a distance dx apart. Consider the volume $dA \cdot dx$ of this " slice " included between two horizontal planes dy apart and distant y from the neutral axis. As the load on the beam increases from zero to its maximum value, the force on dA increases from zero to a maximum, the average value of this force being $SydA/2\,c$. The energy stored in the elementary volume $dAdx$ is the product of average force and deformation and is

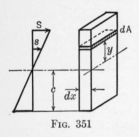

FIG. 351

$$\frac{SydA}{2\,c} \cdot \frac{Sydx}{cE} = \frac{S^2 dx y^2 dA}{2\,c^2 E}$$

Therefore the energy stored in the length dx of the beam is $\dfrac{S^2 dx}{2\,c^2 E}\,I$, and the energy stored in the entire beam is

$$\frac{S^2}{2\,E}\int_0^L \frac{I dx}{c^2}$$

Substituting Ar^2 for I,

$$U = \frac{S^2}{2\,E}\int_0^L \frac{Ar^2 dx}{c^2}$$

For a rectangle, $\dfrac{r^2}{c^2} = \dfrac{1}{3}$. Therefore if the successive cross-sections of the beam are all rectangles (as is frequently the case),

$$U = \frac{S^2}{2\,E} \int_0^L \frac{A\,dx}{3}$$

$$= \frac{S^2}{2\,E} \times \frac{\text{Volume}}{3}$$

Example. A cantilever beam made of spring steel has the dimensions shown in Fig. 352 and carries a load of 250 lb. at the end. (a) What maximum bending stress does this load cause, and how much elastic energy of bending does it store? (b) What is the deflection of the free end of the beam?

Solution: (a) For the cross-section at the face of the wall, $\dfrac{I}{c} = \dfrac{bd^2}{6} = \dfrac{12 \times (\frac{5}{16})^2}{6} = 0.195$ in.^{3} $S = \dfrac{M}{I/c}$.
Therefore

$$S = \frac{250 \times 18}{0.195} = 23{,}050 \text{ lb. per sq. in.}$$

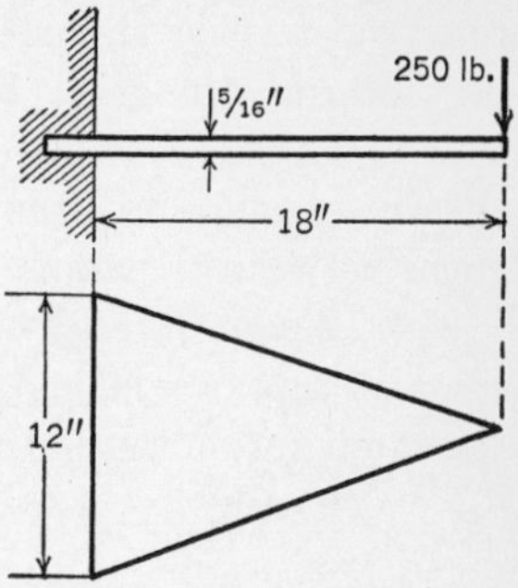

The volume of the beam is

$$\frac{12 \times 18}{2} \times \frac{5}{16} = 33.75 \text{ cu. in.}$$

FIG. 352

$$U = \frac{S^2}{2\,E} \times \frac{\text{Volume}}{3} = \frac{(23{,}050)^2}{2 \times 30{,}000{,}000} \times \frac{33.75}{3} = 99.6 \text{ in-lb.}$$

(b) The work done on the beam by the load $= 250\ \Delta/2$ lb-in.   Therefore

$$\frac{250\ \Delta}{2} = 99.6 \quad \text{and} \quad \Delta = 0.80 \text{ in.}$$

PROBLEM

Suppose that a second load of 250 lb. is applied at the end of the beam of the above example.   What increases in stress, deflection, and elastic energy of the beam result?

215. Leaf Springs. The ordinary leaf spring (Fig. 353) used for cushioning the travel of vehicles is an approximation to a beam of constant strength, if friction between the leaves or plates is disregarded. The cantilever beam of constant strength discussed in the foregoing example has the same material in it as in each arm of the semi-elliptic spring shown in Fig. 353 (a) and (b).   From practical considerations, it is preferable to design the spring as at (c) and (d), however.   Each arm of this spring, it can easily be seen, is equivalent to a cantilever of uniform strength, plus a cantilever of uniform section.   The spring may be (and often is) so designed that instead of being initially straight, and deflecting into a curve under load, it is initially curved and deflects into a straight line under full load.[1]

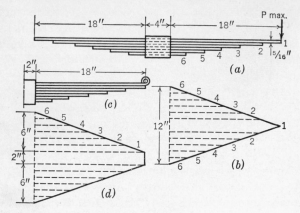

Fig. 353

PROBLEMS

1. Fig. 353(c) and (d) shows one arm of a " semi-elliptical " spring, under a load which causes a maximum stress of 80,000 lb. per sq. in. in the spring. How much elastic energy is stored in the spring at this stress? Does the top leaf add to or subtract from the energy capacity of the spring? All leaves are $\frac{5}{16}$ in. by 2 in.

2. If the tapered leaves remain unchanged in section, what variation in the thickness of the top leaf would add to the capacity of the spring?

3. What thickness should the top leaf have to give the spring maximum capacity?

STRESSES PRODUCED BY MOVING BODIES

216. Introduction. Up to this point in this chapter, consideration has been limited to the relationship between the energy stored in a member and the accompanying stresses and deformations. The energy stored has been recognized as having been transmitted to the member by some moving body which has come in contact with the member; but it has not been necessary to consider what fraction of the energy possessed by the moving body has been stored in the member as elastic energy. The only thing that has been considered is the effect, in stressing and deforming the member, *of that amount of energy which has been stored.*

The articles immediately following this one will make the assumption that all the energy possessed by a moving load is transmitted to the resisting member as elastic energy. On the basis of that assumption,

[1] For a fuller discussion of leaf springs see Maurer and Withey, " Strength of Materials," Second Edition, page 319.

these articles will connect the weight of a moving body and either the vertical distance through which it falls onto a resisting member or the velocity which it has when it comes in contact with the resisting member, with the stresses and deformations produced. A convenient form of equation is one in which the " dynamic " stresses and deformations produced by the moving weight are related to the stresses and deformations which the same amount of weight, acting as a static load, would produce. Such equations will be derived.

The equations derived are never absolutely accurate, since it is never true that all the energy possessed by a moving load is stored as elastic energy in a resisting body. For many situations, however, the equations are sufficiently close to the truth to be acceptable and useful. After the equations have been derived, the limitations of their application to various situations will be discussed in Art. 220.

217. Difference between Gradually Applied Load and Suddenly Applied Load. Attention has already been called to the fact that when a member is elastically deformed by a moving body the energy stored in it is the product of one-half the *maximum* force exerted on the member and the deformation produced by that force. Let us now relate this energy to the energy given up by the body which causes the deformation.

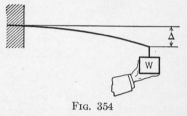

Fig. 354

Suppose that a load W is hung on the end of a cantilever beam (Fig. 354). If " gradually applied " to the beam, it is first entirely supported by something other than the beam (the hand, in the picture). As the external support is gradually lowered, the stiffness of the beam causes more and more of the load to be resisted by the beam, until eventually the beam carries the entire load, W. Since the accompanying deflection is that due to the static load W, let it be called Δ_{st}. The average load on the beam during the production of this deflection Δ_{st} has been $W/2$, and the work done on the beam by the load (or done on the load by the beam) has been $\dfrac{W}{2}\,\Delta_{st}$. The force exerted on the load by the hand has decreased, in proportion to the deflection, from W to 0, and the work the hand has done on the load has been $\dfrac{W}{2}\,\Delta_{st}$. The beam and the hand together have done work on the load equal to the work of gravity, or the loss of potential energy, which is obviously $W\Delta_{st}$.

Suppose now that the weight is brought just in contact with the undeflected beam and then *suddenly* released. Call the deflection of the beam when the weight is brought to rest Δ_1. The force exerted on the weight by the beam at that instant is $\dfrac{\Delta_1}{\Delta_{st}}\,W$, since the force W of the static load deflected the beam Δ_{st} in. and since forces are proportional to the deflections they produce. The work done on the load by the beam during the deflection Δ_1 equals

$$\frac{1}{2}\frac{\Delta_1}{\Delta_{st}}\,W \times \Delta_1 \quad \text{or} \quad \frac{1}{2}\frac{\Delta_1^2}{\Delta_{st}}\,W$$

This equals the work done on the load by gravity. Therefore

$$\frac{1}{2}\frac{\Delta_1^2 W}{\Delta_{st}} = \Delta_1 W$$

whence $\Delta_1 = 2\,\Delta_{st}$. Since the stresses are proportional to the deflections, it is evident that a suddenly applied load causes twice the stress that the same load does if gradually applied. It is also evident that the maximum force which the load exerts on the beam is twice the weight of the load.

Although these relations between a gradually applied load and a sudden load have been worked out for a beam, it is evident that nothing in the derivation limits them to beams. For an axially loaded member, Δ_1 and Δ_{st} represent total *deformations;* for a shaft they represent total torsional deformations, which are proportional to angles of twist; for a helical spring, they represent the shortening or elongation of the spring, etc. In any elastic body, a suddenly applied load causes twice the stress and twice the deformation (or deflection) as the same load applied gradually.

218. Weight Falling a Height h. If the weight W is dropped a distance h before striking the beam (or other elastic member) the beam will deflect a distance Δ which is greater than either Δ_{st} or Δ_1. The work done on the weight by gravity is equaled by the work done on it by the beam, or

$$W.(h + \Delta) = \frac{1}{2}\frac{\Delta}{\Delta_{st}}\,W \times \Delta = \frac{1}{2}\frac{\Delta^2}{\Delta_{st}}\,W$$

or
$$h + \Delta = \frac{1}{2}\frac{\Delta^2}{\Delta_{st}}$$

whence
$$\Delta - \Delta_{st} = \sqrt{2\,\Delta_{st}h + \Delta_{st}^2}$$

and
$$\Delta = \Delta_{st} + \Delta_{st}\sqrt{\frac{2\,h}{\Delta_{st}} + 1} = \Delta_{st}\left(1 + \sqrt{\frac{2\,h}{\Delta_{st}} + 1}\right) \qquad (1)$$

It is also true, since stresses are proportional to deformations or deflections, that

$$S = S_{st}\left(1 + \sqrt{\frac{2h}{\Delta_{st}} + 1}\right) \tag{2}$$

in which S_{st} is the static stress due to a gradually applied weight and S is the stress due to the same weight falling a height h and striking the beam. Note that, if $h = 0$, the above equations give values of $2\,\Delta_{st}$ for Δ and $2\,S_{st}$ for S, as found in the previous article.

For certain values of h/Δ_{st} the following values result for S:

h/Δ_{st}	S
0	$2.0\,S_{st}$
1	$2.7\,S_{st}$
10	$5.6\,S_{st}$
50	$11.1\,S_{st}$

In equations (1) and (2), if Δ_{st} is small in comparison with h, as is often the case (especially for members loaded axially), with negligible error

$$\Delta = \Delta_{st}\left(1 + \sqrt{\frac{2h}{\Delta_{st}}}\right) \quad \text{and} \quad S = S_{st}\left(1 + \sqrt{\frac{2h}{\Delta_{st}}}\right)$$

Example 1. A 1-in. square beam (Fig. 355) is 60 in. long and rests on supports at the ends. A 25-lb. weight falls 2 in., striking the beam at its midpoint. What stress is caused (*a*) if the beam is steel? (*b*) if the beam is duralumin?

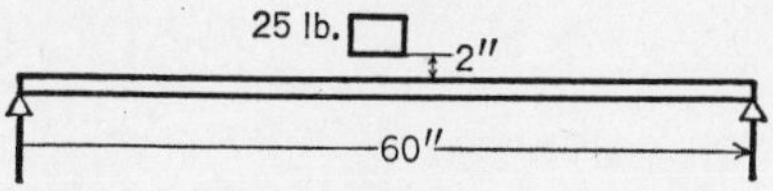

FIG. 355

Solution: For steel beam

$$\Delta_{st} = \frac{PL^3}{48\,EI} = \frac{25 \times 60^3}{48 \times 30{,}000{,}000 \times \frac{1}{12}} = 0.045 \text{ in.}$$

$$S_{st} = \frac{Mc}{I} = \frac{375}{\frac{1}{6}} = 2{,}250 \text{ lb. per sq. in. (for static load)}$$

Therefore

$$S = 2{,}250 + 2{,}250\sqrt{\frac{4}{0.045} + 1} = 2{,}250 + 2{,}250\,\sqrt{89 + 1} = 2{,}250 + 2{,}250 \times 9.5$$

$$= 2{,}250 + 21{,}400 = 23{,}650 \text{ lb. per sq. in.}$$

and

$$\Delta = 0.045 \times 10.5 = 0.473 \text{ in.}$$

(b) For the duralumin beam, $E = 10,000,000$ lb. per sq. in.

$$\Delta_{st} = 0.045 \times 3 = 0.135 \text{ in.}$$

$$S_{st} = 2,250 \text{ lb. per sq. in. (for static load)}$$

$$S = 2,250 + 2,250 \sqrt{\frac{4}{0.135} + 1} = 2,250 + 2,250 \sqrt{30.6} = 2,250 + 2,250 \times 5.54$$

$$= 2,250 + 12,500 = 14,750 \text{ lb. per sq. in.}$$

If grades of steel and duralumin having the same strength are used, the dura-lumin beam has a considerably higher factor of safety. It may be noted, however, that if the load were " suddenly applied " (without falling, or $h = 0$) the stress in either beam would be simply twice the 2,250-lb.-per-sq.-in. stress due to static load, or 4,500 lb. per sq. in.

Example 2. If the steel beam in the previous example is 66 in. long instead of 60 in. and other conditions remain the same, what is the stress?

$$\Delta_{st} = \frac{PL^3}{48\ EI} = \frac{25 \times 66^3}{48 \times 30,000,000 \times \frac{1}{12}} = 0.060 \text{ in.}$$

$$S_{st} = 33 \times 12.5 \times 6 = 2,480 \text{ lb. per sq. in.}$$

$$S = 2,480 + 2,480 \left(\sqrt{\frac{4}{0.060} + 1} \right) = 2,480 + 2,480 \times 8.2 = 22,800 \text{ lb. per sq. in.}$$

Note that this is a smaller stress than that resulting in the shorter beam of the same cross-section and with the same loading. The stress is the sum of the stress due to a static load plus that same stress multiplied by a coefficient which is $\sqrt{\dfrac{2h}{\Delta_{st}} + 1}$. By

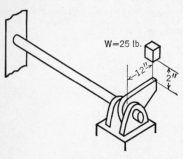

FIG. 356

lengthening the beam a certain amount this coefficient is reduced enough (from 9.5 to 8.2) to make the total stress less in spite of the greater amount of the " static " stress.

Example 3. A 1-in.-diameter steel shaft (Fig. 356) 60 in. long and adequately supported to prevent bending is fixed at one end and carries a 12-in. rigid arm fixed to the other end. A weight of 25 lb. falls 2 in., hitting the arm. What stress results in the shaft?

Solution: The static stress due to the 25-lb. weight acting with a moment arm of 12 in. is

$$S_{st} = \frac{Tc}{J} = \frac{300 \times \frac{1}{2} \times 2}{\pi \times (\frac{1}{2})^4} = 1,530 \text{ lb-in.}$$

$$\theta_{st} = \frac{TL}{E_s J} = \frac{300 \times 60 \times 2}{12,000,000 \times \pi \times (\frac{1}{2})^4} = 0.0153 \text{ rad.}$$

$$\Delta_{st} = 12\ \theta_{st} = 0.184 \text{ in.}$$

Therefore the resulting stress $S = 1,530 \left(1 + \sqrt{\dfrac{4}{0.184} + 1} \right) = 1,530\ (1 + 4.8)$

$$= 8,880 \text{ lb. per sq. in.}$$

PROBLEMS

1. In Example 3, let the moment arm be 6 in., other quantities remaining unchanged. Calculate the stress produced in the shaft. The static stress will have been halved. Why will the total stress not have been more greatly reduced?

2. In Example 3, calculate the stress in the shaft if the length of the shaft is doubled, other quantities remaining unchanged.

3. In Example 3, assume the shaft to be fixed at both ends, and the 12-in. arm to be supported at the midpoint (in such a way as to prevent bending of the shaft). Other conditions remaining unchanged, what is the resulting stress?

4. In Example 1, assume all conditions to remain unchanged except the length of the beam. Find the length that will receive the *minimum* amount of stress from the falling weight.

5. In the example of Art. 214, find from what height the 250-lb. load must fall on the spring to stress it to 80,000 lb. per sq. in.

219. Stresses Produced by a Body of Weight W Moving with a Velocity of v Ft. per Sec. For a falling body, $v^2 = 2\,gh$ or h (ft.) $= v^2/2\,g$, whence h(in.) $= 6\,v^2/g$, where v is in feet per second and g is in feet per second per second. If this value for h is substituted in equation (1), Art. 218, there results $S = S_{st}\left(1 + \sqrt{\dfrac{12\,v^2}{g\Delta_{st}} + 1}\right)$, for the stress produced by the moving body in terms of the stress produced by a body of the same weight if gradually applied.

If, instead of falling on the resisting member, the moving body is traveling horizontally so that there is no gravitational effect but all stress in the resisting member is caused by the kinetic energy of the moving body, it can be shown that

$$S = S_{st}\sqrt{\frac{12\,v^2}{g\Delta_{st}}} = 0.61\,S_{st}\sqrt{\frac{v^2}{\Delta_{st}}}$$

PROBLEM

Prove the truth of the foregoing equation.

220. Limitations of the Foregoing Expressions. The foregoing expressions assume that all the kinetic energy of the moving body is stored in the resisting member as elastic energy of direct elongation or compression, of bending, or of torsion in the cases of axially loaded members, beams, and shafts or helical springs, respectively. This assumption will never be entirely true, and may be far from true. If the velocity of impact is great, the rate of deceleration is likely to be so great that high local stresses and deformations will be produced and in extreme cases (as when a lead bullet strikes a steel beam) almost all the kinetic energy may be transformed into energy of local deformation, largely inelastic, of both the moving body and the resisting member. Even when the velocity of impact is small, if the dimensions of the resisting member are such as to give it a large amount of *stiffness*, the same thing will result. Finally, if the mass of the resisting member is large in comparison with that of the moving body, the *inertia* of the resisting member may cause a large part of the kinetic energy to be consumed in the production of local deformations of the moving body and the resisting member.

All three of these invalidating conditions imply large values of $2 h/\Delta_{st}$. A high velocity of impact is consistent with a large value of h.   Also, generally speaking, the greater the stiffness or the greater the mass of the resisting member, the less will be the value of Δ_{st}.   The formulas are therefore more accurate for small values of $2 h/\Delta_{st}$ $\left(\text{or of } \dfrac{12\ v^2}{g\Delta_{st}}\right)$ than for large values.   In any case in which this ratio is less than 100, values of Δ and S computed from the equations will probably not be in error by more than about 10 per cent.[1]

There is another condition which the equations assume, and which is never present, though in many cases it may be closely approximated. That is immovability of the supports of the member.   If the supports are yielding, and permit the resisting member to be displaced as a whole, the resisting member simply transmits to the supports a part of the energy of the moving load.   If the member itself is very rigid in comparison with the supports, almost all the energy of the moving load may simply pass through the member to the supports.   This fact is utilized when machine parts subject to shock are held in rubber mountings.   In such cases, the stresses produced by an impact load may be only a small fraction of their values as computed by the above equations.

Because of all these circumstances, the equations need to be applied with care and judgment.

221. " Equivalent Static Loads " — Impact Formulas. It has been noted that whatever the nature of a moving load, and whatever the nature of the resisting member, the maximum stresses and deformations of the member are the direct result of the maximum *forces* exerted on the member.   In the case of many members on which moving loads act, there is inevitably a great deal of uncertainty concerning both the amount of energy given up by the moving load, and the proportion of this energy that is stored elastically in the resisting member.   In such cases satisfactory application of the equations developed in the preceding

---

[1] For a discussion of the effect of the inertia of the resisting member, see A. Morley, " Strength of Materials," pages 66 and 235 (Fifth Edition), or M. Merriman, " Mechanics of Materials," pages 331 et seq. (Eleventh Edition).

articles of this chapter would be very difficult, and the results would necessarily be uncertain. As an alternative procedure, it is a common practice to assume some relation between the moving load and the greatest *force* which the moving load exerts on the member. This is accomplished by assuming that the force exerted by the moving load equals the weight of the moving load plus that weight multiplied by some factor. Such a factor is called an " impact factor." The value assumed for it is usually empirical and is based on a consideration of similar members in existing machines or structures.

As an illustration of this procedure the supports for an elevator hoist may have to carry " dead " (or non-moving) loads of 5,000 lb., consisting of the weight of the beams that carry the operating motors and the weight of the operating motors themselves; and " live " loads of 5,000 lb., consisting of the elevator car, the load carried by it, the cables, etc. The supports then might be designed for a total load of 15,000 lb. made up as follows:

Dead load	5,000 lb.
Live load	5,000 lb.
Impact	5,000 lb.

Here the impact factor is 1. This is equivalent to assuming that the force exerted on the supports by the live load may reach twice the static weight of the live load, or that the supporting beams may have to decelerate the downward moving live load (or accelerate the upward moving live load) at a rate equal to that of gravity.

The " equivalent static load " method of taking into account the effect of the energy of a moving load is particularly applicable to situations in which the larger part of the force on a member is due to *weights*, and only a minor part to dynamic effects or energy. Such situations are more likely to occur in the design of structures than of machines. For certain important types of structures, such as bridges, " impact formulas " are used. These provide in a systematic way for the increase in stress that results from the movement of a load. One such formula[1] which is widely used in the design of highway bridges is $I = \dfrac{50}{L + 125}$.

In this equation I represents the impact factor and L represents the " loaded length " or the distance (in feet) which the live load must travel while the value of live-load stress increases from zero to the maximum value.

---

[1] American Association of State Highway Officials, " Specifications for Highway Bridges," 1935.

GENERAL PROBLEMS

+ **1.** A 10-lb. weight falls 36 in. onto the head of the bolt shown in Fig. 357. Assuming all the energy absorbed by the bolt, what is the maximum tensile stress produced in it? What is the maximum shearing stress on the cylindrical surface where the head joins the body of the bolt? How much is the bolt elongated?

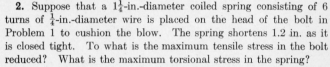

2. Suppose that a $1\frac{1}{4}$-in.-diameter coiled spring consisting of 6 turns of $\frac{1}{4}$-in.-diameter wire is placed on the head of the bolt in Problem 1 to cushion the blow. The spring shortens 1.2 in. as it is closed tight. To what is the maximum tensile stress in the bolt reduced? What is the maximum torsional stress in the spring?

+ **3.** A round carbon-steel bar, 1 in. in diameter, is used as a cantilever beam 48 in. long and carries a load P at the end which causes a maximum stress equal to the proportional limit of 30,000 lb. per sq. in. (a) What is the minimum diameter of a nickel-steel bar which will absorb the same amount of energy if loaded in the same way without stress above the proportional limit of 50,000 lb. per sq. in.? (b) Which of the bars will support the greater static load at the end if stressed to the proportional limit? *Ans.* (a) $d = 0.6$ in.

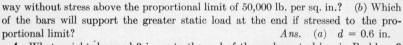

4. What weight dropped 3 in. onto the end of the carbon-steel bar in Problem 3 will cause the maximum bending stress to be 30,000 lb. per sq. in.? What deflection will this weight cause?

CHAPTER XVIII

CONTINUOUS BEAMS

222. Definition. A continuous beam is one which rests upon more than two supports, as in Fig. 358, or, has more than two reactions. Such beams occur frequently in modern structures. There is usually some economy of material in the use of a continuous beam as compared with a series of simple beams over the same spans. In this book the consideration of continuous beams will be limited to beams in which

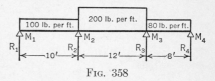

Fig. 358

E and I are constant[1] from end to end and with the supports all on the same level.

223. Theorem of Three Moments. Continuous beams are statically indeterminate structures, and therefore the external reactions cannot be found by the conditions of static equilibrium alone. The most convenient method for finding bending moments in continuous beams is by means of a relation that exists between the bending moments at the three supports of any two adjacent spans of a continuous beam. This relation is expressed as an equation and is commonly called the *theorem of three moments*. By use of this theorem or equation, the bending moments at all the supports of a continuous beam can be found. When these are known it is possible to determine the shears and bending moments at all points and to draw the shear and bending-moment diagrams.

The theorem of three moments is commonly ascribed to the French engineer, E. Clapeyron, who published one form of it in 1857. The derivation of this equation expressing the relation that always exists between the bending moments at three consecutive supports is based on conditions of deflection and continuity of the elastic curve. Consequently the equations expressing these conditions are the necessary additional equations for the solution of this indeterminate type of structure.

It will be seen that if there are n spans in a continuous beam there are

[1] For a method for solving continuous beams with variable EI, see P. G. Laurson, *Engineering News-Record*, Vol. 96, April 15, 1926, p. 604.

$n + 1$ supports.[1]   The bending moment at the end supports is zero if the beam does not overhang the ends.   If it does overhang, the bending moments at the end supports can be calculated.   There are therefore $n - 1$ unknown bending moments at the $n - 1$ intermediate supports.

If a " three moment equation " is written for each group of three consecutive supports, there will be $n - 1$ such equations, which are just sufficient for finding the $n - 1$ bending moments.

224. Solving for Bending Moments at Supports.   Before deriving the theorem of three moments its use will be illustrated by a numerical example.

With uniformly distributed loads on all spans, with constant E and I for all spans, and with all supports at the same level, the theorem of three moments is

$$M_A L_1 + 2\,M_B(L_1 + L_2) + M_C L_2 = -\frac{w_1 L_1^3}{4} - \frac{w_2 L_2^3}{4}$$

In this equation, M_A, M_B, and M_C are the bending moments at *any three consecutive supports*, taken in order from left to right. L_1 is the length of the left-hand span of the two being considered and L_2 is the length of the right-hand span. w_1 is the uniform load *per unit of length* on the left span, and w_2 the uniform load per unit of length on the right span.   In any given specific case w_1, w_2 and L_1 and L_2 are given.   If w_1 and w_2 are expressed in pounds per foot and L_1 and L_2 are in feet, the value found for M_A, M_B, etc., will be in pound-feet.

Example.   Calculate the bending moments at the supports of the continuous beam shown in Fig. 358.

Solution: The " three moment equation " given above is written for the first two spans:

$$10 \times 0 + 2\,M_2(10 + 12) + 12\,M_3 = -\frac{100 \times 1{,}000}{4} - \frac{200 \times 1{,}728}{4}$$

$$44\,M_2 + 12\,M_3 = -25{,}000 - 86{,}400 = -111{,}400$$

Dividing by 12, $3.67\,M_2 + M_3\ = -9{,}283$ lb-ft.   (1)

The equation written for the second two spans is

$$12\,M_2 + 2\,M_3(12 + 8) + 8 \times 0 = -\frac{200 \times 1{,}728}{4} - \frac{80 \times 512}{4}$$

$$12\,M_2 + 40\,M_3 = -86{,}400 - 10{,}240 = -96{,}640\ \text{lb-ft.}$$

Dividing by 40, $0.3\,M_2 + M_3\ = -2{,}416$ lb-ft.   (2)

[1] Assume that these are " knife-edge " supports; that is, that the supports themselves exert no restraint on the beam (although in general, at the supports, there will be bending moments that are due to the continuity of the beam).

Subtracting (2) from (1),

$$3.37 \, M_2 = -6,867$$
$$M_2 = -2,038 \text{ lb-ft.}$$
$$M_3 = -2,416 + 0.3 \times 2,038 = -1,805 \text{ lb-ft.}$$

The bending moments at the two intermediate supports, M_2 and M_3, having been determined, it is possible to calculate the shear at various points, the four reactions, and the bending moments at all points. Methods for performing these calculations will be given later.

THEOREM OF THREE MOMENTS — DOUBLE INTEGRATION METHOD

(Arts. 225 to 228 inclusive may be omitted if the double integration method is not to be studied.)

225. End Slope in Unloaded Beam with Moments at Ends. The derivation of the theorem of three moments by double integration, as given in the following article, makes use of an expression for the slope at one end of a beam without loads but bent by moments at the ends. In Fig. 359, AB is the elastic curve of such a beam with end moments M_A and M_B, respectively. The directions shown for M_A and M_B are the directions of the moments acting on AB if the bending moments at A and B are both positive.

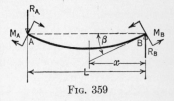

Fig. 359

To calculate R_B, use the equation $\Sigma M = 0$ with A as the moment center. Giving counterclockwise moments the plus sign, $R_B L + M_B - M_A = 0$. Therefore

$$R_B = \frac{M_A - M_B}{L}$$

At any distance, x, from B,

$$M_x = R_B x + M_B = \frac{M_A x}{L} - \frac{M_B x}{L} + M_B$$

Taking the origin at B and regarding x as positive to the left, the equation of the elastic curve is

$$EI \frac{d^2 y}{dx^2} = \frac{M_A x}{L} - \frac{M_B x}{L} + M_B$$

Integrating,

$$EI \frac{dy}{dx} = \frac{M_A x^2}{2L} - \frac{M_B x^2}{2L} + M_B x + C_1$$

in which C_1 is EI times the slope of the elastic curve at B. Integrating again,

$$EIy = \frac{M_A x^3}{6\,L} - \frac{M_B x^3}{6\,L} + \frac{M_B x^2}{2} + C_1 x + C_2$$

But $y = 0$ when $x = 0$. Therefore $C_2 = 0$.
Also $y = 0$ when $x = L$. Therefore

$$C_1 = -\frac{M_A L}{6} - \frac{M_B L}{3}$$

Let the slope of the elastic curve at B (due to the end moments) be β. Then

$$C_1 = EI\beta. \quad \text{Therefore } \beta = -\frac{M_A L}{6\,EI} - \frac{M_B L}{3\,EI}$$

Since in Fig. 359 M_A and M_B are given directions which correspond to the directions of the couples exerted by $+$ bending moments at A and at B, the signs in the expression for β are those corresponding to $+$ bending moments at A and B.

226. Derivation of Theorem of Three Moments. Fig. 360(a) represents any two adjacent spans of a continuous beam. The loads shown

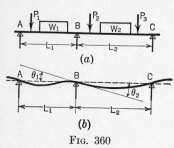

(a)

(b)

Fig. 360

represent *any system of loads*. (b) represents the deflected elastic curve. The shape of this is unknown, and it is unnecessary at present to know its exact form. Since the beam is *continuous* there is one and only one tangent at B. This is shown sloping downward to the right consistent with the assumed elastic curve. As this derivation is confined to the case where the supports remain at the same level, A, B, and C in Fig. 360 (b) are on the original straight, horizontal line.

In the following discussion the origin will be taken at B, the middle support, the positive direction of the Y axis will be assumed upward, and the positive direction of the X axis will be assumed to the right when considering the right-hand span and to the left when considering the left-hand span.

Because of the continuity of the beam at B, it is evident that the slope of the elastic curve of AB at B is opposite in sign to the slope of the elastic curve of BC at B since one slope is upward in the plus direction of x while the other is downward in the plus direction of x. This is true whether the tangent at B slopes downward to the right, as shown, or upward to the right. This fact may be expressed by the equation $\theta_1 = -\theta_2$.

Fig. 361 shows the BC span as a body in equilibrium with the loads, the vertical shears at B and C, and the moments M_B and M_C exerted on this span by the adjacent spans. By the principle of summation of effects, it follows that θ_2 is the algebraic sum of the slope of the beam caused by the loads alone and the slope of the beam caused by the moments at the ends, M_B and M_C, alone. Call the slope due to the loads alone α_2 and the slope due to the end

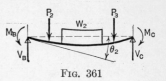

FIG. 361

moments alone β_2. Then $\alpha_2 + \beta_2 = \theta_2$. For the left-hand span, $\alpha_1 + \beta_1 = \theta_1$. Then equation $\theta_1 = -\theta_2$ becomes

$$\alpha_1 + \beta_1 = -(\alpha_2 + \beta_2)$$

or

$$\beta_1 + \beta_2 = -\alpha_1 - \alpha_2 \tag{1}$$

Substituting for β_1 and β_2 the values based on the value of β found in the preceding article, there results

$$-\frac{M_A L_1}{6\ EI} - \frac{M_B L_1}{3\ EI} - \frac{M_C L_2}{6\ EI} - \frac{M_B L_2}{3\ EI} = -\alpha_1 - \alpha_2 \tag{2}$$

from which

$$M_A L_1 + 2\ M_B(L_1 + L_2) + M_C L_2 = 6\ EI\alpha_1 + 6\ EI\alpha_2 \tag{3}$$

in which α_1 is the slope that would be caused at end B in a *simple* beam (without restraint at the ends) of span L_1 by the same loads that are on the left-hand span of the two spans of the continuous beam. α_2 is the corresponding slope at B for the right-hand span. This is a general form of the theorem of three moments for beams with constant E and I and supports at the same level. The theorem of three moments for a particular type of loading is derived from the above equation by substituting the values of α_1 and α_2 for the particular type of load.

227. Theorem of Three Moments — Uniformly Distributed Load. In Art. 113 the value of C_1 (EI times the slope at the origin which was taken at the end of the beam) for a beam on two supports with a uniformly distributed load of w lb. per unit of length was found to be

$$C_1 = -\frac{wL^3}{24}$$

from which the end slope is found to be $-\dfrac{wL^3}{24\ EI}$. Substituting this value with the proper subscripts (Fig. 362), there results the theorem of three moments for uniformly distributed loads:

$$M_A L_1 + 2 M_B (L_1 + L_2) + M_C L_2 = -\frac{w_1 L_1^3}{4} - \frac{w_2 L_2^3}{4}$$

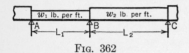

Fig. 362

The use of this equation was illustrated in Art. 224.

If, as often happens, the spans are all of the same length and the load is the same on all spans, this reduces to

$$M_A + 4 M_B + M_C = -\frac{wL^2}{2}$$

PROBLEMS

1. A continuous beam rests on three supports with spans of 15 ft. and 20 ft. It carries a uniform load of 200 lb. per ft. Calculate the moment at the intermediate reaction.   *Ans.* $M_B = -8{,}125$ lb-ft.

2. If the beam in Problem 1 overhangs 5 ft. beyond the 15-ft. span, calculate the moment at the intermediate reaction.

3. Calculate the moments at the reactions for a continuous beam of four equal spans of L ft. carrying a uniform load of w lb. per ft. Note that because of symmetry $M_2 = M_4$.

228. Theorem of Three Moments — Concentrated Load. The theorem of three moments for concentrated loads is obtained by substituting the proper values of α_1 and α_2 in equation (3), Art. 226. Fig. 363 shows a simple beam of length L with a single load P, at a distance a from reaction A. In Art. 114 the slope at the right reaction is C_2/EI. The value of C_2, found from equations (5) and (6) of that article, and with $L_1 - a$ substituted for b, is

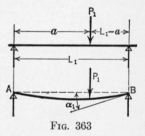

Fig. 363

$$C_2 = -\frac{P_1 a(L_1 - a)}{6 L_1}(L_1 + a) = -\frac{P_1 a(L_1^2 - a^2)}{6 L_1}$$

But

$$\alpha_1 = \frac{C_2}{EI} = -\frac{P_1 a(L_1^2 - a^2)}{6 EIL_1}$$

By changing the notation, for the right-hand span of Fig. 364,

$$\alpha_2 = -\frac{P_2 b(L_2^2 - b^2)}{6 EIL_2}$$

Substituting these values of α_1 and α_2 in equation (3), there results

$$M_A L_1 + 2\,M_B(L_1 + L_2) + M_C L_2 = -\frac{P_1 a(L_1^2 - a^2)}{L_1} - \frac{P_2 b(L_2^2 - b^2)}{L_2}$$

It must be kept in mind that a and b are measured from the *outside* supports of the respective spans (Fig. 364). The factor $L_1^2 - a^2$ equals $(L_1 + a)(L_1 - a)$ and may be computed in that form if more convenient.

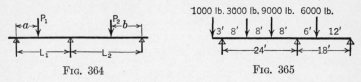

FIG. 364   FIG. 365

In order to cover cases involving more than one load in a span, the above equation is usually written as follows:

$$M_A L_1 + 2\,M_B(L_1 + L_2) + M_C L_2$$
$$= -\sum \frac{P_1 a(L_1^2 - a^2)}{L_1} - \sum \frac{P_2 b(L_2^2 - b^2)}{L_2}$$

The summation sign, $\sum$, before each term of the right-hand member indicates that the term is to be written for each load.

Example. Calculate the bending moment at the intermediate support of the beam shown in Fig. 365.

Solution:

$$-24 \times 3,000 + 84\,M_B + 18 \times 0 = -\frac{3,000 \times 8}{24}\,(576 - 64)$$

$$-\frac{9,000 \times 16}{24}\,(576 - 256) - \frac{6,000 \times 12}{18}\,(324 - 144)$$

$$-72,000 + 84\,M_B = -512,000 - 1,920,000 - 720,000$$

$$M_B = -\frac{3,080,000}{84} = -36,700 \text{ lb-ft.}$$

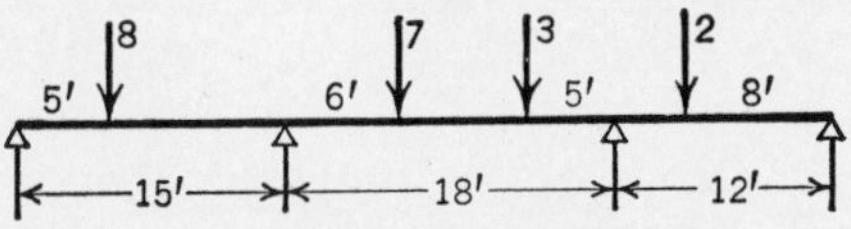

FIG. 366

PROBLEM

Calculate the moments at the supports of the beam shown in Fig. 366. (Loads are given in thousands of pounds.)

THEOREM OF THREE MOMENTS — AREA-MOMENT METHOD

(Arts. 229 to 232 inclusive may be omitted if the area-moment method is not to be studied.)

229. Derivation of Theorem of Three Moments. Fig. 367 (a) represents any two adjacent spans of a continuous beam. The loads shown represent *any system of loads.* (b) represents the deflected elastic curve.

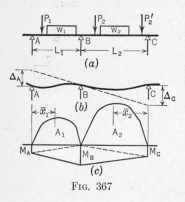

(a)

(b)

(c)

FIG. 367

The shape of this is unknown, and it is unnecessary at present to know its exact form. Owing to the fact that the beam is *continuous* there is one and only one tangent at B. This is shown sloping downward to the right consistent with the assumed elastic curve. Since this derivation is confined to the case where the supports remain at the same level, A, B, and C in Fig. 367 (b) are on the original straight, horizontal line. Δ_A is the displacement of A from the tangent at B, and Δ_C is the displacement of C from the same tangent. By similar triangles

$$\frac{\Delta_A}{L_1} = -\frac{\Delta_C}{L_2}$$

The minus sign must precede one of the members of this equation because the displacements Δ_A and Δ_C are in opposite directions. This equation introduces two conditions: continuity, and no settlement of supports. The similar triangles do not exist unless both these conditions exist. Δ_A and Δ_C are easily expressed in terms of the bending-moment diagrams for the left and right spans, respectively, by means of the second area-moment proposition.

In Art. 143 it was shown that a loaded beam fixed at the ends is equivalent to a simple beam having the same span and load, and also having applied to it end moments of such magnitude as to make the tangents at the ends of the span horizontal. In the case of a continuous beam, the tangents at the end of a span are not, in general, horizontal. But any span of a continuous beam can be considered equivalent to a simple beam having the same span and load and acted on by end moments of sufficient amount to give the tangents at the ends of the beam the slope which the elastic curve of the continuous beam has at the supports in question. Since this is true, the bending-moment diagram for each of the spans under consideration may be drawn in two parts (as in Art. 143). One part is the M diagram for a simple beam with the given loading. Since the bending moment is always positive in a simple beam with downward loads this part is shown above the base line in (c) of Fig. 367. The other part of the diagram represents the bending moment throughout the beam caused by the restraint or bending moments at the supports. The magnitude of these moments not being known, this part of the diagram cannot be drawn to scale (which does not interfere with its use for the present purpose). The sign of these moments is also unknown, although they are generally negative. In the equations below they will be assumed positive, and the sign resulting from the solution of the equations will then be the true sign. (See footnote, Art. 133.) To simplify the appearance of the diagram these areas are drawn below the base line.

Let A_1 be the area of the positive part of the M diagram for the left span, and let x_1 be the distance to its centroid from support A (the support which is displaced from the tangent). A_2 and x_2 are corresponding values for the right span.

By the second area-moment proposition,

$$\Delta_A = \left(A_1 x_1 + M_A \times \frac{L_1}{2} \times \frac{L_1}{3} + M_B \times \frac{L_1}{2} \times \frac{2\,L_1}{3} \right) \frac{1}{EI}$$

$$\frac{\Delta_A}{L_1} = \left(\frac{A_1 x_1}{L_1} + \frac{M_A L_1}{6} + \frac{M_B L_1}{3} \right) \frac{1}{EI}$$

In the same way

$$\frac{\Delta_C}{L_2} = \left(\frac{A_2 x_2}{L_2} + \frac{M_C L_2}{6} + \frac{M_B L_2}{3} \right) \frac{1}{EI}$$

Since

$$\frac{\Delta_A}{L_2} = - \frac{\Delta_C}{L_2}$$

$$\frac{A_1 x_1}{L_1} + \frac{M_A L_1}{6} + \frac{M_B L_1}{3} = - \left(\frac{A_2 x_2}{L_2} + \frac{M_C L_2}{6} + \frac{M_B L_2}{3} \right)$$

Multiplying by 6 and collecting terms:

$$M_A L_1 + 2\,M_B(L_1 + L_2) + M_C L_2 = - \frac{6\,A_1 x_1}{L_1} - \frac{6\,A_2 x_2}{L_2}$$

This is a form of the theorem of three moments which applies to *any type of loading whatever*, provided that the three supports are on a straight line and EI is constant throughout both spans.

230. Theorem of Three Moments for Uniformly Distributed Loads. For the case of uniformly distributed loads of w_1 and w_2 lb. per ft. on the left and right spans respectively, with no concentrated loads, the M

curves for simple beams are parabolas.   The maximum ordinate for the left one is $w_1L_1^2/8$, and the area under the curve is $2\,L_1/3 \times w_1L_1^2/8 = w_1L_1^3/12$.   The distance x_1 to the centroid is equal to $L_1/2$. Hence

$$-\frac{6\,A_1x_1}{L_1} = -\frac{w_1L_1^3}{4}$$

for this particular case of loading.

The theorem of three moments for uniform loads covering the spans is therefore

$$M_AL_1 + 2\,M_B(L_1 + L_2) + M_CL_2 = -\frac{w_1L_1^3}{4} - \frac{w_2L_2^3}{4}$$

The use of this equation was illustrated in Art. 224.   If the spans are all of the same length and the load is the same on all spans, this reduces to

$$M_A + 4\,M_B + M_C = -\frac{wL^2}{2}$$

PROBLEMS

1. Same as Problem 1, Art. 227.
2. Same as Problem 2, Art. 227.
3. Same as Problem 3, Art. 227.

231. Theorem of Three Moments for Concentrated Loads.   Let Fig. 368 represent any two adjacent spans of a continuous beam, each span having a single concentrated load as shown.

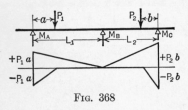

FIG. 368

The theorem of three moments for this case may be derived by substituting in the equation

$$M_AL_1 + 2\,M_B(L_1 + L_2) + M_CL_2 = -\frac{6\,A_1x_1}{L_1} - \frac{6\,A_2x_2}{L_2}$$

the particular value for A_1x_1 and A_2x_2.   Notice that these are statical moments.   It is not necessary actually to determine x_1 and x_2.

The bending-moment diagram for each span *as a simple beam* is drawn by parts below the sketch of the beam.   The statical moment of the diagram for the left span with respect to the left reaction is:

$$A_1x_1 = P_1a \times \frac{L_1}{2} \times \frac{L_1}{3} - P_1a \times \frac{a}{2} \times \frac{a}{3} = \frac{P_1aL_1^2}{6} - \frac{P_1a^3}{6}$$

Therefore

$$-\frac{6\,A_1 x_1}{L_1} = -\frac{P_1 a}{L_1}\,(L_1^2 - a^2)$$

In exactly the same way:

$$-\frac{6\,A_2 x_2}{L_2} = -\frac{P_2 b}{L_2}\,(L_2^2 - b^2)$$

The theorem of three moments for concentrated loads is therefore:

$$M_A L_1 + 2\,M_B(L_1 + L_2) + M_C L_2$$
$$= -\frac{P_1 a}{L_1}\,(L_1^2 - a^2) - \frac{P_2 b}{L_2}\,(L_2^2 - b^2)$$

It must be kept in mind that a and b are measured from the outside supports of the two spans. The factor $(L_1^2 - a^2)$ may be computed in the form $(L_1 + a)\,(L_1 - a)$ if more convenient.

In order to cover cases involving more than one load in a span, the above equation is usually written as follows:

$$M_A L_1 + 2\,M_B(L_1 + L_2) + M_C L_2$$
$$= -\sum \frac{P_1 a(L_1^2 - a^2)}{L_1} - \sum \frac{P_2 b(L_2^2 - b^2)}{L_2}$$

The summation sign, $\sum$, before each term of the right-hand member indicates that the term is to be written for each load.

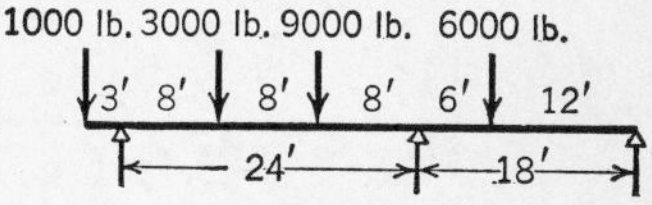

FIG. 369

Example. Calculate the bending moment at the intermediate support of the beam shown in Fig. 369.
Solution:

$$-24 \times 3{,}000 + 84\,M_B + 18 \times 0 = -\frac{3{,}000 \times 8}{24}\,(576 - 64)$$

$$-\frac{9{,}000 \times 16}{24}\,(574 - 256) - \frac{6{,}000 \times 12}{18}\,(324 - 144)$$

$$-72{,}000 + 84\,M_B = -512{,}000 - 1{,}920{,}000 - 720{,}000$$

$$M_B = -\frac{3{,}080{,}000}{84} = -36{,}700 \text{ lb-ft.}$$

PROBLEM

Same as Problem 1, Art. 228.

MOMENTS, SHEARS AND REACTIONS[1]

232. Theorem of Three Moments — Concentrated and Distributed Loads. The theorem of three moments may be written to cover the cases of both concentrated and uniformly distributed loads, as follows:

$$M_A L_1 + 2 M_B (L_1 + L_2) + M_C L_2 = - \sum \frac{P_1 a}{L_1} (L_1^2 - a^2)$$

$$- \sum \frac{P_2 b}{L_2} (L_2^2 - b^2) - \frac{w_1 L_1^3}{4} - \frac{w_2 L_2^3}{4}$$

As an illustration of the substitution of numerical values in the four terms of the right-hand member of the equation consider the two spans

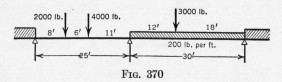

Fig. 370

shown in Fig. 370. Substituting numerical values in the right-hand member of the equation, it becomes,

$$- \frac{2,000 \times 8}{25} (25^2 - 8^2) - \frac{4,000 \times 14}{25} (25^2 - 14^2)$$

$$- \frac{3,000 \times 18}{30} (30^2 - 18^2) - 0 - \frac{200 \times 30^3}{4}$$

There are two loads P_1 and no w_1 in this example.

233. Symmetrical Beams. In case a beam is symmetrical in all respects the bending moments at symmetrically located supports are equal. This reduces the number of unknowns (unless the beam has but two spans) and the number of equations required. In such cases the equal bending moments should be given the same subscripts in writing the equation.

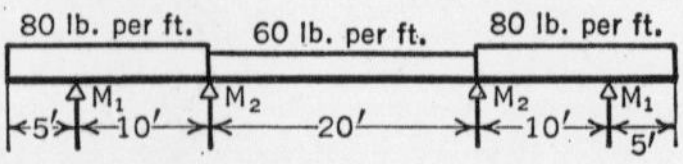

Fig. 371

Example. Calculate the moments at the supports of the beam shown in Fig. 371.

[1] The remainder of this chapter is based on either the double integration method or the area-moment method of deriving the three-moment equation, and should be studied no matter which of those methods (if only one) was studied.

Solution:

$$M_1 = -400 \times 2.5 = -1{,}000 \text{ lb-ft.}$$

$$M_A L_1 + 2 M_B (L_1 + L_2) + M_C L_2 = -\frac{w_1 L_1^3}{4} - \frac{w_2 L_2^3}{4}$$

$$-1{,}000 \times 10 + 2 M_2 \times 30 + 20 M_2 = -\frac{80 \times 1{,}000}{4} - \frac{60 \times 8{,}000}{4}$$

$$-10{,}000 + 80 M_2 = -20{,}000 - 120{,}000 = -140{,}000$$

$$80 M_2 = -130{,}000$$

$$M_2 = -1{,}625 \text{ lb-ft.}$$

PROBLEMS

1. A continuous beam of four equal spans, of L ft. each, overhangs $\frac{1}{3}$ L ft. at each end and carries a uniform load of w lb. per ft. Calculate the moments at the supports.

2. A continuous beam of three equal spans, of L ft. each, carries a load of P lb. at the midpoint of each span. Calculate the moments at the supports.

234. Calculation of Shears and Reactions. The bending moments at all supports having been calculated, it is possible to compute the shears at either end of a span by applying $\Sigma M = 0$ with the other end of the span as the moment center. The shear at a reaction will be designated by a large V with two subscripts, the first being the letter of the reaction and the second being R or L, indicating whether the shear is just to the right or to the left of the reaction.

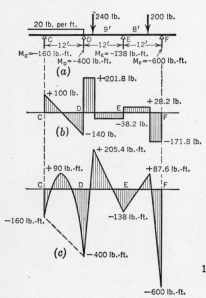

Fig. 372

Example. Three spans of a continuous beam are shown in Fig. 372(a). The bending moments at the supports have been found by the theorem of three moments. Calculate all the shears and the reactions at D and E.

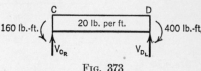

Fig. 373

Solution: Consider as a free body the length of beam between supports C and D. Since the bending moments at C and D are negative, the couples acting on the ends of the segment are as shown (Fig. 373).

Since $\Sigma M_D = 0$, $12 \, V_{CR} + 400 - 160 - (20 \times 12) \, 6 = 0$.
Whence $V_{CR} = +100$ lb. Then

$$V_{DL} = +100 - 240 = -140 \text{ lb.}[1]$$

Considering as a free body the segment between supports D and E, $\Sigma M_E = 0$ gives
$12 \, V_{DR} + 138 - 400 - 240 \times 9 = 0$.
Whence $V_{DR} = +201.8$ lb.
Then $V_{EL} = +201.8 - 240 = -38.2$ lb.
By similar procedures, V_{ER} may be found to be $+28.2$ lb., and V_{FL}, -171.8 lb.
(The student should verify these.) With these values known, the shear diagram
can be drawn for the three spans. It is shown in Fig. 372(b).

Equilibrium of the short length of beam over a support establishes the
amount of the reaction as the *numerical* sum of the shears on either side
of the reaction, if the shears on the two sides are of opposite sign (as they
usually are). If the shears are of the same sign, the reaction equals their
numerical difference.

235. Bending Moments at Intermediate Points. If the shears and
moments at supports are known, the bending moment at any intermediate point is easily determined by applying the definition of bending
moment to the segment of the beam extending from one of the adjacent
supports to the point in question. In the example above, the maximum
bending moment in the CD span occurs where the shear changes sign,
5 ft. from C. At this point $M_5 = -160 + 100 \times 5 - 100 \times 2.5 =
-160 + 250 = +90$ lb-ft. The M curve for this span is a parabola
since the load is uniformly distributed. It should be noted that this

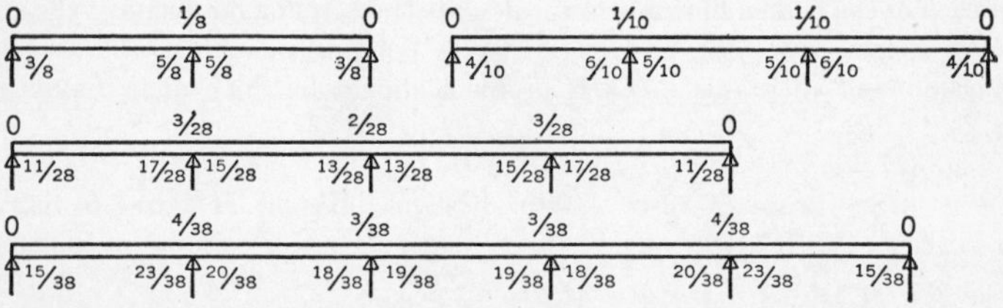

0	⅛	0	0	1/10	1/10	0
⅜	⅝ ⅝	⅜	4/10	6/10 5/10	5/10 5/10	4/10

0	3/28	2/28	3/28	0
11/28	17/28 15/28	13/28 13/28	15/28 17/28	11/28

0	4/38	3/38	3/38	4/38	0
15/38	23/38 20/38	18/38 19/38	19/38 18/38	20/38 23/38	15/38

Coefficients for Moments at Reactions and Shears at ends of Spans for
Continuous Beams with Equal Spans and same Uniform Load over all Spans.

FIG. 374

parabola has the same ordinate as the parabola which is the M diagram
for a simple beam of 12-ft. span with a load of 20 lb. per ft. But in this
case these ordinates for the " combined " M diagram are measured
upward from the sloping straight line the ordinate of which at C is
-160 lb-ft. and at D is -400 lb-ft.

In the DE span the maximum positive bending moment occurs at the

[1] This is the *external shear* at D, and is minus in accordance with the convention
given in Art. 74. This negative external shear is consistent with the upward
resisting shear that acts on the segment just to the left of D.

concentrated load and is 205.4 lb-ft.   The student should verify this and the value of $+87.6$ lb-ft. for the bending moment at the concentrated load in the EF span.

The " combined " bending-moment diagram for these three spans is shown in Fig. 372(c).

Coefficients for shears and bending moments in uniformly loaded beams of equal spans are given in Fig. 374.

PROBLEMS

1. Calculate the shears and bending moments, and draw shear diagram and combined bending-moment diagram for the span of a continuous beam shown in Fig. 375.

2. Calculate the shears and bending moments, and draw shear diagram and combined bending-moment diagram for the span of a continuous beam shown in Fig. 376.

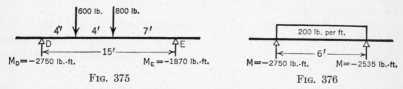

Fig. 375   Fig. 376

3. Calculate shears and bending moments, and draw shear and bending-moment diagrams for the beam of Fig. 371.   For bending moments at the supports, use the values found in the example.

GENERAL PROBLEMS

For each of the beams shown below, calculate the bending moments at the supports. Find the shears, reactions, and intermediate bending moments.   Draw shear and bending-moment diagrams.   (Each problem should be done on a single sheet of paper.)

1. Fig. 377.   *Ans.* $M_B = -576$ lb-ft.

2. Fig. 378.   Beam is 12-in., 40-lb. I-beam.   Weight of beam is included in given loads.   *Ans.* $M_B = -40,000$ lb-ft.

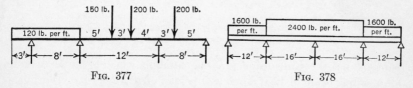

Fig. 377   Fig. 378

3. Using the results found in Problem 2, calculate the maximum bending stress in the beam of Fig. 378.   If this beam were cut at each intermediate support, forming four simple beams, how would the maximum bending stress in each of these compare with the maximum bending stress in the continuous beam?

4. A continuous beam rests on three supports without overhang.   The length of the left-hand span is L ft., and of the right-hand span $L/3$ ft.   A load P is applied at the midpoint of the left-hand span.   How much greater is the reaction of the intermediate support than it would be if the right-hand reaction did not exist?

CHAPTER XIX

BEAMS OF TWO MATERIALS

236. Introduction. Concrete and steel are very often used together in beams. Some use is also made of wood beams strengthened with strips of steel and of beams made of two different metals (Fig. 379). If the two materials are attached to each other so that no slipping can occur, there is a definite distribution of stress which can be determined.

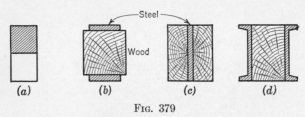

(a)   (b)   (c)   (d)

Fig. 379

A convenient way of attacking such problems is by a method which may be called " equivalent areas."

237. Equivalent Area in Bending. Fig. 380(a) is a cross-section of a beam made of wood and steel. The common assumption that a plane section before bending remains a plane after bending is made for this type

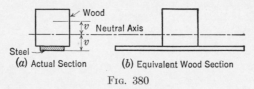

(a) Actual Section   (b) Equivalent Wood Section

Fig. 380

of beam. It follows that the unit stress in any fiber of the wood is proportional to its distance from the neutral axis.

Let $E_s/E_w = n$, the ratio of the modulus of elasticity of the steel to that of the wood.

A " fiber " of steel v in. from the neutral axis will have the same unit deformation as a fiber of wood v in. from the neutral axis. Consequently the unit stress in any steel fiber will be n times the unit stress in a fiber of the wood which is the same distance from the neutral axis. A unit area of steel therefore has n times as much total stress as a unit area of wood the same distance from the neutral axis. If for the area of steel

316

at a given distance from the neutral axis there were substituted n times that area of wood (at the same distance from the neutral axis), the resisting moment of the beam would be the same. The deformations of the substituted fibers would also be the same as the deformation of the actual steel fibers.

From these facts it follows that the position of the neutral axis and the stresses (or resisting moment) may be found by using an equivalent section of one material as shown in Fig. 380(b). The value of I for this equivalent section can be used in the relation $S = Mc/I$.

Example. Calculate the allowable bending moment for a beam made of a 4-in.-by-6-in. timber with a 3-in.-by-$\frac{1}{2}$-in. steel strap adequately fastened to the under side (Fig. 381[a]). How does this compare with the allowable bending moment for the timber alone? Assume that allowable stresses are 1,200 lb. per sq. in. for wood and 18,000 lb. per sq. in. for steel. E for wood = 1,500,000 lb. per sq. in. E for steel = 30,000,000 lb. per sq. in.

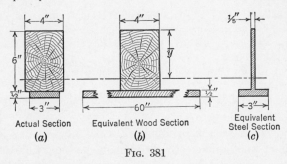

Actual Section	Equivalent Wood Section	Equivalent Steel Section
(a)	(b)	(c)

FIG. 381

Solution: Either the equivalent wood section or the equivalent steel section may be used to calculate the stresses. Using the equivalent wood section (Fig. 381[b]),

$$\bar{y} = \frac{24 \times 3 + 30 \times 6.25}{54} = \frac{72 + 187.5}{54} = 4.81 \text{ in.}$$

$$I_0 = \frac{4 \times 6 \times 6 \times 6}{12} + 24 \times 1.81^2 + \frac{60 \times \frac{1}{2} \times \frac{1}{2} \times \frac{1}{2}}{12} + 30 \times 1.44^2$$

$$= 72 + 78.7 + 0.6 + 62.2 = 213.5 \text{ in.}^4$$

The bending moment must not be greater than that which would cause a stress of 1,200 lb. per sq. in. on the most remote fiber of the wood. The bending moment causing this stress is

$$M = \frac{SI}{c} = \frac{1{,}200 \times 213.5}{4.81} = 53{,}300 \text{ lb-in.}$$

This bending moment may be applied to the beam, provided it does not cause a stress in the steel in excess of 18,000 lb. per sq. in. The stress in the lowest wood fiber of the equivalent section which results from a bending moment of 53,300 lb-in. is $\frac{53{,}300 \times (6.5 - 4.81)}{213.5} = 422$ lb. per sq. in. Since $E_s/E_w = 20$, the bending moment causing a stress of 422 lb. per sq. in. in the wood would cause a stress of 422 × 20 = 8,440 lb. per sq. in. in the steel, which is satisfactory. The bending moment could be increased in the ratio 18,000/8,440 without causing excessive stress in the steel, but any increase above 53,300 lb-in. would cause stresses greater than 1,200 lb. per sq. in. in the wood fibers at the top of the beam.

For the plain timber used as a beam,

$$\frac{I}{c} = \frac{4 \times 6 \times 6}{6} = 24 \text{ in.}^3$$

$M = 1,200 \times 24 = 28,800$ lb-in. (which is only about 54 per cent of the allowable bending moment for the reinforced beam).

The device of an equivalent section can be used just as effectively if the adjoining surfaces of the two materials lie in a plane parallel to the line of action of the loads (Fig. 379[c], [d]).

PROBLEMS

1. A wood beam 10 in. by 16 in. in cross-section is reinforced by securely bolting a 6-in.-by-$\frac{1}{2}$-in. steel plate of the same length to the lower 10-in. face of the beam. Calculate the allowable bending moment if the stress in the wood is not to exceed 1,200 lb. per sq. in. and the stress in the steel is not to exceed 15,000 lb. per sq. in. Assume E for the wood to be 1,200,000 lb. per sq. in.   *Ans.* $M = 703,000$ lb-in.

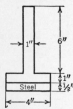

FIG. 382

2. Calculate the allowable bending moment if a 3-in.-by-$\frac{1}{2}$-in. plate is added to the top of the beam in Problem 1.

3. A beam is made by adequately attaching a 4-in.-by-$\frac{1}{2}$-in. steel plate to a T-section of cast iron. The cross-section is shown in Fig. 382. The steel is on the tension side. Calculate the maximum tensile and compressive stresses in the cast iron and the maximum tensile stress in the steel caused by a bending moment of 100,000 lb-in. Assume E for cast iron to be 0.4 E for steel.

4. Two 8-in., 11.5-lb. channels are adequately bolted to an 8-in.-by-8-in. (actual size) oak beam as shown in Fig. 379(d). If E for oak is 1,500,000 lb. per sq. in., calculate the allowable bending moment. Allowable stresses are, for steel, 18,000 lb. per sq. in.; for oak, 800 lb. per sq. in.

238. Shearing Stress in Beams of Two Materials.

An equation giving the shearing unit stresses (horizontal and vertical) at any point in any cross-section of a beam was derived in Chapter VIII. This equation, $S_s = VQ/Ib$, can also be applied to beams of two materials, by using the equivalent cross-section for a beam of one of the two materials, as explained in the previous article. The reason is as follows:

In deriving the equation for shearing unit stresses, the shearing *force* on the horizontal surface of a block (which was taken as a free body) was equated to the difference between the forces exerted by the bending stresses on the ends of the block. Since the *forces* on the equivalent cross-section are the same as the forces on the cross-section of the original beam, it is apparent that the equation for shearing unit stress may be used in connection with an equivalent section.

Example. As an example, let Fig. 383(a) be the cross-section of a composite beam of brass and steel for which values of E may be taken as 15,000,000 lb. per sq. in. and 30,000,000 lb. per sq. in., respectively. The equivalent cross-section for a steel beam is shown in (b) and the equivalent cross-section for a brass beam is shown in (c). The neutral axes of the two equivalent cross-sections are shown and are necessarily at the same distance from the lower edges of the cross-sections.

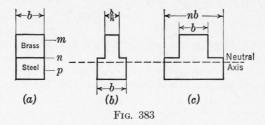

FIG. 383

The equation $S_s = VQ/Ib$ may be applied to *either* equivalent section, but it is somewhat simpler to use the equivalent section which has the width of the original beam at the point where the shearing stress is desired. Thus, to calculate shearing stresses at m and n, the section shown in (c) should be used. To calculate the shearing stress at p, the section shown in (b) should be used.

PROBLEM

Calculate the allowable total shear in a beam with the cross-section shown in Fig. 381 if the allowable shearing stress along the grain for the wood is 120 lb. per sq. in.

239. Deflection of Beams of Two Materials. The curvature of a beam may be regarded as the result of the changes in length of the " fibers " in the beam. Since the fibers at any point in a beam of two materials change in length by the same amount as the fibers at the corresponding point in the beam of one material with " equivalent

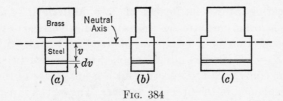

FIG. 384

cross-section," it follows that the deflections of the two beams are the same. Consequently the deflection at any point of a beam of two materials may be found by calculating the deflection of a beam of equivalent cross-section of one material.

The methods used in this book for calculating deflections of beams are based on the relationship expressed by the equation $1/\rho = M/EI$, in which EI is a function involving the shape and size of the cross-section and the stiffness of the material. Fig. 384 shows (a) the cross-section of a beam of two materials (say brass and steel), (b) the equivalent cross-section of a steel beam, and (c) the equivalent cross-section of a brass beam. By considering elementary strips such as the one shown at a distance v from the neutral axis, it is apparent that EI for the steel beam (b) equals EI for the brass beam (c) and that this value of EI also equals the E for brass times the I (with respect to the neutral axis) of the area of brass plus the E for steel times the I (with respect to the neutral axis) of the area of steel. The quantity EI can therefore be computed from either of the equivalent sections or from the cross-section of the actual beam after the neutral axis has been found from an equivalent cross-section.

PROBLEM

The beam shown in Fig. 381 is 12 ft. long and carries a uniform load of 250 lb. per ft. Calculate the deflection at the midpoint. $E = 1,500,000$ for the wood.

240. Reinforced-Concrete Beams. The most common use of two materials in beams occurs in reinforced-concrete construction. Concrete beams without reinforcing could be used only for relatively short spans and light loads because of the weakness of concrete in tension.

In reinforced-concrete construction, the reinforcing steel is placed in the forms before the concrete is poured. When the concrete sets it adheres very firmly to the steel. This adherence is called " bond." Fortunately, steel and concrete contract and expand about the same amount with change in temperature. The firm bond and the roughly equal thermal expansion of steel and concrete are both essential to the success of reinforced concrete.

Reinforcing steel is generally in the form of bars which may be round or square, or twisted, or otherwise " deformed." Sometimes woven wire mesh, welded wire mesh, or " expanded " metal is used as reinforcing.

241. Assumptions in Reinforced Concrete. Because of the low tensile strength of concrete it is common practice to assume that the concrete in a reinforced-concrete beam carries *no tensile stress at all*. It is also generally assumed that the compressive unit stress in the concrete at a given cross-section is proportional to the distance from the neutral axis. The steel at a given cross-section is assumed to be uniformly stressed, since it is so placed that all of it is at nearly the same distance from the neutral axis (see Fig. 385[c]). The force exerted by the steel is therefore the product of the stress in the steel and the cross-sectional area of

the steel and is assumed to act at the center of the cross-section of
the steel.   These assumptions are not exact but are probably as near
to the truth as the assumed values for strength and modulus of elasticity
of concrete.

242. Resisting Moment.   The result of the assumptions made is
illustrated in Fig. 385(*b*).   The unit stress in the concrete varies from

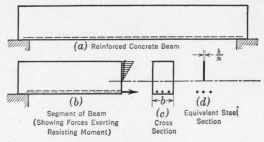

FIG. 385

zero at the neutral axis to a maximum at the top of the beam.   This
variation of stresses is represented by short arrows, increasing in length
from the neutral axis to the top.   The distance from the top of the beam
to the resultant compressive force is one-third of the distance from the
top of the beam to the neutral axis.   The resultant force equals the
product of the *average* unit compressive stress in the concrete (which
is one-half the maximum compressive stress) and the area of the cross-
section above the neutral axis.   The amount and position of this resultant as here stated occur in the solution of many problems and
should be kept in mind.   The resisting moment at any section may be
regarded as a couple.   One of the forces is the resultant of the compressive stresses in the concrete, and the other force is the resultant of
the tensile stress in the steel.

The equivalent steel section is shown in Fig. 385(*d*).   This consists of
the actual cross-sectional area of the reinforcing steel and the steel
equivalent of the concrete above the neutral axis.   This is a rectangle
with a width $1/n$ times the width of the beam.   The position of the
neutral axis of the cross-section must be computed.   It does not pass
through the centroid of the actual cross-section of the beam, but through
the centroid of the equivalent steel section.

243. Investigation of a Rectangular Reinforced-Concrete Beam.
The steps that are taken in the investigation of a reinforced-concrete
beam will be illustrated with an assumed numerical example.   Let the
assumed beam be 6 in. by $11\frac{1}{2}$ in. in cross-section.   The reinforcing consists of three $\frac{5}{8}$-in. round rods 10 in. below the top of the beam as shown

in Fig. 386(a). Assume $E_s = 30,000,000$ and $E_c = 2,000,000$ lb. per sq. in., making $n = 15$. It is desired to find the maximum stress in the concrete and the stress in the steel which result from a bending moment of 75,000 lb-in.

The position of the neutral axis is most easily found by determining the position of the centroid of the equivalent steel section, shown in

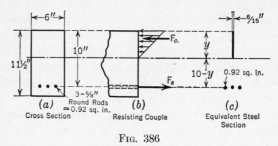

(a) Cross Section   Round Rods = 0.92 sq. in.   (b) Resisting Couple   (c) Equivalent Steel Section

FIG. 386

Fig. 386(c). The moments of the area above the neutral axis equal the moment of the area below it. Whence,

$$\frac{6}{15} y \times \frac{y}{2} = 0.92 \, (10 - y)$$

$$0.2 \, y^2 = 9.2 - 0.92 \, y$$

$$y^2 + 4.6 \, y = 46$$

Whence $y = 4.86$ in.

The resultant compressive force acts $y/3$ in. below the top of the beam. The distance between F_c and F_s is $10 - \dfrac{4.86}{3} = 10 - 1.62 = 8.38$ in. The resisting moment equals $8.38 \, F_c = 8.38 \, F_s$. For the given bending moment of 75,000 lb-in.

$$F_c = F_s = \frac{75,000}{8.38} = 8,950 \text{ lb.}$$

The stress in the steel, $S_s = 8,950/0.92 = 9,730$ lb. per sq. in.

The stress in the equivalent steel section at the top may be calculated by $F_c = 0.2 \, S'_s \times 4.86$

$$S'_s = \frac{8,950}{0.2 \times 4.86} = 9,200 \text{ lb. per sq. in.}$$

This could also have been calculated by proportion

$$\frac{S'_s}{S_s} = \frac{4.86}{5.14} \qquad S'_s = 9,730 \times \frac{4.86}{5.14} = 9,200 \text{ lb. per sq. in.}$$

The actual stress in the concrete at the top of the beam is $\frac{1}{15}$ of the stress at the top of the equivalent steel section.

$$S_c = \frac{9,200}{15} = 613 \text{ lb. per sq. in.}$$

Many specifications for reinforced concrete limit the maximum stress in the concrete to 650 lb. per sq. in. For the beam in the present example this stress in the concrete would occur with a bending moment of $650/613 \times 75,000 = 79,500$ lb-in. For this bending moment the stress in the steel would become $650/613 \times 9,730 = 10,300$ lb. per sq. in. Most specifications permit a stress of 18,000 lb. per sq. in. in the reinforcing steel. It is obvious that the steel is not working up to its full capacity. The beam is poorly designed.

244. Determination of Cross-Section of a Rectangular Reinforced-Concrete Beam. At the cross-section of maximum bending moment, safety requires that the materials in a concrete beam be not overstressed and economy requires that they be not greatly understressed. The designer should meet both these conditions. A method of determining a suitable cross-section to resist a given bending moment will now be illustrated.

Let it be assumed that the beam is required to carry a bending moment of 330,000 lb-in. Allowable stresses are 650 lb. per sq. in. compression in concrete and 18,000 lb. per sq. in. tension in steel. Use $n = E_s/E_c = 15$.

Let y in. be the unknown depth from the top of the cross-section to the neutral axis. The equivalent steel section is shown in (c) and the

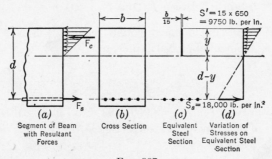

(a) Segment of Beam with Resultant Forces   (b) Cross Section   (c) Equivalent Steel Section   (d) Variation of Stresses on Equivalent Steel Section

FIG. 387

corresponding stresses are shown in (d) of Fig. 387. The stress in the equivalent steel at the top of the beam would be $15 \times 650 = 9,750$ lb. per sq. in. compression, if the actual stress in the concrete is 650 lb. per sq. in.

Since a plane section before bending remains a plane after bending, it follows that the stress at any point in the equivalent steel section is proportional to the distance from the neutral axis. In this beam the position of the neutral axis is determined by the fact that the stress at the top of the section will be 9,750 lb. per sq. in. when the stress in steel is 18,000 lb. per sq. in., and by the additional fact that both of these stresses are proportional to the distances from the neutral axis. Hence, by similar triangles, as shown in Fig. 387(d)

$$\frac{y}{d - y} = \frac{9,750}{18,000}$$

$$18,000\, y = 9,750\, d - 9,750\, y$$

$$27,750\, y = 9,750\, d$$

$$y = \frac{9,750}{27,750}\, d = 0.351\, d \text{ in.}$$

The distance between the resultant compressive force, F_c, and the tensile force, F_s, is

$$d - \frac{y}{3} = d - 0.117\, d = 0.883\, d \text{ in.}$$

The resultant compressive force,

$$F_c = \frac{15 \times 650}{2} \times \frac{b}{15} \times 0.351\, d = 114\, bd$$

The resisting moment is F_c times the distance between F_c and F_s. This must equal 330,000 lb.-in.

Therefore 114 bd × 0.883 d = 330,000

$$bd^2 = \frac{330,000}{114 \times 0.883} = 3,280 \text{ in.}^3$$

Any cross-section for which $bd^2 = 3,280$ will meet the requirements. It is apparent, however, that the deeper the beam, the larger will be the moment arm of the resisting moment and the smaller the force. A deep beam will therefore require less steel and less concrete than a shallower beam. There are practical limits to the depth. These will not be discussed here. A satisfactory cross-section which is practicable and reasonably economical is one in which d is about $1\frac{1}{2}\, b$.

If these proportions are chosen,

$$bd^2 = \tfrac{9}{4}\, b^3 = 3,280$$

$$b^3 = 1,460$$

$$b = 11.3$$

If b is made even 11 in.,

$$d^2 = \frac{3,280}{11} = 298$$

$d = 17.25$ in. from top of beam to *center of steel*

The moment arm of the resisting couple is $0.883 \times 17.25 = 15.20$ in. The cross-sectional area of steel can be calculated from the relation $18,000 \, A_s \times 15.20 = 330,000$, giving

$$A_s = \frac{330,000}{18,000 \times 15.20} = 1.21 \text{ sq. in.}$$

If round rods are used (the available diameters being in multiples of $\frac{1}{8}$ in.), it may not be possible to provide exactly 1.21 sq. in. of steel. For three suitable sizes of round rods the areas of steel that could be used are:

7 rods $\frac{1}{2}$ in. in diameter $= 1.37$ sq. in.

4 rods $\frac{5}{8}$ in. in diameter $= 1.23$ sq. in.

3 rods $\frac{3}{4}$ in. in diameter $= 1.33$ sq. in.

If the rods $\frac{5}{8}$ in. in diameter are selected there is a very slight excess of steel. The resulting unit stress in the steel will be slightly less than 18,000 lb. per sq. in., the stress in the concrete will be slightly less than 650 lb. per sq. in., and the position of the neutral axis will be lowered a little. These changes are very small and may be neglected. There should be $1\frac{1}{2}$ in. of concrete below the rods to insure adequate " bond " and protection to the reinforcing. The total depth of the beam will be $17.25 + \frac{5}{16} + 1.5 = 19$ in.

PROBLEMS

1. A rectangular reinforced-concrete beam is 10 in. wide, 20 in. deep. There are four $\frac{1}{2}$-in. square reinforcing rods 18.25 in. below the top of the beam. Calculate, by the method of this article, the allowable bending moment if stress in the concrete is not to exceed 650 lb. per sq. in. and stress in the steel is not to exceed 18,000 lb. per sq. in.

2. By the method of this article, find the dimensions of the cross-section of a reinforced-concrete beam to carry a bending moment of 260,000 lb-in. Also select suitable square steel rods for reinforcing. (The bottom of the rods is to be $1\frac{1}{2}$ in. above bottom of beam.) Allowable stresses are 18,000 lb. per sq. in. for steel, and 650 lb. per sq. in. for concrete. Make depth of beam approximately twice the width. Compare the weight of this beam with the weight of a steel I-beam which will carry this bending moment with a stress not exceeding 18,000 lb. per sq. in.

245. Formulas for Reinforced-Concrete Beams. The design of concrete structure is complicated by many considerations which cannot be taken up in a book of this scope. The foregoing articles have developed the relationships which determine the tensile stress in the steel and the compressive stress in the concrete due to the bending of a rectangular beam. There is not space here to do more than merely mention other problems in concrete design, such as provision of reinforcement to help resist the shearing stress in a beam, methods of securing proper bond between steel and concrete to keep the steel from slipping, the design of beams having a T-shaped cross-section, etc.

Although the method developed in the two preceding articles can be used in the design and investigation of concrete beams, it is customary in practice to make use of a number of formulas which are derived from the principles just developed. If specific values for known quantities are substituted in these formulas, required values can be found. The terminology and symbols used are quite well established. The principles discussed in the preceding articles will now be applied to the derivation of some of these formulas, in order that the student may become familiar with them and with the symbols.

Study of the following articles will not qualify one to design concrete structures, but it should form a foundation for a more intelligent reading of the literature of the subject, and for further study.

246. Symbols Commonly Used in Concrete Beam Formulas. The following notation is commonly used:

b = width of beam (inches).

d = depth of beam *to center of reinforcing* (inches).

A_s = area of cross-section of reinforcing steel (square inches).

p = " per cent " of reinforcing. Actually not a percentage, but the ratio of the area of reinforcing steel to the area bd. Hence $A_s = pbd$.

kd = distance from top of beam to neutral axis (inches).

jd = moment arm of resisting couple, or distance (inches) between resultant compressive force and resultant tensile force.

n = E_s/E_c the ratio of the modulus of elasticity of steel to that of concrete.

f_c = compressive unit stress in the extreme fibers of concrete.

f_s = tensile unit stress in reinforcing steel.

(Note that k and j are always less than unity.)

This notation will be used in the following articles except that, instead of f, S will be used to designate unit stress, as heretofore.

247. Position of Neutral Axis, Given n and p. For a given n (ratio of E_s to E_c) and a given " percentage " of steel, p, there is a definite value of k. When this is found the distance from the top of the beam to the neutral axis is found by multiplying the depth of the beam (to the center of the steel) by k. A formula will now be derived which gives the value of k in terms of n and p. In Fig. 388 a typical cross-section of a reinforced concrete beam is shown in (a) and the resisting moment or couple is shown in (b).

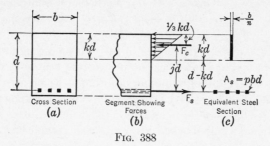

FIG. 388

Since $\Sigma H = 0$, $F_c = F_s$. Therefore

$$kd\frac{b}{n} \times \frac{S'_s}{2} = pbdS_s$$

(in which S'_s is the stress at the top of the equivalent steel section).

Hence

$$\frac{S'_s}{S_s} = \frac{2\,pn}{k}$$

Also

$$\frac{S'_s}{S_s} = \frac{kd}{d - kd} = \frac{k}{1 - k}$$

(since, in the equivalent steel section, the stress is proportional to the distance from the neutral axis).

Equating these values of S'_s/S_s,

$$\frac{k}{1 - k} = \frac{2\,pn}{k}$$
$$k^2 = 2\,pn - 2\,pnk$$
$$k = \sqrt{2\,pn + p^2n^2} - pn$$

The values of n commonly used are those specified by the " Joint Committee."[1] They are given on page 328. These depend on the specified compressive strength of the concrete 28 days after mixing.

[1] Progress Report of Joint Committee on Standard Specifications for Concrete and Reinforced Concrete, January, 1937. The " Joint Committee " includes representatives of the following five organizations: American Society of Civil Engineers, American Society for Testing Materials, American Railway Engineering Association, American Concrete Institute, Portland Cement Association.

Strength of Concrete, lb. per sq. in.	Specified Value of n
2,000–2,400	15
2,500–2,900	12
3,000–3,900	10
4,000–4,900	8
Above 5,000	6

The value of $n = 15$ applies to the concrete usually specified in rein-forced-concrete construction.

In the diagram (Fig. 389), values of k are plotted for different values of p and for values of n of 10, 12, and 15. From this diagram, values of k can be found without calculation with sufficient accuracy.

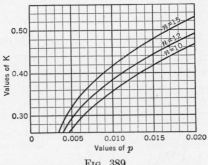

FIG. 389

248. Balanced Reinforcing. Building codes and other specifications state allowable stresses for reinforcing steel and for concrete of given strength or proportions. If the percentage of reinforcing steel is chosen at random, the bending moment which stresses the concrete to the specified value will cause a stress in the steel more or less than the spec-ified allowable stress for steel.

For a given value of n there is only one value of p which will result in a beam section in which the allowable bending moment causes the allowable stresses in both the steel and the concrete. This value of p gives the most economical cross-section, since both materials are work-ing to the allowed limit.

If S_s and S_c represent the specified allowable stresses, this value of p can be found in terms of S_s/S_c and n. The assumption that a plane section before bending remains a plane after bending gives the relation

$$\frac{nS_c}{S_s} = \frac{kd}{d - kd} = \frac{k}{1 - k}$$

from which

$$k = \frac{nS_c/S_s}{1+\dfrac{nS_c}{S_s}} = \frac{1}{\dfrac{S_s}{nS_c}+1}$$

The requirement of statics that $F_c = F_s$ gives

$$kdb\frac{S_c}{2} = pbdS_s$$

from which

$$p = \frac{k}{2\dfrac{S_s}{S_c}}$$

Substituting in this the value for k found above,

$$p = \frac{1}{2\dfrac{S_s}{S_c}\left(\dfrac{S_s}{nS_c}+1\right)}$$

When p has the value which results in the specified stresses in both steel and concrete, with the beam subjected to the allowable bending moment, the reinforcing is said to be *balanced*.

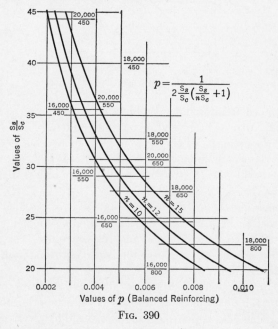

FIG. 390

Fig. 390 is a diagram from which the value of p for balanced reinforcing may be found for any value of S_s/S_c.

249. Formulas for Investigation of a Beam. Several formulas can be derived for the allowable resisting moment (which equals the allowable bending moment) in a concrete beam of given cross-section and with a given amount of reinforcing, provided the value of n is known or assumed. Since the amount of reinforcing is known, the value of p can be determined. The value of p and n fix the value of k, as shown in Art. 247. With these terms known, the allowable bending moment can be very simply expressed, either in terms of the allowable stress in the steel, or of the allowable stress in the concrete. For a given unit stress in the steel the resisting moment equals the resultant force exerted by the steel multiplied by the distance between the resultant tensile and compressive forces.

Hence

$$M = F_s jd = S_s A_s jd$$

But

$$A_s = pbd, \quad \text{so that} \quad M = S_s pbjd^2$$

Substituting $1 - k/3$ for j (see Fig. 388),

$$M = S_s pbd^2 (1 - k/3)$$

In a similar way, the resisting moment in terms of the maximum stress in the concrete is

$$M = F_c jd = \frac{S_c}{2} bkd(jd) = \frac{1}{2} S_c kj(bd^2)$$

These two equations for the bending moment can, of course, be used for the determination of the stresses caused in the steel and the concrete of a given beam by a given bending moment.

250. Steps in the Design of a Concrete Beam. The starting point in the design of a reinforced-concrete beam which is to resist a known bending moment is the selection of the allowable stresses to be used and a decision as to the most probable value of n. Generally these stresses and n are prescribed by a building code or some other specification. Sometimes the designer must himself decide on appropriate values. When the allowable stresses and the value of n have been decided on, the value of p for greatest economy can be determined from the equation of Art. 248 or from a diagram such as Fig. 390. When the value of p has been selected, the value of k is found by the formula developed in Art. 247. With all the foregoing quantities known, the next step in the design is the determination of the dimensions b and d of the concrete cross-section. (These determine the cross-section of the steel, since p is known.) Either of the foregoing formulas may be used to determine the product bd^2. With this product found, an assumption can be made as to the relative values of b and d and each dimension determined. With b, d, and p known, suitable reinforcing bars are selected. After this is done, shearing and bond stresses must also be investigated and provided for. These steps are not within the scope of this book.

PROBLEMS

1. A rectangular concrete beam is 12 in. wide and 28 in. deep. At the center cross-section there are four steel rods, $\frac{3}{4}$ in. square. The center of the rods is 2 in. above the bottom of the beam. Calculate the maximum bending moment that will not cause stresses exceeding 18,000 lb. per sq. in. in the steel and 650 lb. per sq. in. in the concrete. Assume $n = 15$. *Ans.* $M = 854,000$ lb-in.

2. Solve Problem 1 if the beam has five rods $\frac{3}{4}$ in. square, instead of four.

3. Calculate the depth and the number of square inches of reinforcing steel for a beam 10 in. wide which is to resist a bending moment of 35,000 lb-ft. Allowable stresses are: $S_c = 650$ lb. per sq. in. and $S_s = 18,000$ lb. per sq. in. Assume $n = 15$. Use balanced reinforcing.

CHAPTER XX

BEAMS — ADDITIONAL TOPICS

251. Introduction. This chapter is divided into the following parts:

Maximum Normal and Shearing Stresses in Beams.
Longitudinal Shear in " Built-up " Beams.
Shearing Deflection of Beams.
Beams of Materials That Do Not Follow Hooke's Law.
Buckling of Beam Flanges and Webs.
Curved Beams.
Beams Having Loads Not in the Plane of a Principal Axis of
Inertia.
Beams Whose Cross-section Has No Vertical Axis of Symmetry;
Shear Center.

The first three of these divisions treat problems in the design or use of beams that were not considered sufficiently fundamental for inclusion in the chapters where ordinary problems in beam stresses and deflections were considered. The remaining five divisions discuss situations to which the ordinary flexure formula, $S = Mc/I$, does not apply, and present modifications of the basic formula or present supplemental formulas that must also be used; or they specify and discuss the conditions that must be introduced if the ordinary formula is to be valid.

MAXIMUM NORMAL AND SHEARING STRESSES IN BEAMS

252. Maximum Stresses in Beams. It is evident from the results of Art. 191 that the " bending stress " at a given point in a beam calculated by the flexure formula is not the maximum stress at that point if shearing stress exists at that point. It is also true that the shearing unit stress (horizontal and vertical) at a point in a beam calculated from $S_s = VQ/Ib$ is not the maximum shearing stress at that point if tensile or compressive stress exists at that point.

Before discussing the importance of these maximum stresses an example will be solved to illustrate the calculation of maximum stresses in a steel beam.

Example. An 18-in., 96-lb. wide-flange beam is used as a cantilever projecting 4.96 ft. and carrying a uniformly distributed total load of 111,600 lb. Determine the maximum normal and shearing stresses at the fixed end. (This loading is such as to give a maximum bending stress of 18,000 lb. per sq. in. and a shearing stress on the gross area of the web of 12,000 lb. per sq. in., which are the allowable stresses of the New York City Building Code, 1938.)

Solution: The dimensions and properties of this beam are given below: Depth of beam, 18.16 in.; width of flange, 11.75 in.; thickness of web, 0.512; thickness of flange, 0.831; $I_1 = 1674.7$ in.[4]; $I/c = 184.4$ in.[3]

Fig. 391(a) shows the upper half of the cross-section of the beam; (b) shows the variation of the bending stress; and (c), the variation of the horizontal shearing stress. For four points on the cross-section the maximum normal stresses (principal stresses) are shown in (e), and for the same four points the maximum shearing stresses are shown in (d).

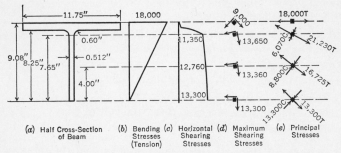

(a) Half Cross-Section of Beam   (b) Bending Stresses (Tension)   (c) Horizontal Shearing Stresses   (d) Maximum Shearing Stresses   (e) Principal Stresses

FIG. 391. Maximum stresses in a wide-flange beam.

The computations for these values at the point on the web where the fillets begin will be shown. The other values are found in a similar way.

$$S_s = \frac{VQ}{Ib} = \frac{111,600(11.75 \times 0.831 \times 8.664 + 0.60 \times 0.512 \times 7.949)}{1,674.7 \times 0.512}$$
$$= 11,350 \text{ lb. per sq. in.}$$

$$S_t = \frac{My}{I} = \frac{3,320,000 \times 7.649}{1,674.7} = 15,170 \text{ lb. per sq. in.}$$

$$S_s\text{max.} = \sqrt{\left(\frac{S_t}{2}\right)^2 + S_s^2} = \sqrt{7,585^2 + 11,350^2} = 13,650 \text{ lb. per sq. in.}$$

$$S_n = \frac{S_t}{2} \pm S_s \text{ max.} = 7,580 \pm 13,650 = +21,230 \text{ lb. per sq. in., tension}$$
$$\text{or} \quad -6,070 \text{ lb. per sq. in., compression}$$

The two planes on which the maximum normal stresses (principal stresses) act make an angle θ with the horizontal such that $\tan 2\theta = \dfrac{-2 S_s}{S_t} = \dfrac{-22,700}{15,170} = -1.497.$ $2\theta = 123° 44'$, or $303° 44'$, and $\theta = 61° 52'$ or $151° 52'$. The planes on which the maximum shearing stresses exist are inclined 45° to those on which the principal stresses act.

It will be noticed that, although this beam is not overstressed according to the New York City Building Code, 1938, the maximum tensile stress calculated above exceeds the allowable bending stress by 18 per cent. Structural specifications do not specify that the maximum tensile stress in a beam shall not exceed the specified allowable stress, but instead it is specified that the maximum *bending stress on the extreme fibers* shall not exceed a stated allowable stress (by *bending stress* is meant the stress computed by $S = Mc/I$). This may be regarded as one example of the " inaccuracy in the calculation of stress " for which the factor of safety may legitimately be expected to provide.

Although the loading assumed above may occur (as in footings, etc.), in the majority of beams such unfavorable combinations of large bending moment and large shear on the same cross-section are not found. For many beams supported at the ends the shear is small at points where bending moments are large, and vice versa. Furthermore, on any cross-section of most beams the shearing stress is small at points where bending stresses are large. (The wide-flange beam considered in the above example has exceptionally high shearing stresses in the web near the flanges because it combines heavy flanges with a thin web.) In the majority of beams, because of the conditions just mentioned, the maximum bending stresses in the extreme fibers are, in fact, the maximum principal stresses.

Also in the majority of beams the maximum *total shear* occurs at a section where the bending moment is small; and on the cross-section where the greatest total shear occurs the maximum shearing stress occurs at the neutral axis where there is no bending stress. Consequently, in the majority of cases the maximum longitudinal (and vertical) shearing stress is, in fact, the maximum shearing stress in the beam. But a designer should know when this will not be true.

Fig. 392.   Directions of principal stresses.

A more general study of the principal stresses in beams is of help in understanding the behavior of beams and their possible failure. Fig. 392 represents a side view of a beam of rectangular cross-section carrying a uniformly distributed load. For simplicity it will be assumed that the load carried by the beam is its own weight only and that it is supported at the ends without concentrated reactions.[1]

[1] Concentrated loads and reactions cause local stresses which will not be considered here. A uniformly distributed load resting on the top of the beam also causes compressive stresses on the top surface which extend into the beam. In order to avoid, for the present, the complication of local stresses due to reactions, the beam may be thought of as the middle segment of a beam fixed at both ends, the segment extending between the two points of zero bending moment.

The lines drawn on the face of the beam indicate the direction of the principal stresses, the tangent and normal to a curve at any point being the directions of the two principal stresses at that point. The set of curves concave downward indicate the directions of compressive principal stresses (there is tensile stress normal to the curve at every point, its magnitude being zero at all points above the neutral axis on a vertical line at the midpoint of the beam). In the same way the set of curves concave upward follow the directions of tensile principal stresses. Wherever a curve of one set crosses a curve of the other set the intersection is necessarily at a right angle. The shear being zero at the midsection of the beam, the principal stresses at the midsection are the bending stresses calculated from $S = My/I$. Therefore all curves are horizontal at the midpoint of the beam. At the end of the beam the bending moment is zero and the principal stresses are those resulting from shearing stresses on vertical and horizontal planes. These principal stresses are inclined 45° to the horizontal and vertical and are equal in intensity to the unit shearing stress at any point. Since bending stresses are zero along the neutral axis the principal stresses there result from shear alone and all the lines cross the neutral axis with an inclination of 45°. It should be clearly kept in mind that these lines are not lines of constant intensity of stress.

The occurrence of the tensile principal stresses inclined 45° at the ends of the beam is of significance in beams of materials with low tensile strength such as concrete. In reinforced-concrete beams there are steel rods embedded in the concrete to carry the tensile stresses. These are placed near the bottom of the beam (if the bending moment is positive). Near the ends, some are bent upwards at an angle of about 45° as shown in Fig. 393.

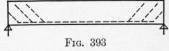

Fig. 393

This inclined reinforcing is commonly called " shear " reinforcing but actually resists the tensile stresses resulting from shearing stresses. The concrete itself has ample compressive strength to resist the compression stresses caused by the shear.

It should be understood that the distribution of stresses in a composite beam is not exactly the same as in a beam of homogeneous material.

PROBLEM

Calculate the maximum shearing and normal stress at a point 6 in. above the neutral axis at the cross-section of the beam considered in the preceding example. Also calculate the inclinations of the planes on which these stresses act, and represent stresses as acting on small cubes properly oriented.

LONGITUDINAL SHEAR IN "BUILT-UP" BEAMS

253. Connection of Cover Plates to Flanges. Fig. 394(a) represents the cross-section of an I-beam with a cover plate riveted to each flange to increase the section modulus of the beam, a method frequently used. Obviously, as the beam bends (it may be assumed that the loads are applied to the web of the I-beam), the compressive stresses in the top cover plate are the result of the forces exerted on it by the rivets which serve the same function as the longitudinal shearing stresses in a beam made of one piece. The problem is to determine the necessary spacing of the rivets.

It is evident from the relation already established (Chapter VIII) between the vertical shear V and the longitudinal shearing stresses that the rivets should be most closely spaced where the vertical shear V is greatest.

As shown in Art. 91, the force on the B end of the segment of cover plate (Fig. 394(c)) is $F_B = M_B Q/I$, where Q is the statical moment of

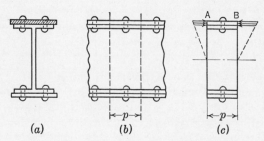

(a)   (b)   (c)

FIG. 394.   Rolled beam with cover plates.

the cross-section of the cover plate with respect to the neutral axis of the entire cross-section.[1] On the A end, the force is $F_A = M_A Q/I$. Hence the force which the rivets between A and B must exert is $F_B - F_A = (M_B - M_A)Q/I$. Since the change in bending moment equals the area of the shear diagram between the two points A and B, $M_B - M_A = pV_{av.}$, in which $V_{av.}$ is the average value of V in the distance AB. Hence, $F_B - F_A = pV_{av.}Q/I$. This gives the value of the force which must be supplied by the rivets in a distance of p in. If R is the value of one rivet in shear or bearing (whichever is least), and if there are n rivets in a group ($n = 2$, in the case illustrated), $nR = pV_{av.}Q/I$, or $p = \dfrac{nRI}{V_{av.}Q}$ for the distance between groups of rivets.

[1] Q is computed from the gross area of the cross-section of the cover plate, making no allowance for the rivet holes.

Practical considerations limit the distance between rivet groups where the vertical shear is small. Specifications for structural details contain rules governing such matters. For instance, it is frequently specified that for $\frac{7}{8}$ or $\frac{3}{4}$-in. rivets the pitch shall not exceed 6 in., or 16 times the thickness of the cover plate, whichever is less.[1]

When a cover plate is to be *welded* to the flange of an I-beam, the welds must furnish the force provided by the rivets in the above discussion. If the unit length of flange to be considered, p, is taken as 1 ft. or 12 in., and R is the allowable load on 1 in. of fillet of a given size, then n, the number of inches of fillet per foot length of flange, is given by

$$n = \frac{12 \, V_{av.} Q}{RI}.$$

Specifications establish minimum allowable lengths of fillet and maximum spacings between welds.[2]

254. Connection of Flange to Web of Girder. A plate girder is a " built-up " beam consisting of a web plate to which angles and generally one or more cover plates are attached to form each flange (Fig. 395). If loads are applied to the web of the girder, as in the preceding article, the spacing of rivets is given by the same equation $p = \dfrac{nRI}{V_{av.} Q}$ (in this case, of course, Q is the statical moment of the cross-section of the entire flange). It should be remembered that the rivets are in double shear. The value of a rivet will generally be determined by bearing against the web.

FIG. 395. Plate girder.

PROBLEMS

1. A plate girder is made up of a 48-in.-by-$\frac{1}{2}$-in. web plate, and each flange consists of 2 angles 6 in. by 6 in. by $\frac{3}{4}$-in. and 1 cover plate 14 in. by 1 in. arranged as in Fig. 395. At a section where the total shear is 256,000 lb. determine the required spacing of the pairs of rivets connecting the cover plate to the angles. Rivets are $\frac{7}{8}$ in.; $S_s = 12,000$ lb. per sq. in.; and $S_c = 24,000$ lb. per sq. in. The distance " back to back of angles " is $48\frac{1}{2}$ in.

2. Calculate the required distance between the rivets connecting the flange to the web of the girder of Problem 1.

3. A 14-in.-by-1-in. cover plate is to be welded to each flange of a 16-in., 88-lb. wide-flange beam. Calculate the length of $\frac{3}{8}$-in. fillet required per foot of beam to attach one cover plate if the shear causes an average stress of 12,000 lb. per sq. in. over the web.   *Ans.* $n = 14.2$ in.

[1] " Standard Specifications for Highway Bridges " (1935), American Association of State Highway Officials.

[2] See, for example, " Standard Specifications for Arc Welding Metal Bridge Structures," American Association of State Highway Officials.

SHEARING DEFLECTION OF BEAMS

255. Shearing Deflection of Beams. The methods of calculating beam deflections which were explained in Chapter X give the deflection due to bending only. Additional deflections result from shearing deformation. In most cases these deflections due to shear are so small in comparison with deflections due to bending that they can be disregarded. In short, deep beams, however, the deflections due to shear may sometimes be important.

Art. 212 shows how the principles of elastic energy can be used to determine the bending deflections of a beam. The same principles can be utilized for finding the deflections due to shear, and Problem 1, Art. 212, gives the shearing deflection due to a load P at the end of a prismatic cantilever beam of rectangular cross-section as $\Delta_s = \dfrac{6\,PL}{5\,E_sA}$.

The *bending* deflection for this beam and loading is $\Delta_b = \dfrac{PL^3}{3\,EI}$. The ratio of the shearing deflection to the bending deflection is therefore $\dfrac{3}{10}\dfrac{E}{E_s}\left(\dfrac{d}{L}\right)^2$, where d is the depth of the cross-section. This shows that the relative importance of shearing deflection decreases very rapidly as the slenderness of the beam increases.

The expression $\dfrac{\Delta_s}{\Delta_b} = k\dfrac{E}{E_s}\left(\dfrac{d}{L}\right)^2$ is a general expression true for all beams of constant cross-section. The value of k is determined by the shape of the cross-section, the arrangement of the supports, and the kind of loading. Values of k for four cases are tabulated below.[1]

	Cross-Sections	
	Circular	Rectangular
Cantilever beam, load at end.......	$k = \frac{5}{24}$	$k = \frac{3}{10}$
Simple beam, load at midpoint	$k = \frac{5}{6}$	$k = \frac{6}{5}$

PROBLEM

Two aluminum beams each 3 in. by 4 in. in cross-section rest on supports which are 20 in. and 40 in. apart, respectively. Each carries a load of 12,000 lb. at the midpoint. Calculate the deflection due to bending and the deflection due to shearing for each beam.

[1] Maurer and Withy, " Strength of Materials."

BEAMS OF MATERIALS THAT DO NOT FOLLOW HOOKE'S LAW

256. Beams of Materials That Do Not Follow Hooke's Law. Beams made of materials for which the stress-strain diagram is not a straight line (e.g., cast iron, concrete, etc.) or beams stressed beyond the proportional limit do not conform to the common theory of flexure and the stresses are not correctly given by the common flexure formula.

The assumption that transverse sections which were planes before bending remain planes after bending is made for beams of such materials and is closely true. It follows from this assumption that deformations of fibers vary directly as their distances from the neutral axis. However, since in the cases under consideration the stresses are not proportional to the deformations, the variation of the tensile and compressive stresses is not the straight-line variation that follows from the same assumption in the common beam theory.

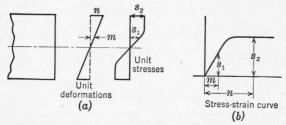

Fig. 396. Stress distribution in beam of ductile steel, stressed above the yield point.

In Fig. 396 is shown a stress variation diagram for a steel beam stressed beyond the yield point. For ductile steel with a pronounced yield point the unit stress remains constant for a considerable increase in unit deformation after the yield point has been reached. After the stress in the extreme fibers in a beam of this steel reaches the yield point considerable further bending does not increase the stress but more and more of the cross-section is stressed to the yield point as the bending moment increases. It is evident that the resisting moment increases only slightly as this change takes place. This results in a large increase in deflection with small increase in load, or in other words, there is a yielding in bending analogous to that in tension.

The tensile and compressive stress-strain curves for cast iron are shown in Fig. 397, together with diagrams showing deformation and bending stresses in a cast-iron beam. Since for cast iron the modulus of elasticity is greater in compression than in tension it follows that, for the same unit deformation, the compressive stress is greater than the tensile stress. But the sum of the tensile forces equals the sum of the compressive forces, and consequently the neutral axis shifts so as to decrease the area in compression and increase the area in tension as shown in Fig. 397.

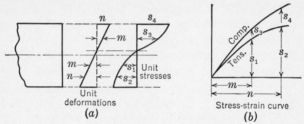

Unit deformations
(a)

Stress-strain curve
(b)

Fig. 397. Shift of neutral axis in beam of material with different moduli of elasticity in tension and compression.

BUCKLING OF BEAM FLANGES AND WEBS

257. Sidewise Buckling of Compression Flange. If a long beam with a compression flange which is not supported against sidewise deflection is gradually loaded until it fails, it is probable that the failure will result from a sidewise " buckling " of the compression flange. This can be illustrated by a simple experiment. The ends of a thin wooden yardstick are rested on two tables about 30 in. apart. The stick is kept resting on its edge by holding the ends. A downward force is applied at the midpoint by pulling vertically on a string tied around the yardstick. (The string is used since it offers no lateral support.) As the pull increases, the top surface of the stick will rather suddenly deflect sidewise. This sidewise buckling is greatest at the midpoint, decreasing toward the ends.

An unsupported compression flange of a beam is somewhat comparable to a column, stiffened in the direction of its least r by the web of the beam. (The web, in addition, stiffens the flange somewhat against sidewise deflection, but only slightly.) The loading is not that of the columns considered in Chapters XII and XIV, since, instead of being applied at the ends and therefore being the same at all cross-sections, the load is applied all along the length of the flange and the load on any cross-section of the flange is proportional to the bending moment at that section. The theoretical analysis of the stress in such a flange is very complex, and in the design of beams with unsupported compression flanges, an empirical procedure analogous to that used in column design is ordinarily resorted to.

Because of the great complexity of the situation presented by an unsupported compression flange, it is difficult to say just what reduction should be made in the *average* stress in any flange in order to have some particular *maximum* stress value. This is the same difficulty that exists in column design. More important than making just the proper reduction is recognition of the danger inherent in a narrow (easily deflected) unsupported compression flange, the avoidance of such flanges where possible, and the making of an adequate allowance for the condition where it cannot be avoided.

The New York City Building Code (1938) provides that for structural steel beams no reduction in compression flange stress need be made until the ratio L/b (the unsupported length of the flange divided by the flange width) reaches 15. No beam for which the ratio L/b exceeds 40 may be used. Between these two values of L/b the average stress at the outer surface of the compression flange is to be determined by the equation $S = \dfrac{20,000}{1 + \dfrac{1}{2,000}\,(L/b)^2}$.[1]

For a beam with a flange of rectangular cross-section, such as a wide-flange beam, $b^2 = 12\,r^2$. Making this substitution, the above equation becomes S (or P/A) $= \dfrac{20,000}{1 + \dfrac{1}{24,000}\left(\dfrac{L}{r}\right)^2}$. This equation is similar in form to the Rankine column formula. It is somewhat less conservative than the A.I.S.C. Rankine formula for columns, in making a reduction in the average stress. The less conservatism is based on the fact that the compression flange does not carry the maximum load throughout its length, by the stiffening effect of the web, etc. The " flat " stress of 18,000 lb. per sq. in. applies up to $L/r = 52$ (i.e., $15\,L/b \times \sqrt{12}$) and the greatest slenderness allowed is 139 (i.e., $40\,L/b \times \sqrt{12}$).

Example. An 18-in., 50-lb. wide-flange beam is simply supported and has a span of 22 ft. If the top flange is not braced laterally, what is the greatest bending moment to which the beam may be subjected, using the formula given above?

Solution: For this beam, $b = 7\frac{1}{2}$ in. Therefore $L/b = \dfrac{22 \times 12}{7.5} = 35.2$.

Therefore the average stress at the top surface of the beam at the section of greatest bending moment is to be limited to

$$S = \frac{20,000}{1 + \dfrac{1}{2,000}\,(35.2)^2} = 12,350 \text{ lb. per sq. in.}$$

For this beam $I/c = 89.0$ in.^{3}

$$M = SI/c = 12,350 \times 89.0 = 1,100,000 \text{ lb-in.} = 91,700 \text{ lb-ft.}$$

[1] This equation gives S a value of 18,000 lb. per sq. in. when L/b equals 15.

Owing to lack of support of the compression flange, the capacity of the beam is reduced in the ratio $\dfrac{18,000 - 12,350}{18,000} = 31$ per cent.

As in the case of a column, the *design* of a beam with an unsupported compression flange is usually best carried out by a process of trial and error.

Fortunately in most structures the beams are well supported laterally. In the case of floor beams and roof beams in buildings, the floor or roof generally rests on and supports the compression flange. Where this is not the case, it is often possible to provide bracing between two beams so that the two beams together with the system of bracing form a sufficiently rigid horizontal truss, which furnishes the lateral support. Where there is a single beam or where bracing or other supports are not feasible, it is necessary to reduce the bending stress.

PROBLEMS

1. If a 9-in.-by-$\frac{1}{2}$-in. plate is riveted to the compression flange of the beam in the example above, what does the allowable moment become? (*Hint:* In this case it is possible that the allowable moment will be limited by tension in the bottom flange, or by compression in the top flange. Investigate both possibilities.)

2. A 12-in., 40.8-lb. American Standard beam rests on supports 14 ft. 0 in. center to center. Calculate the allowable uniform load (*a*) if the top flange is not laterally supported; (*b*) if the top flange is supported at the midpoint; (*c*) if the top flange is supported at the " third-points."   *Ans.* (*a*) $w = 2,020$ lb. per ft.

258. Buckling of Beam Webs. If the web of a beam is thin in relation to the depth of the beam, there is a tendency for the web to buckle. This tendency may be serious in some beams.

To illustrate the tendency of a thin web to buckle, Fig. 398 shows the loading and some of the principal stresses in the web of a beam under concentrated load.[1] These stresses were determined by actual strain gage measurements. Now suppose that a narrow strip of the web having the line *AB* as its longitudinal axis is considered (Fig. 398*b*). It may be seen that compressive stresses of considerable magnitude exist on successive cross-sections of the strip. This small part of the beam web is therefore somewhat similar to a column completely braced in one direction by the adjacent web material, but only slightly restrained in a direction perpendicular to the plane of the web. If the web is sufficiently thin in relation to its length, the strip is likely to deflect laterally. If this lateral deflection becomes sufficiently great, the

[1] See discussion by R. L. Moore and E. C. Hartman, Transactions, American Society of Civil Engineers, Vol. 100, 1935, page 696.)

web may fail through elastic instability somewhat as a slender column fails.

An empirical procedure which is widely used to guard against such failure is to limit the allowable shear, V, on a thin-webbed beam in accordance with an equation similar to a Rankine column formula.   The 1934 specifications of the American Institute of Steel Construction, for example, require that the average shear V/A on the web of a beam shall not exceed 12,000 lb. per sq. in., nor $\dfrac{18,000}{1 + \dfrac{1}{7,200}\left(\dfrac{h}{t}\right)^2}$, whichever is smaller.

The dimensions of the standard rolled steel beams are such that h/t is less than 60 in all cases.   Therefore use of the above formula is limited to " built-up " girders.[1]

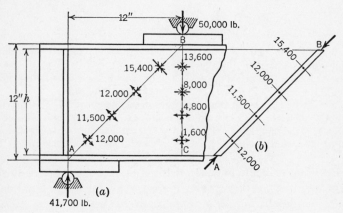

Fig. 398

259. Web " Crippling " under a Concentrated Load.

Reference to Fig. 398(a) shows that in the web directly under the concentrated load there are compressive stresses which become increasingly large as the flange is approached.   Very close to the junction of flange and web the compression in the web on planes parallel to the axis of the beam may become so great as to lead to a horizontal wrinkling or " crippling " of the web.   The shorter the length of the beam along which a concentrated load is applied to the web, the higher is the compressive stress in the web and the greater is the danger of this crippling.   Therefore it is necessary that the load be applied along a sufficiently great

[1] An alternative procedure to this stress reduction is the " stiffening " of the web by means of pairs of " stiffening angles " placed vertically, one on either side of the web at a distance not over 60 t apart.

length of the beam. The same condition exists with respect to a reaction.

In determining the minimum allowable length of end bearing for a reaction or the minimum length of bearing plate through which a load is transmitted to a beam, it has been found experimentally[1] that the

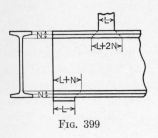

Fig. 399

load may be assumed to " spread " through the thickness of the flange on a 45° plane (Fig. 399). Therefore the necessary length of a bearing plate under a concentrated load is given by $L = \dfrac{P}{S_c t} - 2 N$, where L is the required length of bearing plate, N is the flange thickness (to the toe of the fillet), P is the load, t is the web thickness, and S_c is the allowable compressive stress in resisting this type of failure. An end reaction should be distributed over a length $L = \dfrac{P}{S_c t} - N$. The 1937 Specifications of the American Institute of Steel Construction permit S_c to have a value of 24,000 lb. per sq. in.

CURVED BEAMS

260. Curved Beams. The term " curved beam " is applied to a beam in which the neutral surface of the *unloaded* beam is not a plane surface. The slight deflection of ordinary beams under load is not sufficient to make them " curved beams."

The common flexure formula is not theoretically correct when applied to curved beams. Nevertheless, in some cases it may be applied to them without causing errors that are prohibitive. For instance, if the inner radius is four times the depth of the beam, the maximum stresses as calculated from the common flexure formula will be too small by about 10 per cent. If the ratio of radius of curvature to depth is greater, the error is less. On the other hand, as the ratio of inner radius to depth decreases, the error resulting from use of the common flexure formula increases rapidly.

The reason for the failure of the common flexure formula to apply to curved beams is evident from consideration of the diagram in Fig. 400. This shows part of a curved beam subject to a bending moment of value M. The assumption is made (and has been experimentally verified) that every plane radial surface remains a plane after bending. This is

[1] I. Lyse, and H. J. Godfrey, " Web Buckling in Steel Beams " (discussion) Transactions, American Society of Civil Engineers, Vol. 100 (1935), page 706.

the same assumption that is the basis of the common flexure formula. It follows that in a curved beam subjected to bending moment the *total* deformations of the various fibers are proportional to the distances of these fibers from the neutral axis or surface. Since, however, the lengths of the fibers between two radial planes such as AB and DC are not all the same, it follows that in a curved beam the unit deformations and consequently the unit stresses do not vary as the total deformations. In a curved beam, the fibers at the concave surface are shorter than those fibers which are the same distance from the neutral axis on the convex side. Consequently, at a given distance from the neutral axis *toward* the center of curvature, the unit deformations and consequently the unit stresses are greater than they are at the same distance from the neutral axis *away* from the center of curvature. The manner of stress variation is indicated in Fig. 400(b).

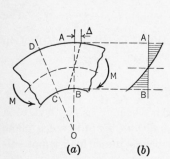

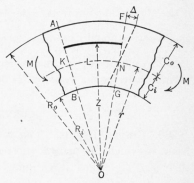

(a)   (b)

Fig. 400.   Variation of bending stress in a curved beam.

Fig. 401

The laws of equilibrium require the total tensile force on one face of a radial segment to equal the total compressive force. Since the unit stresses increase more rapidly from the neutral surface towards the center of curvature than they do from the neutral surface away from the center of curvature, it follows that the neutral axis for a curved beam is shifted from the centroid of the cross-section toward the center of curvature.

261. The Flexure Formula for Curved Beams.   Fig. 401 represents part of a curved beam subjected to bending moment M, represented by couples. Consider a segment between two radial planes (AB and FG), the distance between the planes at the neutral surface being L. The total change in length of the fiber AF at the convex surface is Δ (shown as elongation in the diagram). The change in curvature of the beam due to bending is not shown. The length AF equals LR_0/r, in which r is the radius to the neutral surface. (An expression for the value of r will be found later.) The stress at the outer fibers, S_0, equals $\delta E = \dfrac{\Delta E}{L R_0 / r}$.

The elongation of a fiber at a distance z from O is $\dfrac{z - r}{c_0} \Delta$, and the unit stress S_z at any distance z is

$$S_z = \frac{\dfrac{(z - r)}{c_0} \Delta E}{L z / r}$$

Therefore

$$\frac{S_z}{S_0} = \frac{R_0}{c_0} \frac{(z - r)}{z} \quad \text{or} \quad S_z = \frac{S_0 R_0}{c_0} \frac{(z - r)}{z}$$

The force on an area dA of the cross-section at distance z from O equals $\dfrac{S_0 R_0}{c_0} \dfrac{(z - r)}{z} \, dA$. Taking moments with respect to O, the resisting moment,

$$M = \frac{S_0 R_0}{c_0} \int_{R_i}^{R_0} (z - r) dA = \frac{S_0 R_0}{c_0} \left[\int_{R_i}^{R_0} z \, dA - \int_{R_i}^{R_0} r \, dA \right]$$

But $\displaystyle\int_{R_i}^{R_0} z \, dA$ is the statical moment of the cross-section with respect to O. If $\overline{R}$ is the distance to the centroid,

$$\int_{R_i}^{R_0} z \, dA = \overline{R} A. \quad \text{Also} \quad \int_{R_i}^{R_0} r \, dA = r A.$$

Hence

$$M = \frac{S_0 R_0}{c_0} (\overline{R} A - r A) = \frac{S_0 R_0}{c_0} (\overline{R} - r) A$$

But $(\overline{R} - r)$ is the shift or displacement of the neutral axis due to curvature. Let $\overline{R} - r = j$. Then $M = S_0 R_0 j A / c_0$, which is the flexure formula for curved beams giving M in terms of the stress in the extreme (convex) fibers. In the same way (or by substituting for S_0 its value in terms of S_i) there results

$$M = \frac{S_i R_i j A}{c_i}$$

Note that these formulas are analogous to $M = SI/c = SAk^2/c$, but with $R_0 j$ and $R_i j$ taking the place of k^2 (k = radius of gyration).

Before stresses or resisting moments can be calculated by the above formulas it is necessary to determine j for the beam in question. As in straight beams the neutral axis is so placed that the tensile force on one side equals the compressive force on the other side, or the total force on one end of any segment is zero. Since $S_z = \dfrac{S_0 R_0}{c_0} \dfrac{(z - r)}{z}$, the total force on the cross-section equals

$$\int S_z dA = \frac{S_0 R_0}{c_0} \int_{R_i}^{R_0} \frac{(z - r)}{z} dA = 0$$

Therefore

$$\int_{R_i}^{R_0} dA - r \int_{R_i}^{R_0} \frac{dA}{z} = 0$$

whence

$$r = \frac{\displaystyle\int_{R_i}^{R_0} dA}{\displaystyle\int_{R_i}^{R_0} \frac{dA}{z}} = \frac{A}{\displaystyle\int_{R_i}^{R_0} \frac{dA}{z}}$$

which, evaluated for a particular cross-section, gives the distance from the center of curvature to the neutral axis.

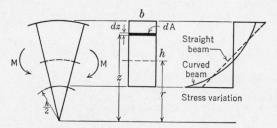

FIG. 402.   Shift of neutral axis in a curved beam.

Example.   Fig. 402 shows a beam of rectangular cross-section the depth of which is twice the inner radius. The beam is bent by couples of M lb-in. applied to its ends.   Calculate the unit stresses at the concave and convex surfaces and compare them with the maximum bending stress in a straight beam of the same cross-section and subject to the same moment.

Solution: The distance to the neutral axis is

$$r = \frac{A}{\displaystyle\int_{R_i}^{R_0} \frac{dA}{z}} = \frac{bh}{\displaystyle\int_{R_i}^{R_0} \frac{b\,dz}{z}} = \frac{h}{\log_e z \Big]_{R_i}^{R_0}} = \frac{h}{\log_e \dfrac{R_0}{R_i}}$$

For the beam in this example $R_0/R_i = 3$. Therefore $r = \dfrac{h}{\log_e 3} = \dfrac{h}{1.09862} = 0.9103\,h$; whence $j = \bar{R} - r = h - 0.9103\,h = 0.0897\,h$.

The unit stress at the concave inner surface is

$$S_i = \frac{M c_i}{R_i j A} = \frac{M(0.5 - 0.0897)h}{0.5\,h \times 0.0897\,h \times bh} = \frac{9.14\,M}{bh^2}$$

The unit stress at the convex surface is

$$S_0 = \frac{Mc_0}{R_0 jA} = \frac{M(0.5 + 0.0897)h}{1.5\, h \times 0.0897\, h \times bh} = \frac{4.38\, M}{bh^2}$$

In a straight beam the unit stress in the extreme fibers is

$$S = \frac{Mc}{I} = \frac{6\, M}{bh^2}$$

Owing to the curvature, the stress at the inner (concave fibers) is about 52 per cent greater than the stress in a straight beam, and the stress at the outer fibers is only 73 per cent of the stress in a straight beam.

For beams of rectangular and circular cross-sections, Fig. 403 gives, for different ratios of depth to inner radius, the ratios of the stress in a curved beam to that in a straight beam.

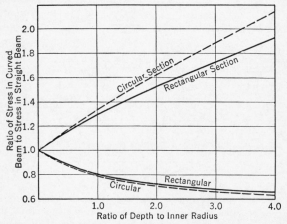

FIG. 403.   Ratios of stresses in curved beams to stresses in straight beams.   Upper curves are stresses on concave surface.

Values for the distance r from the axis of curvature to the neutral axis are given below for several types of cross sections.

CURVED BEAMS

Values of $r = \dfrac{A}{\displaystyle\int \frac{dA}{z}}$ (r is distance from axis of curvature of beam to neutral axis of cross-section)

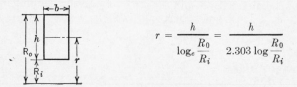

$$r = \frac{h}{\log_e \dfrac{R_0}{R_i}} = \frac{h}{2.303 \log \dfrac{R_0}{R_i}}$$

$$r = \frac{b_1 h_1 + b_2 h_2}{2.303 \left(b_1 \log \dfrac{R_i + h_1}{R_i} + b_2 \log \dfrac{R_0}{R_i + h_1} \right)}$$

$$r = \frac{b_1 h_1 + b_2 h_2 + b_3 h_3}{2.303 \left(b_1 \log \dfrac{R_i + h_1}{R_i} + b_2 \log \dfrac{R_0 - h_3}{R_i + h_1} + b_3 \log \dfrac{R_0}{R_0 - h_3} \right)}$$

$$r = \frac{\dfrac{h}{2}(b_1 + b_2)}{b_2 - b_1 + \left(b_2 + \dfrac{R_0}{h}(b_1 - b_2) \right) \times 2.303 \log \dfrac{R_0}{R_i}}$$

$$r = \frac{F + \sqrt{F^2 - a^2}}{2}$$

$$j = F - r = \frac{F - \sqrt{F^2 - a^2}}{2}$$

Triangular section: put b_2 equal to zero in trapezoid.

PROBLEM

A beam of circular cross-section is curved so that the inner radius equals the radius of the cross-section. Calculate the stress on the inner and on the outer fibers caused by a bending moment of M lb-in. Compare these stresses with the maximum bending stresses in a straight beam of the same cross-section with the same bending moment.

262. Curved Beams Subject to Bending Combined with Direct Stress.
Curved beams subject to bending moment alone are of rare occurrence, but examples of curved beams subject to bending and direct stress are numerous. Hooks, rings or other links, frames of machines, " C " clamps, and tools of various sorts afford common examples.

The stress at any point on a cross-section of such a member is the algebraic sum of the direct stress and the stress due to the bending moment as in straight beams or prisms with eccentric loads. For curved beams this resultant stress is given by these formulas:

At the inner surface $S_i = \pm \dfrac{P}{A} \pm \dfrac{M c_i}{R_i j A}$

At the outer surface $S_0 = \pm \dfrac{P}{A} \pm \dfrac{Mc_0}{R_0 jA}$

These formulas are analogous to $S = \pm \dfrac{P}{A} \pm \dfrac{Mc}{I}$

In the solution of problems involving curved beams, a question arises as to the correct moment arm to use in calculating M. In straight beams this moment arm is the distance from the line of action of the load to the centroid of the cross-section and also to the neutral axis (which passes through the centroid). In curved beams the moment arm is the distance from the line of action of the load to the centroid of the cross-section and not to the neutral axis. The actual load P is regarded as equivalent to an imaginary load P at some point on the cross-section and a couple or bending moment Pe (Fig. 404). If this imaginary load is to produce uniformly distributed stress on the cross-section it must act through the centroid, and consequently e must be measured from the centroid.

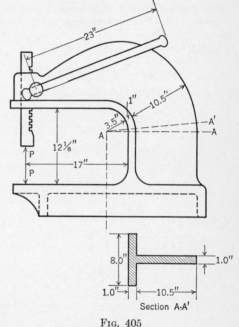

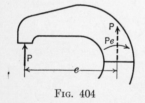

Fig. 404

Fig. 405

Example. A small hand press for performing odd jobs in a machine shop (Greenerd Arbor press) has a cast-iron frame with the dimensions shown in Fig. 405. (a) Calculate the stresses which a load, P, of 1,000 lb. causes to act on a radial section $A-A'$, making a small angle with $A-A$, the end of the straight part of the frame. (b) Compare these stresses with those in the straight part of the frame.

Solution: (a) The distance r from the center of curvature to the neutral axis of the section $A-A'$ is given by $r = \dfrac{b_1 h_1 + b_2 h_2}{2.30 \left(b_1 \log \dfrac{R_i + h_1}{R_i} + b_2 \log \dfrac{R_0}{R_i + h_1} \right)}$

$\dfrac{R_i + h_1}{R_i} = \dfrac{3.5 + 1}{3.5} = 1.285 \qquad \dfrac{R_0}{R_i + h_1} = \dfrac{15}{3.5 + 1} = 3.333$

Therefore

$$r = \frac{8 \times 1 + 10.5 \times 1}{2.30(8 \times 0.1089 + 1 \times 0.5224)} = \frac{18.5}{2.30 \times 1.392} = 5.74 \text{ in.}$$

The distance from the center of curvature to the centroid of the cross-section is

$$\overline{R} = \frac{8 \times 4 + 10.5 \times 9.75}{18.5} = 7.26 \text{ in.}$$

Therefore $j = 7.26 - 5.74 = 1.52$ in. Also

$$c_i = 3.76 - 1.52 = 2.24 \text{ in.}$$

$$c_0 = 11.5 - 2.24 = 9.26 \text{ in.}$$

Moment arm of load P with respect to centroid of cross-section $= 17.0 + 3.76 = 20.76$ in. Therefore the bending moment of the load $P = 1,000 \times 20.76 = 20,760$ lb-in. Whence

$$S_i = \frac{Mc_i}{R_i j A} + \frac{P}{A} = + \frac{20,760 \times 2.24}{3.5 \times 1.52 \times 18.5} + \frac{1,000}{18.5} = +472 + 54$$

$$= 526 \text{ lb. per sq. in., tension}$$

$$S_0 = -\frac{Mc_0}{R_0 j A} + \frac{P}{A} = -\frac{20,760 \times 9.26}{15.0 \times 1.52 \times 18.5} + \frac{1,000}{18.5}$$

$$= -456 + 54 = -402 \text{ lb. per sq. in. (compression)}$$

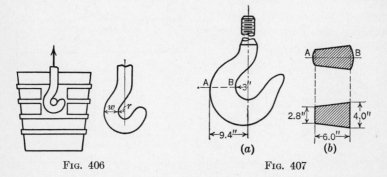

FIG. 406   FIG. 407

(b) The moment of inertia of the cross-section with respect to the centroidal axis (which is also the neutral axis of the straight part of the frame) $= 243$ in.[4] Therefore

$$S_i = \frac{20,760 \times 3.76}{243} + \frac{1,000}{18.5} = +321 + 54 = 375 \text{ lb. per sq. in., tension}$$

$$S_0 = \frac{-20,760 \times 7.74}{243} + \frac{1,000}{18.5} = -660 + 54 = -606 \text{ lb. per sq. in. (compression)}$$

The maximum tensile stress in the curved part of the frame is 40 per cent greater than in the straight part; the maximum compressive stress is 34 per cent less.

PROBLEMS

1. Fig. 406 shows one of a pair of hooks used for lifting the 125-ton ladles in a steel works. The width w of the hook is $16\frac{1}{16}$ in., and the thickness of the metal is $5\frac{1}{4}$ in. The inner radius r is $6\frac{1}{16}$ in. Calculate the maximum stress in the hook if the load on the hook is 135,000 lb. *Ans.* $S_i = 15,150$ lb. per sq. in.

2. A typical 20-ton crane hook is shown in Fig. 407(a). The cross-section at AB and an approximately equivalent trapezoidal cross-section are shown in (b). Calculate the stress caused by a load of 20 tons. Use the simplified cross-section and assume the resultant of the load to act 3.3 in. from the 4.0 in. edge of the cross-section.

BEAMS HAVING LOADS NOT IN THE PLANE OF A PRINCIPAL AXIS OF INERTIA

263. Maximum Stresses Resulting from Inclined Moment. One of the limitations stated when considering the common flexure formula was that the loads must be in the plane of a principal axis of inertia of the beam cross-section.[1] The effect of loads that do not lie in the plane of a principal axis of inertia will now be considered.

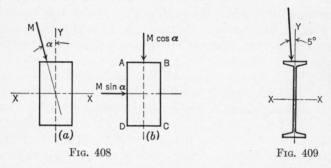

FIG. 408   FIG. 409

For simplicity consider first a beam with a rectangular cross-section and with loads in a plane passing through the centroid of the cross-section and making an angle α with the principal axis, as shown in Fig. 408(a). The law of summation of effects shows that the stresses at any point can be found by adding the stresses caused by each of the two components of the loads (or moments) parallel, respectively, to the two axes (Fig. 408(b)). If this beam is a beam on two supports, the stress at A is found by adding two compressive stresses; the stress at C is the sum of two tensile stresses. The stress at B is the algebraic sum of compressive stress due to $M \cos \alpha$ and tensile stress due to $M \sin \alpha$, and the stress

---

[1] The principal axes of inertia at any point of any given area are the two rectangular axes through that point for which the values of I are a maximum and a minimum, respectively. If the point is the centroid of the area, the axes are called the *principal centroidal axes*. In this discussion, whenever " principal axes " are referred to, it will be understood that the centroidal axes are meant. If an area has an axis of symmetry, that axis is one of the principal axes. See Appendix B.

at D is the algebraic sum of compression due to $M \sin \alpha$ and tension due to $M \cos \alpha$.

A convenient expression for the maximum stress at a cross-section of this beam is derived as follows: Let M be the bending moment at the cross-section, and let the moment act in a plane making an angle α with the Y axis. Let the section modulus with respect to the X axis be Z_x, and the section modulus with respect to the Y axis be Z_y. Let n be the ratio of Z_x to Z_y, or $Z_x = nZ_y$. The maximum bending stress (at C) due to the given bending moment M is

$$ S = \frac{M \cos \alpha}{Z_x} + \frac{M \sin \alpha}{Z_y} = \frac{M}{Z_x} (\cos \alpha + n \sin \alpha) \tag{1} $$

But M/Z_x is the maximum bending stress that would result from a bending moment M in the plane of the Y axis. Hence the maximum stress due to an inclined bending moment is $(\cos \alpha + n \sin \alpha)$ times the maximum bending stress caused by the same bending moment if applied in the plane of the Y axis. For small angles, $\cos \alpha$ is very nearly unity ($\cos 8° = 0.99$), and consequently for small angles of inclination of load the percentage *increase* in stress due to the inclination of the bending moment is very closely $100\, n \sin \alpha$.

Equation (1) applies to solid and hollow rectangular sections, to I and H sections. It also applies to all sections that contain two axes of symmetry and have such a shape that the point where the stress is maximum under the oblique moment is a point that is as remote as any other point on the cross-section from both the X axis and the Y axis.

It should also be noted that, for equation (1) (which is derived from the ordinary flexure formula) to apply, the plane of loading must be such that no torsional forces act on the beam. This condition is met, for all beams that have two axes of symmetry, if the plane of loading passes through the centroid of the cross-section.

Example. A bending moment, M, acts at an inclination of 5° with the Y axis of the cross-section of a 24-in., 100-lb. American Standard I-beam (Fig. 409). Compare the resulting maximum stress with that which would be produced by the same moment acting in the plane of the Y axis.

Solution: For this beam, $Z_x = 197.6$ and $Z_y = 13.4$, whence $n = 14.75$, $\cos 5° = 0.996$, and $\sin 5° = 0.0872$, whence $n \sin \alpha = 14.75 \times 0.0872 = 1.29$. Inclination of the plane of loading therefore increases the maximum stress by 129 per cent, or the maximum stress under the inclined moment is 2.29 times what it would be if the moment were in the plane of the Y axis.

For most I-beams, the ratio, n, of the section moduli is very large, and this makes any slight obliquity of loading very severe in its effects. The value of n is smaller for the wide-flange beams, so that obliquity of loading is less important, but even in them it has serious effects, as the following table shows.

Beam	$\dfrac{Z_x}{Z_y} = n$		Ratio of $\dfrac{\text{Maximum stress for inclined moment}}{\text{Maximum stress when } \alpha = 0}$ for the following values of α		
			1°	2°	5°
24″–100# I	$\dfrac{197.6}{13.4}$	14.75	1.26	1.51	2.29
24″–100# WF	$\dfrac{248.9}{33.9}$	7.35	1.13	1.26	1.64
12″–31.8# I	$\dfrac{36.0}{3.8}$	9.48	1.16	1.33	1.82
12″–32# WF	$\dfrac{40.7}{6.3}$	6.46	1.11	1.23	1.56

264. Position of Neutral Axis. When a beam is stressed by a bending moment which is in one of the principal planes of the beam, the neutral axis of the cross-section is perpendicular to the plane of the bending moment. But when the moment acts in a plane inclined to the principal axes of the beam, *the neutral axis is not perpendicular to the plane of bending.*

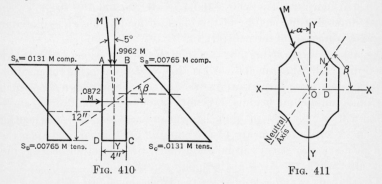

FIG. 410   FIG. 411

Considering the beam of rectangular cross-section pictured in Fig. 410, and using the procedure discussed in Art. 263, it is found that the stresses at the four corners of the cross-section have the values shown. But if all stresses are within the proportional limit, the stress at any point of the cross-section is proportional to the distance of the point from the neutral axis. By proportion, therefore, the point of zero stress along the line BC is located at 4.43 in. from B, and the corresponding point along AD at the same distance from D. The neutral axis therefore has the position shown. Let β be the angle which it makes with the X axis. Then $\tan \beta = 1.57/2 = 0.785$, and $\beta = 38° 08'$. A shift of 5 degrees in the plane of loading has produced a shift of 38 degrees in the direction of the neutral axis.

A general expression for the value of the angle β in terms of the moments of inertia I_x and I_y and the angle α will now be derived. The area shown in Fig. 411 represents the cross-section of a beam the principal axes of which are X–X and Y–Y. The vector marked M represents the resultant bending moment and lies in the plane of the loads. Let N be any point on the neutral axis. Since the bending stress at N is zero, the tensile stress at N due to the horizontal component of M equals the compressive stress at N due to the vertical component of M, or

$$\frac{M \sin \alpha \times OD}{I_y} = \frac{M \cos \alpha \times ND}{I_x}$$

$$\frac{ND}{OD} = \frac{I_x \sin \alpha}{I_y \cos \alpha} = \frac{I_x}{I_y} \tan \alpha$$

But $\dfrac{ND}{OD} = \tan \beta$. Therefore $\tan \beta = \dfrac{I_x}{I_y} \tan \alpha$.

Applying this expression to the first of the beams included in the table of Art. 263, and letting $\alpha = 1°$, $I_x/I_y = 2{,}372/48.4 = 49.0$, and $\tan 1° = 0.0175$. Whence $\tan \beta = 49.0 \times 0.0175 = 0.858$, and $\beta = 40° 38'$. An almost imperceptible change in the plane of loading has caused a large shift in the direction of the neutral axis.

The bending stress *at any given point* on the cross-section of a beam can be determined by the principles of Art. 263, without locating the position of the neutral axis. But if the cross-section of the beam has a shape such that, under an oblique loading, it is not obvious what point of the cross-section will be most distant from the neutral axis (Fig. 411), the neutral axis can be located by means of the equation just given, and then the point of maximum stress can be determined by inspection or measurement, after which the stress at that point can be found.

The following example applies the principles developed in this and the previous articles to a beam which possesses the additional complication that the directions of the principal axes are not initially known, but have to be determined.

Example.   Calculate the allowable bending moment for a 5-in.-by-3-in.-by-$\frac{1}{2}$-in. L (Fig. 412) if the allowable bending stress is 16,000 lb. per sq. in. The bending moment is due to vertical loads and the angle is placed with the 5-in. leg vertical and above the 3-in. leg. Assume that the plane of bending moments is properly placed so as to avoid twisting (see *shear center*, Art. 267). Compare the allowable bending moment thus found with one-half of the allowable bending moment for two similar angles with the 5-in. legs fastened back to back to form a symmetrical section.

Solution: For an angle such as this, the moments of inertia given in structural handbooks are not the principal moments of inertia. The first step in determining the principal moments is to find the angle θ at which the principal axes $X'-X'$ and $Y'-Y'$ are inclined to the axes $X-X$ and $Y-Y$. (Since the bending moment acts in a plane parallel to the $Y-Y$ axis, the angle θ will evidently equal the angle α which measures the obliquity of the loading.) After θ has been found the values of the principal moments of inertia, $I_{x'}$ and $I_{y'}$, can be determined.

Appendix B derives the equations from which θ, $I_{x'}$, and $I_{y'}$ can be found, and an example in that Appendix shows that for a 5-in.-by-3-in.-by-$\frac{1}{2}$-in. angle, $\theta = 19°\ 40'$, $I_{x'} = 10.45$ in.^{4}, and $I_{y'} = 1.583$ in.^{4}

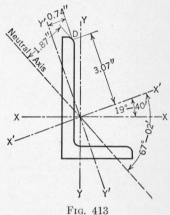

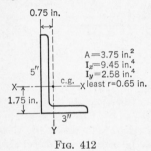

$$A = 3.75 \text{ in.}^2$$
$$I_x = 9.45 \text{ in.}^4$$
$$I_y = 2.58 \text{ in.}^4$$
least r = 0.65 in.

Fig. 412   Fig. 413

Fig. 413 shows the cross-section of the beam with the principal axes. The neutral axis will evidently lie in the second and fourth quadrants, making an angle with $X'-X'$ given by the equation

$$\tan \beta = \frac{I_{x'}}{I_{y'}} \tan \alpha = \frac{10.45}{1.583} \tan 19°\ 40' = 2.36, \text{ whence } \beta = 67°\ 02'^1$$

It can now be determined that D is the point most distant from the neutral axis, and it is at this point that the maximum stress will occur. The relation between stress at D and bending moment M is given by

$$S_D = \frac{M_{x'}c_{x'}}{I_{x'}} + \frac{M_{y'}c_{y'}}{I_{y'}} = \frac{M \cos 19°\ 40'\ c_{x'}}{I_{x'}} + \frac{M \sin 19°\ 40'\ c_{y'}}{I_{y'}}$$

Whence $$16,000 = \frac{0.942\ M \times 3.07}{10.45} + \frac{0.336\ M \times 0.74}{1.583}$$

$$= 0.277\ M + 0.157\ M = 0.434\ M$$

[1] The physical necessity for this large inclination of the neutral axis may be understood by considering the 5-in.-by-3-in.-by-$\frac{1}{2}$-in. angle of this example. The bending moment here is in a vertical plane. The resisting moment must therefore be a couple in the same vertical plane. That is, the resultant of the compressive forces acting on the shaded part of the cross-section must lie in the same vertical line as the resultant of the tensile forces acting on the unshaded part of the cross-section (Fig. 414). It should be kept in mind that the resultants of the forces do not act through the centroids of the areas, since the forces vary in intensity from the neutral axis outward.

Therefore $M = \dfrac{16,000}{0.434} = 36,900$ lb-in.

For two 5-in.-by-3-in.-by-$\frac{1}{2}$-in. angles fastened back to back forming a symmetrical section,

$$S = \frac{Mc_x}{I_x} \quad \text{or} \quad 16,000 = \frac{M \times 3.25}{2 \times 9.45}$$

whence $M = 93,000$ lb-in. for the two angles, or 46,500 lb-in. allowable for each of the angles.

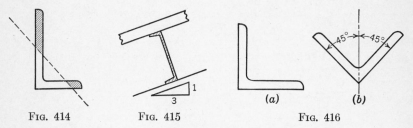

FIG. 414   FIG. 415   FIG. 416

PROBLEMS

1. The purlins of a roof consist of 8-in., 11.5-lb. channels resting on roof trusses 16 ft. center to center. The inclination of the roof is 1 to 3, as shown in Fig. 415. Each purlin supports 48 sq. ft. of roof which weighs 25 lb. per sq. ft. Calculate the maximum stress in the channels, assuming that torsional stresses do not occur.

$Ans.$ $S = 14,900$ lb. per sq. in.

2. A 4-in.-by-4-in.-by-$\frac{1}{2}$-in. angle is used as a cantilever beam. Calculate the maximum stress resulting from a given bending moment M in a vertical plane (a) if the angle is turned as shown in Fig. 416(a); (b) if the angle is turned as shown in Fig. 416(b).

265. Deflection of Beams Due to Loads Not in Plane of Principal Axis.

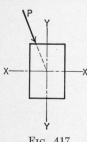

FIG. 417

If a load is applied to a beam not in the plane of the principal axis of inertia but with its line of action passing through the centroid of the cross-section as shown in Fig. 417, the deflection at any point may be regarded as the vector sum of two displacements. The beam will be deflected horizontally by the horizontal component of the load and vertically

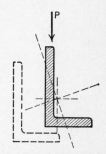

Direction of deflection of angle under vertical load

FIG. 418

by the vertical component of the load. It is obvious that the horizontal deflection is a function of the horizontal component of the load and I_y, while the vertical deflection is a function of the vertical component of the load and I_x.

In the angle discussed in the foregoing example, the component of the bending moment in the direction of the $Y'-Y'$ axis causes a deflection in that direction, and the component of the moment in the direction of the $X'-X'$ axis causes a deflection in that direction. An angle loaded in this manner therefore does not deflect straight downward, but deflects sidewise as well (Fig. 418).

PROBLEMS

1. If the angle in the example of Art. 264 is a simply supported beam, 100 in. between supports, what are the vertical and horizontal displacements of the midsection of the beam when it is loaded with a concentrated vertical load at the midsection which is sufficient to produce the allowable bending moment of 36,900 lb-in.?

2. A beam of rectangular cross-section h in. deep and b in. wide has a load inclined $\alpha°$ to the horizontal. Calculate α in order that H and V components of the deflection shall be equal.

3. A 12-in., 31.8-lb. American standard beam rests on two supports 20 ft. center to center and carries a vertical, uniform load of 6,000 lb. The web of the beam is tilted 4.0° from the vertical. Calculate the horizontal and vertical components of the deflection of the midpoint of the beam.

4. A 4-in.-by-4-in.-by-$\frac{1}{2}$-in. angle is used as a cantilever beam 10 ft. long. It carries a vertical concentrated load at the end of 230 lb. The legs of the angle are vertical and horizontal respectively. Calculate the horizontal and vertical components of the deflection at the end caused by the concentrated load.

266. Stresses Caused by Loads Not in a Single Plane.

The beam AB shown in Fig. 419 carries loads the lines of action of which do not lie in a single plane but all of which are perpendicular to the longitudinal axis of the beam. If the deflections are small,

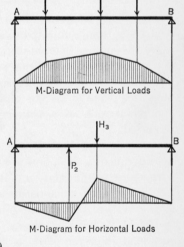

M-Diagram for Vertical Loads

M-Diagram for Horizontal Loads

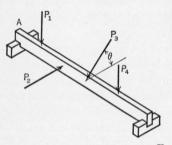

FIG. 419

the stresses and deflections may be found as follows: Resolve each load into its two components parallel respectively to the two planes containing the principal axes of inertia.

Draw a bending-moment diagram for the components in the X plane and a separate bending-moment diagram for the components in the Y plane. Then for any point of any cross-section the bending stress may be calculated from

$$S = \pm \frac{M_V c_x}{I_x} \pm \frac{M_H c_y}{I_y}$$

If deflections in either the H or V direction are large, twisting of the beam results from the fact that the loads in the other direction no longer lie in a *plane*.

PROBLEMS

1. A 4-in.-by-6 in. wood beam 12 ft. long, with the 6-in. face vertical, is supported at the end and carries a vertical load of 600 lb. at the midpoint and two horizontal loads of 100 lb. each 32 in. from the midpoint. Calculate the maximum bending stress.

2. Solve Problem 1 if one of the horizontal loads is omitted.

3. In Fig. 419 the beam is a wooden beam 4 in. by 10 in. (actual size) and 10 ft. long. $P_1 = 100$ lb., $P_2 = 100$ lb., $P_4 = 150$ lb., $V_3 = 120$ lb., $H_3 = 160$ lb. Distances from the left reaction to the respective loads are 1.8 ft., 3.6 ft., 5.3 ft., and 7.7 ft. Calculate the maximum bending stress.

BEAMS WHOSE CROSS-SECTION HAS NO VERTICAL AXIS OF SYMMETRY; SHEAR CENTER

267. Shear Center. The common theory of flexure assumes that the bent beam is not subjected to any resultant torque which would tend to cause the successive cross-sections of the beam to rotate with respect to one another. This condition is ordinarily met by using beams that have a vertical plane of symmetry, so that each cross-section of the beam intersects this plane in an axis of symmetry. If the resultant of the loads applied at any cross-section coincides with this axis, no torsion is produced.

Beams having cross-sections without a vertical axis of symmetry are not infrequently used, however. The ordinary channel section (Fig. 420 a and b) is an illustration. It might be supposed that such a section would not be twisted about its longitudinal axis if loads were applied to it in the vertical plane containing the centroids of the successive cross-sections. Experiment shows, however, that this is not true. Under such load, the beam twists as shown.

This can easily be proved by use of a small model. A strip of tin 3 in. wide and about 20 in. long is formed into a channel by means of two bends parallel to the long dimensions.[1] One end is rigidly fastened to a

---

[1] Even a cardboard model will give fairly satisfactory results.

block of wood, and a small square tin plate is soldered to the other end (Fig. 421). The beam is supported as a cantilever by attaching the block of wood to a fixed support. A load is applied to the upper edge of the square of tin by a pencil or other object held in the hand. If a vertical load is first applied at the edge of the flange away from the_web,

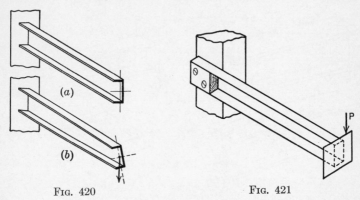

FIG. 420   FIG. 421

the beam twists as would be expected. But when the load is moved closer to the web until it is over the centroid of the cross-section, the twist does not disappear. *A vertical centroidal load causes torsion.* However, if the plane of the load is shifted *to the other side of the web* a position can be found where no twisting of the beam is apparent. If loads are applied vertically in this plane of bending, they do not cause any torsion of the beam, and the flexure formula may be correctly used. The intersection of the horizontal axis of symmetry of the cross-section with the line of action of a vertical load so applied as not to cause any twist of the beam is called the *shear center* of the cross-section.

It is obvious that for any beam the plane of loading should pass through the shear centers of the successive cross-sections, and it is important, therefore, to be able to locate the shear center. For a beam with a vertical axis of symmetry, the shear center is simply the centroid of the cross-section. For a channel section, and for certain other sections that do not possess a vertical axis of symmetry, the position of the shear center may be found, closely enough for practical purposes, by the reasoning that will be given in Art. 269.

268. Transverse Shearing Stresses in Beams. First, however, it is desirable to consider the existence of certain horizontal shearing stresses which may occur on transverse planes of a beam. Consider as an example a beam (Fig. 422) of *I* cross-section used as a cantilever and loaded at the end with a load *P* (not shown) applied directly over the top of the web. This beam is shown in (*a*). As it bends, the top flanges lengthen.

The forces which stretch these flanges must be shearing forces exerted by the web (which is considered as extending through the flanges) on the vertical surface of each flange where it joins the web.   If the material is weak in shear, failure in shear along these surfaces may result and the flanges may separate from the web as shown in (b).

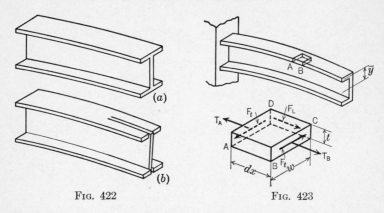

FIG. 422   FIG. 423

Fig. 423 shows a beam of channel cross-section bent by loads (not shown).   Consider a segment of the top flange in the form of a rectangular block between two transverse planes at A and B.   On the BC face there is a resultant tensile force T_B, and on the AD face a force T_A.   For the cantilever beam shown, T_A is greater than T_B since the bending moment at A is greater than that at B.   There must be a force equal to $T_A - T_B$ acting on the DC face, as shown.   This is the resultant F_L of the shearing stresses.

$$F_L = T_A - T_B$$

Then if S_s is assumed uniform over the thickness t,

$$S_s t dx = \frac{M_A \bar{y}}{I} wt - \frac{M_B \bar{y}}{I} wt$$

whence

$$S_s = \left(\frac{M_A - M_B}{dx} \right) \frac{w\bar{y}}{I} = \frac{V w \bar{y}}{I}$$

Shearing stresses must also exist on the transverse faces AD and BC in the directions shown by the arrows.   These stresses are variable, being of the same intensity as S_s at the edge of the face adjoining the web and being zero at the outer edge of the flange.   It follows from the above equation that for a flange of uniform thickness (as in the diagram) this variation in shearing stress is uniform.

269. Location of Shear Center. The transverse force F_T is the average shearing stress times the area

$$F_T = \frac{Vw\bar{y}}{2\,I}\,wt = \frac{Vw^2\bar{y}t}{2\,I}$$

The effect of these transverse shearing forces which act on the flanges will now be considered. In Fig. 424 is shown a segment of the free end of the cantilever beam shown in Fig. 423, cut off by a section through AD. This is shown as viewed from the cut end. The resultant forces acting on this cut end are shown by vectors and are as follows: (1) the resultant tensile and compressive forces T and C constituting the resisting moment; (2) the resultants of the transverse shearing stresses on the cross-section of the flanges, designated F_t and acting in the directions indicated; (3) the resultant V of the vertical shearing stresses on the

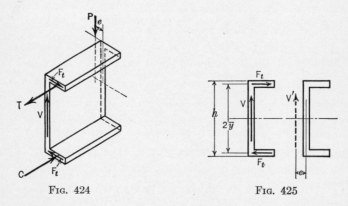

FIG. 424   FIG. 425

plane AD which is, of course, upward on the segment shown. The actual vertical shearing unit stresses on this plane have been shown to vary from zero at the top and bottom to a maximum at the neutral axis, and consequently the vertical force on the flanges is a very small part of the total. The resultant on the entire section in any ordinary channel acts not far from the center of the web and in this discussion is assumed to act at the center of the web.

It can now be seen why the force P, if it is not to twist the beam, must act *not* through the centroid of the cross-section, but through a point on the opposite side of the web. The resultant of the force V and the couple $2\,\bar{y}F_t$ (Fig. 425) is a force V' (which equals V) and which acts to the left of the line of action of V a distance e such that $V'e = 2\,\bar{y}F_t$. Therefore unless P is applied e in. to the left of the line of action of V, it will rotate the segment (clockwise as seen in Fig. 425).

Since $V' = V$,

$$e = \frac{2\,\bar{y}F_t}{V} = \frac{2 \times Vw^2\bar{y}t \times \bar{y}}{2\,I \times V} = \frac{w^2\bar{y}^2 t}{I}$$

$$= \frac{\text{Area of flange} \times w\bar{y}^2}{I}$$

Since $wt\bar{y}^2$ is approximately the I of one flange, a close approximation to the above value for e is $\dfrac{I \text{ of flange} \times w}{I}$.

But the I of one flange is approximately $\bar{y}^2 \times$ area of one flange, and the I of the rectangular web equals $Ak^2 = $ area of web $\times\ h^2/12$. Also $\bar{y}$ is generally only slightly less than $h/2$. Substituting the above values for the I of one flange, the I of the web and $h/2$ for y, there results the equation

$$e = \cfrac{w}{2 + \cfrac{\text{Area of web}}{3 \times \text{area of one flange}}}$$

If the thickness of the web equals the thickness of the flange, this becomes

$$e = \cfrac{w}{2 + \cfrac{h}{3w}}$$

which shows that for this type of section e is less than $\frac{1}{2}\,w$ and approaches $\frac{1}{2}\,w$ as the width of the flange increases relative to the depth of the section. If $h = 3\,w$, $e = \frac{1}{3}\,w$, which is a reasonable value for common structural channels.

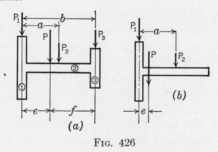

Fig. 426

Two other types of cross-section that have no vertical axis of symmetry and that are in common use are shown in Fig. 426. The section shown in (a) may be regarded as equivalent to three beams each of rectangular cross-section. In order that bending shall occur without twisting, each of these three beams must have the same deflection, which is also the deflection of the beam as a whole. For this to be the case

$$\frac{P_1}{I_1} = \frac{P_2}{I_2} = \frac{P_3}{I_3} = \frac{P}{I} = \frac{P}{I_1 + I_2 + I_3}$$

in which P_1, P_2, and P_3 are components of the applied load P. Whence

$$P_1 = \frac{I_1}{I_1 + I_2 + I_3} P, \quad P_2 = \frac{I_2}{I_1 + I_2 + I_3} P, \quad \text{and } P_3 = \frac{I_3}{I_1 + I_2 + I_3} P$$

These three beams can receive the required loads only if P is applied where the resultant of P_1, P_2, and P_3 falls. This is the case if

$$Pe = P_2a + P_3b = \frac{PI_2a + PI_3b}{I_1 + I_2 + I_3} \quad \text{or } e = \frac{aI_2 + bI_3}{I}$$

If I_2 is negligible in comparison with I_1 and I_3, as it often is, then $e = bI_3/I$ and $f = b - e = bI_1/I$, whence $e/f = I_3/I_1$.

By similar reasoning for the section shown in (b),

$$Pe = P_2a = \frac{PaI_2}{I_1 + I_2}$$

Therefore

$$e = a\frac{I_2}{I}$$

If I_2 is negligible compared with I_1 (as it is if the thickness of the horizontal web is small), $e = 0$, which indicates that the load should be applied at the center of the vertical part of the cross-section.

PROBLEMS

1. A 10-in., 31.7-lb. ship channel has flanges which are $3\frac{5}{8}$ in. wide and $\frac{9}{16}$-in. thick (average). The web is $\frac{9}{16}$ in. thick. Calculate the distance from the back of the channel to the plane of loads if torsion is to be avoided.

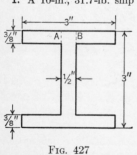

2. A beam has a cross-section like that shown in Fig. 426 (a). The metal is all 1 in. thick. The over-all width is 10 in., and the heights of the flanges are 8 in. and 5 in., respectively. Calculate the position of the plane of loading if torsion is to be avoided.
                                              Ans. $e = 1.8$ in.

3. The cross-section of a small wooden beam is shown in Fig. 427. Calculate the shearing stress on the planes A and B when the total shear on

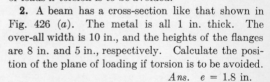

Fig. 427

the cross-section is 80 lb.

CHAPTER XXI

THICK-WALLED CYLINDERS SUBJECT TO INTERNAL AND EXTERNAL PRESSURE

270. Introduction. The relation between unit pressure and circumferential stress which was developed for "thin-walled" cylinders in Chapter IV does not hold for "thick-walled" cylinders. The reasoning which was applied to the thin-walled cylinder gives a correct value for the *average* circumferential stress in the wall of any circular cylinder subjected to internal pressure. But if the cylinder wall is thick (in comparison with the internal radius) the *maximum* unit stress is higher than the average. If the wall thickness is 2/10 of the inner radius, the maximum stress is 10 per cent above the average stress. For greater relative thicknesses, the maximum stress increases more rapidly than the thickness.

271. Lamé's Formulas for Stresses in Thick-Walled Cylinders. A formula will now be derived for the maximum "hoop-tension" in a thick cylinder. Consider a cylinder (Fig. 428) with inside radius R_1 and outside radius R_2 and subject to pressures (pounds per square inch) of P_1 on the interior and P_2 on the outside.[1] From this take a thin half-hoop the radius of which is ρ, the thickness $d\rho$, and the length (perpendicular to the plane of the paper) unity. Let the hoop tension or circumferential stress in this thin half-hoop be S_t lb. per sq. in. Let the radial stress normal to the inner curved surface be S_r, and the radial stress normal to the outer curved surface be $S_r + dS_r$.

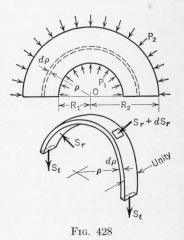

Fig. 428

To this thin half-hoop the methods used for thin cylinders may be correctly applied, and, equating the sum of the vertical forces to zero,

$$2 S_r \rho - 2(S_r + dS_r)(\rho + d\rho) - 2 S_t d\rho = 0$$

---

[1] In thin-walled pressure containers subject to both internal and external pressures, the stresses were found by using the difference between the internal and external pressures. In thick-walled cylinders, such a simple procedure cannot be followed.

whence

$$S_t d\rho = -S_r d\rho - \rho dS_r - d\rho dS_r$$

Neglecting the term $d\rho dS_r$ since it is small compared with the other terms,

$$S_t = -S_r - \rho \frac{dS_r}{d\rho} \tag{1}$$

An additional relation between S_t and S_r is found from the assumption that plane cross-sections of the cylinder remain plane as stresses due to the pressures develop. In other words, the longitudinal unit stress is uniform over the cross-section. (This is reasonable for sections not too close to the ends.) Let S_z be this longitudinal unit stress. At a distance ρ from the axis of the cylinder the longitudinal unit deformation δ_z is

$$\delta_z = \frac{S_z}{E} - m\frac{S_t}{E} + m\frac{S_r}{E} = \frac{1}{E}\left[S_z - m(S_t - S_r) \right]$$

where m is Poisson's ratio.

In this equation, δ_z, E, S_z, and m are all constants, hence $S_t - S_r$ is a constant throughout the cross-section. Let $S_t - S_r = 2\,a$ (where a is merely a convenient constant). Then $S_t = S_r + 2\,a$. This, substituted in (1) gives

$$S_r + 2\,a = -S_r - \rho\frac{dS_r}{d\rho}$$

or

$$S_r + a = -\rho\frac{dS_r}{2\,d\rho}$$

whence

$$-2\frac{d\rho}{\rho} = \frac{dS_r}{S_r + a}$$

Integrating both members of this equation,

$$\log_e (S_r + a) = -2\log_e \rho + C' = -\log_e \rho^2 + C'$$

Let $C' = \log_e C$. Then

$$S_r + a = \frac{C}{\rho^2}$$

and

$$S_r = \frac{C}{\rho^2} - a$$

Since

$$S_t - S_r = 2\,a$$

$$S_t = \frac{C}{\rho^2} + a$$

To determine the values of the constants C and a, note that $S_r = P_1$ when $\rho = R_1$, so that $P_1 = \dfrac{C}{R_1^2} - a$ and also that $S_r = P_2$ when $\rho = R_2$

or $P_2 = \dfrac{C}{R_2^2} - a$.   These two equations solved for a and C give

$$a = \frac{P_1 R_1^2 - P_2 R_2^2}{R_2^2 - R_1^2} \quad \text{and} \quad C = \frac{(P_1 - P_2) R_1^2 R_2^2}{R_2^2 - R_1^2}$$

Values for these constants may be readily calculated for any given internal and external pressures and for given (or assumed) values for the radii.

The radial and circumferential stresses at any distance ρ from the axis are found by substituting the values for C, a, and ρ in the respective formulas

$$S_r = \frac{C}{\rho^2} - a \quad \text{and} \quad S_t = \frac{C}{\rho^2} + a$$

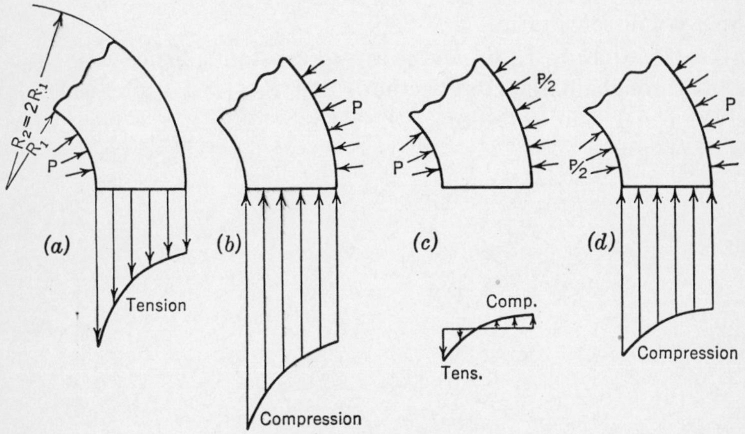

Fig. 429.   Variation of circumferential stress in a thick-walled cylinder for four cases of pressure.

The circumferential stress is obviously maximum when $\rho = R_1$ or at the inner surface for which case

$$\text{max. } S_t = \frac{P_1(R_2^2 + R_1^2) - 2\,P_2 R_2^2}{R_2^2 - R_1^2}$$

For the common case of internal pressure only, the above expression for the maximum tangential stress is

$$\text{max. } S_t = \frac{P_1(R_2^2 + R_1^2)}{R_2^2 - R_1^2}$$

In deriving the above formulas, the first expression for radial stress was written as positive and the stress resulting from the force on the free body as pictured is compression. Consequently a plus value obtained from the expression for radial stress means that the stress is compression, which is always the case. The circumferential stress in the free body was written as plus when the forces were assumed to be such as to cause it to be tension. Consequently a plus value obtained from the expression for circumferential stress means that the stress is tension. In Fig. 429 the variation of circumferential stress for a cylinder in which $R_2 = 2\,R_1$ is shown for four cases of pressure.

The formulas for stresses in thick cylinders were first derived by the French elastician Gabriel Lamé (1795–1870) and are known as the Lamé formulas for thick cylinders.

272. Maximum Stress in Terms of Average Stress. Because of the ease of finding the average circumferential stress in any cylinder subject to internal pressure only, it is convenient to have an expression for the maximum circumferential stress in terms of the average. This may be done as follows:

Let $R_2 = KR_1$, or $R_2/R_1 = K$. Then

$$S_t \text{ max.} = P_1 \frac{K^2 + 1}{K^2 - 1}$$

The *average* hoop tension as correctly given by the method used for thin cylinders is

$$S_t = \frac{P_1 R_1}{R_2 - R_1} = \frac{P_1}{(K - 1)}$$

The ratio of the maximum to average is

$$\frac{\text{max. } S_t}{\text{average } S_t} = \frac{K^2 + 1}{K + 1}$$

The curve in Fig. 430 shows the ratio of the maximum hoop tension to the average for varying values of the ratio of wall thickness to inner radius.

PROBLEMS

1. Eight hydraulic jacks with the diameters given in Fig. 431 were used in raising the suspended span of the Quebec bridge. The total load on eight jacks was 5,540 tons. This results in a working pressure of about 3,640 lb. per sq. in. The jacks were tested by the manufacturer with an oil pressure of 6,000 lb. per sq. in. The ram was 22 in. in diameter and hollow with an internal diameter of 12 in. as shown. Calculate the maximum circumferential stress in the chamber of the jack due to the test pressure. Calculate the maximum circumferential stress in the ram due to the test pressure.

2. It is desired to lower a piece of apparatus into the ocean to a depth of 10,000 ft. The apparatus can be contained in a cylinder with an internal diameter of 10 in. The cylinder is to be made of cast iron with ultimate strengths of 110,000 lb. per sq. in. in compression, 24,000 lb. per sq. in. in tension, and 32,000 lb. per sq. in. in shear. A tentative thickness of 2.5 in. has been assumed. Calculate the factors of safety in shearing and compression.

(NOTE: The longitudinal stress may be computed on the assumption that it is uniform over a transverse section.)   *Ans.* Shearing factor of safety = 8.0.

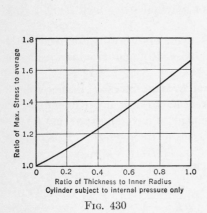

FIG. 430

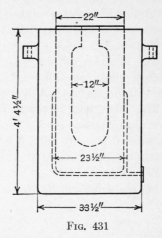

FIG. 431

3. The chrome-vanadium steel shell of a synthesis converter used in the manufacture of ammonia has an inside diameter of 24 in. and an outside diameter of 32 in. It is operated with an internal pressure of 300 atmospheres and at a temperature which may be somewhat higher than that of boiling water. Calculate the maximum stress caused by this pressure.

CHAPTER XXII

ECCENTRICALLY LOADED CONNECTIONS

273. Introduction. When members of a frame are joined to one another by rivets, the most satisfactory distribution of loads on the various rivets results when the line of action of the force on each of the members passes through the centroid of the cross-sections of the group of rivets which connect that member to the others (Fig. 432[a]). Similarly, in a welded joint the line of action of the load should pass through the centroid of the welds (Fig. 432[b]). In the case of a member with a

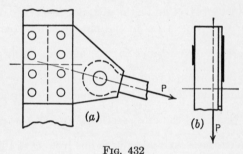

(a)

(b)

Fig. 432

cross-section having a centroid unequally distant from the edges of the member this leads to the use of unequal lengths of fillet on the two edges, as noted in Art. 42.

When the above conditions are met it can generally be assumed that the same amount of load is carried by each rivet, or by each inch of fillet. But there are situations in which it is not possible to have the rivets or fillets so placed that their centroid lies on the action line of the load. The stresses that exist in cases of this sort will now be discussed.

274. Eccentrically Loaded Riveted Connection. In Fig. 433 the load P is equivalent to an equal and parallel force P passing through the centroid of the rivet areas, and a couple Pe. The centroidal force P may be assumed to load each of the rivets equally, so that the force which each exerts on the bracket is P/n and is in a direction opposite to P. The couple Pe tends to rotate the bracket clockwise (and indeed does rotate it slightly, since the materials involved are not absolutely rigid). The point about which this rotation occurs is *the centroid of the rivet areas*. This will now be shown.

370

In Fig. 434 let O be the center about which the slight rotation of a plate occurs in consequence of a moment M applied to the plate.   It is here assumed that the position of O with respect to the centroid of the rivet cross-sections is unknown and is to be determined.   Assume any pair of rectangular axes through O as shown.   Let c be the distance from

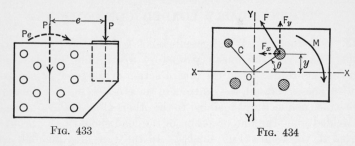

FIG. 433   FIG. 434

O to the most distant rivet and r the distance from O to any other rivet. If S is the shearing unit stress in the most distant rivet, the shearing unit stress in a rivet at a distance r is $\dfrac{r}{c} S$, since the shearing deformation in each rivet is proportional to the distance of that rivet from the center of rotation.   The force exerted by a rivet at a distance r from O is $F = \dfrac{r}{c} SA$, in which A is the cross-sectional area of the rivet.   Let θ be the angle between the X axis and the radius from O to the rivet.   Then the component of F parallel to the X axis is $F_x = \dfrac{r}{c} SA \sin \theta$.   But for any rivet $r \sin \theta$ is y, the distance from the X axis to that rivet.   Hence $F_x = \dfrac{S}{c} Ay$.   For all the rivets $\Sigma F_x = 0$, or

$$\frac{S}{c} \Sigma Ay = 0$$

Since S/c does not equal zero, $\Sigma Ay = 0$.   But if $\Sigma Ay = 0$, the X axis passes through the centroid of the cross-sectional areas of all the rivets.

Similar reasoning shows that the Y axis also passes through the centroid of the cross-sectional areas of all rivets.   Consequently the point about which the plate rotates coincides with the centroid of the cross-sectional areas of all the rivets.

It follows that the force F_r developed by each rivet in resisting the moment Pe is proportional to the distance of that rivet from the centroid of the rivet cross-sections.   The sum of the moments of these forces must equal Pe.   These facts make possible the determination of the force which each rivet develops in resisting the torque Pe. The total force on any rivet is found by adding, vectorially, the " direct " shearing force, P/n, to the force F_r.

Example. Find the resultant force exerted on the bracket (Fig. 435[a]) by each of the rivets when $P = 6,000$ lb.

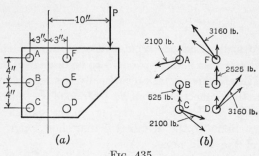

(a)   (b)

FIG. 435

Solution: The load is equivalent to a vertical force of 6,000 lb. through the centroid of the group of rivets and a couple or torque of 60,000 lb-in. To resist the centroidal force of 6,000 lb. each rivet exerts an upward force on the bracket of 1,000 lb.

Let F_A be the tangential force which rivet A exerts on the bracket to resist the torque. Evidently $F_A = F_C = F_D = F_F$. It is also evident that $F_B = F_E = \frac{3}{5} F_A$.

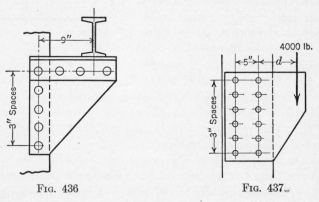

FIG. 436   FIG. 437

Since $\Sigma M = 0$,

$$4(F_A \times 5) + 2(\tfrac{3}{5} F_A \times 3) - 60,000 = 0$$

Whence $F_A = 2,540$ lb.

Also $F_B = \tfrac{3}{5} F_A = 1,525$ lb.

The resultant force which each rivet exerts on the bracket is shown in Fig. 435 (b). The corner rivets on the side toward the load exert the greatest resultant forces.[1]

[1] It should be noted that rivets near to the centroid of the group are inefficient in respect to resistance to torque.

PROBLEMS

1. The reaction of the beam shown in Fig. 436 is 8,350 lb. The rivets are $\frac{3}{4}$ in. Calculate the maximum shearing stress. Is this stress permitted by A.I.S.C. specifications? Assume that bearing stress does not govern.

Ans. S_s = 11,950 lb. per sq. in.

2. The rivets connecting the plate shown in Fig. 437 are $\frac{7}{8}$-in. rivets and the allowable shearing stress is 13,500 lb. per sq. in. Calculate the maximum allowable value of d. Plate thickness is such that bearing stress does not govern.

275. Eccentrically Loaded Welded Connections. The process of reasoning that has just been applied to riveted connections establishes the fact that the torque on an eccentrically loaded welded connection tends to rotate the connection about *the centroid of the group of weld areas.* The force exerted (as a result of the torque) on any short length of fillet is therefore proportional to the distance of that short length of fillet from the centroid of the weld areas. Also the sum of the moments of these forces must equal the torque. These facts can be used to develop an expression connecting the torque Pe with the maximum force (in pounds per linear inch of fillet) exerted on the weld.

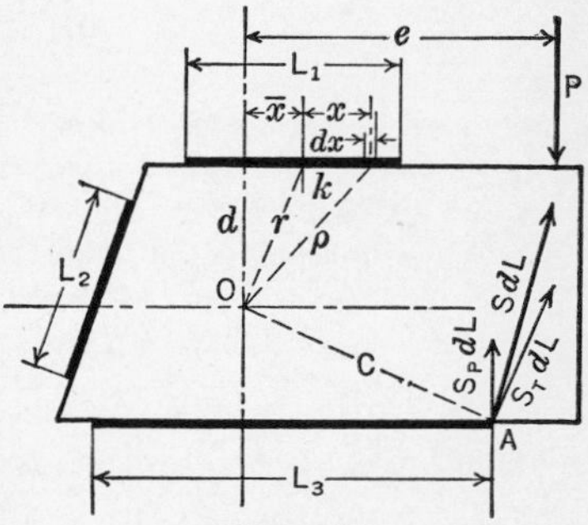

Fig. 438 represents a member welded to a fixed support and carrying loads, the resultant of which is an eccentric load P. The three fillet welds shown represent any arrangement of straight

FIG. 438

fillets. Let O be the centroid of the lines of fillets and let c be the distance from the centroid to the most distant point of fillet.

Let S_P be the load per inch of fillet due to direct loading. Then $S_P = P/L$. This is vertical and, if the force which the fillet exerts on the member is considered, upward.

Each elementary length of fillet is also exerting a force perpendicular to the radius from O. The sum of the moments of these forces equals Pe. The magnitudes of these forces exerted by equal elementary lengths are proportional to the distances of the elementary lengths from O. Consider a length dL at point A which is most remote from O. The vertical force exerted by this is $S_P dL$. If S is the allowable load (as given in specifications) per inch of fillet, then the *total* force which this length dL can exert according to the specifications is $S dL$. This force will be the resultant of the component $S_P dL$ parallel to the load P and the tangential component $S_T dL$ (perpendicular to OA) in which S_T is the allowable tangential load per inch at the point most remote from O.

It is apparent that with S given and S_P calculated it is possible to determine S_T by a simple vector diagram in which dL may be taken as unity.

It is necessary to derive a formula relating S_T, the available tangential load per inch at the most remote point, the lengths and arrangement of the lines of fillets, and the rotating moment of the load Pe. Consider an elementary length dx of the top line of fillet the distance of which from O is ρ.

The tangential force (pounds) exerted by dx and resisting rotation is $\dfrac{S_T \rho\, dx}{c}$. The moment of this force is $\dfrac{S_T \rho^2 dx}{c}$. The total moment exerted by this one line of fillet is therefore

$$M = \frac{S_T}{c} \int_{-L/2}^{+L/2} \rho^2 dx$$

A value for $\displaystyle\int_{-L/2}^{+L/2} \rho^2 dx$ will now be derived for a straight fillet. Let d be the perpendicular distance from O to this line, let $\bar{x}$ be the distance from the foot of this perpendicular to the midpoint K of the line, let r be the distance from O to K, and let x be the distance from K to the elementary length dx. Then

$$\rho^2 = d^2 + (x + \bar{x})^2 = d^2 + x^2 + 2\,x\bar{x} + \bar{x}^2$$

but
$$d^2 + \bar{x}^2 = r^2$$

Therefore
$$\rho^2 = r^2 + x^2 + 2\,\bar{x}x$$

and
$$\int_{-L/2}^{+L/2} \rho^2 dx = r^2 x\Big]_{-L/2}^{+L/2} + \frac{x^3}{3}\Big]_{-L/2}^{+L/2} + \bar{x}x^2\Big]_{-L/2}^{+L/2}$$

$$= r^2 L + \frac{L^3}{12} + 0$$

Hence the allowable moment for this line of fillet is $\dfrac{S_T L}{c}\left(r^2 + \dfrac{L^2}{12}\right)$, and the total allowable moment for the joint is

$$M = \frac{S_T}{c} \sum \left[L\left(r^2 + \frac{L^2}{12}\right) \right]$$

Example. A steel member to carry a vertical eccentric load of 20,000 lb. is welded to a column with three lines of $\frac{3}{8}$ fillet welds as shown in Fig. 439. Specifications for steel structures permit a load in any direction of 3,000 lb. per in. of fillet, for $\frac{3}{8}$-in. fillet. Determine the maximum allowable distance a.

Solution: The number of pounds per inch of fillet required for direct stress = 20,000/22 = 910 lb. per in. The position of the centroid is given by

$$\bar{x} = \frac{16 \times 6 + 6 \times 0}{22} = 4.36 \text{ in.,}$$

and the distance to the most remote point is $c = \sqrt{5.64^2 + 4^2} = \sqrt{31.8 + 16}$
$= \sqrt{47.8} = 6.91$ in.

$$r_1^2 = 4^2 + 1.64^2 = 16 + 2.7 = 18.7; \quad r_1 = 4.33 \text{ in.}$$

also $r_2 = 4.36$ in.

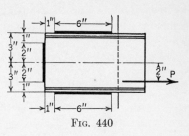

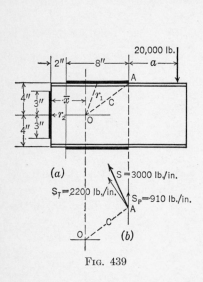

Fig. 440

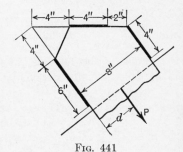

Fig. 439

Fig. 441

The number of pounds per inch at the most remote point of the fillet available for resisting the moment of the load is determined by the vector diagram shown in (b) and is $S_T = 2,200$ lb. per in. The allowable moment is

$$M = \frac{2,200}{6.91}\left[2 \times 8 \left(18.7 + \frac{64}{12}\right) + 6 \left(4.36^2 + \frac{36}{12}\right)\right]$$

$$= 318 \ (384 + 132) = 164,000 \text{ lb-in.}$$

Hence

$$e = \frac{164,000}{20,000} = 8.20 \text{ in.} \quad \text{and} \quad a = 8.20 - 5.64 = 2.56 \text{ in.}$$

PROBLEMS

1. The welded joint shown in Fig. 440 resists a load P of 24,000 lb. applied as shown. Is the resulting maximum load per inch of fillet within the specifications for $\frac{5}{16}$-in. fillet?   *Ans.* Load per inch is 2,430 lb.

2. A welded connection is shown in Fig. 441. Determine the distance d for which the allowable value of P will be greatest. If the fillets are $\frac{3}{8}$ in. what is the allowable P when d has the value found? What is the allowable value of P if d is increased by 1 in.?

CHAPTER XXIII

COMPREHENSIVE PROBLEMS

1. A cableway with a span of 1,200 ft. and designed to handle 150-ton loads was used for handling material and equipment during the construction of the Boulder Dam. To adjust the six $3\frac{1}{2}$-in. wire ropes to the same tension (and sag) there were six toggles operated by hydraulic jacks. (See *Engineering News-Record*, Dec. 21, 1933, p. 760.)

You are asked to determine certain dimensions for a somewhat similar toggle shown in Fig. 442. The pull on the toggle is 175 tons. The dimension H may vary from 3 ft., minimum to 4 ft., maximum. All eyebars are 5.30 ft. long, center to

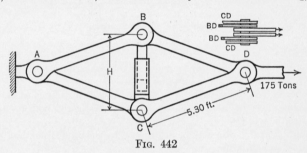

FIG. 442

center of pins. The jack will be operated by oil under a pressure of 3,000 lb. per sq. in. This pressure acts on the end area of the ram. The ram and cylinder will be ground to a close running fit, and suitable packing to insure oil tightness is to be provided but is not shown.

Determine the following:

(*a*) Number of inches of motion of *D*.

(*b*) Required diameter of ram. Make the diameter the next larger one-tenth inch.

(*c*) The shell thickness of the cylinder. It may be necessary to consider this a " thick cylinder " (see Fig. 430).

(*d*) Thickness of eyebars. The width of these will be 6 in.

(*e*) Diameter of pins at *A* and *D*.

(*f*) Diameter of pins at *B* and *C*.

For the cylinder use an allowable stress of 12,000 lb. per sq. in., tension; for other parts use 0.8 of the A.I.S.C. (1936) stresses.

2. The jib crane shown in Fig. 443 is to be constructed to carry a load of $2\frac{1}{2}$ tons, which may be in any position on the boom not less than 18 in. from either end. One hundred per cent is to be added to the load for impact. The combined weight of trolley and hoist is to be assumed to be 500 lb. Allowable stresses are those given by New York City Building Code, 1938. In calculating any particular stress, the load is to be so placed as to make that stress a maximum. Calculate the following:

(*a*) Necessary size of beam. For this determination, the load should be placed at the midpoint of the beam. Both bending and direct compression must be taken into consideration, but in figuring the maximum bending moment on the beam, the effect of deflection of the beam may be disregarded. The combined bending and direct stress in the unsupported top flange must not exceed the stress allowed by the specification covering such cases.

(*b*) Size of rods from *A* to *B*. It may be assumed that the forged loop at *B* will be as strong as the rod, the lower end of which is threaded.

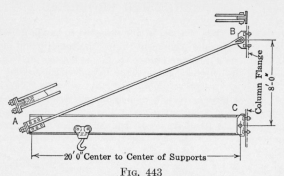

Fig. 443

(*c*) Size of bolt at *B*. This may be determined by shearing strength of bolt, or by its bearing strength against the $\frac{3}{4}$-in. thick angles.

(*d*) Number of $\frac{3}{4}$-in. bolts required to connect angles to column at *B*. An even number of bolts must be used. Bolts should be investigated both for tensile and shearing strength.

(*e*) Size of bolt at *C*. Size may be determined by shearing strength of bolt, or by bearing against web of beam.

(*f*) Number of $\frac{3}{4}$-in. bolts required to connect the angles at *C* to the column. Use an even number and not less than four.

(*g*) Number of $\frac{3}{4}$-in. rivets required to connect the bent plates at *A* to the beam. Use an even number.

3. In a certain plant it is desired to install a hot-water tank to hold water under a pressure of 50 lb. per sq. in. There is available a cylindrical steel tank 70 in. in diameter and 15 ft. long. The tank is made of $\frac{5}{16}$-in. steel plate. Circumferential joints are single-riveted lap joints, diameter of rivet holes $\frac{13}{16}$ in., rivet pitch 2 in. Longitudinal joints are single-riveted butt joints, cover plates $\frac{1}{4}$ in. thick, diameter of rivet holes $\frac{13}{16}$ in., rivet pitch $2\frac{1}{2}$ in.

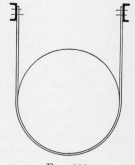

It is proposed to hang this tank from two steel channels by means of steel straps, riveted to the channels, as shown in Fig. 444. The channels are to frame between two I-beams 18 ft. apart. The straps are to be symmetrically located on the tank, 10 ft. apart and 4 ft. from the ends of the channels. The channels are to be carried by 18-in., 70-lb. I-beams, 16 ft. long, the back of one channel being 12 in. from the end of the beams. There

Fig. 444

is adequate bracing to fix the top flanges of the beams and channels against lateral deflection. Before installation of the tank each I-beam is carrying a distributed load of 70,000 lb. To enable them to carry the additional load of the channel reactions, they are to be strengthened by welding a steel plate to the lower face of each beam. It is possible to unload or to support the I-beams so that there is no bending stress in them while the plates are being welded on.

(a) Investigate the tank to see with what factor of safety it will carry the 50-lb.-per-sq.-in. pressure.

(b) Design the strap hangers and their connection to the channels, using $\frac{3}{4}$-in. rivets for this purpose. Assume tank full of water, and allow 10 per cent of the net weight of the tank plates to cover overlap at joints, etc.

(c) Using a steel handbook, select suitable channels to carry the tank.

(d) Determine the size of the plates that must be welded to the lower flange of the I-beams. Make width of plate 8 in.

(e) Determine the number of inches of $\frac{5}{16}$-in. fillet required per foot of plate.

Use 18,000 lb. per sq. in. for the allowable bending stress in steel, and shearing and bearing stresses consistent with this in structural members. Use A.S.M.E. boiler code strengths in determining the factor of safety of the tank.

4. The diagrams of Fig. 445 show approximate dimensions of an automobile jack which is manufactured from steel plates and rolled rods. The threaded rod has a

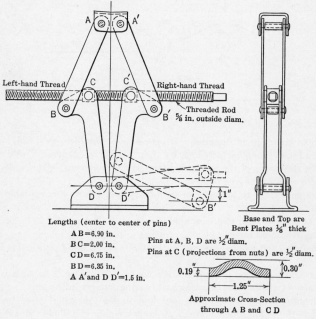

Lengths (center to center of pins)
A B = 6.90 in.
B C = 2.00 in.
C D = 6.75 in.
B D = 6.35 in.
A A′ and D D′ = 1.5 in.

Pins at A, B, D are ½″ diam.
Pins at C (projections from nuts) are ½″ diam.

Base and Top are Bent Plates ⅛″ thick

0.19″   0.30″
1.25″

Approximate Cross-Section through A B and C D

Fig. 445

square end to which a socket bar can be fitted. The threaded rod is turned by this bar. At C and C' there are nuts through which the threaded bar passes. As the rod is turned, the nuts C and C' are either brought nearer together (raising the load) or separated (lowering the load). Additional devices for increasing the stability are used, but not shown in the diagram. They do not affect the stresses.

The low position is shown approximately by the dotted diagram of the right-hand members.

When the jack is in such a position that pins B, D, D', and B' are all in the same horizontal plane, and is carrying a load of 1,200 lb., calculate the following unit stresses:

(a) Tensile stress in screw.

(b) Shearing stress in pins of nuts at C and C'.

(c) Shearing stress in pins at A and B and A' and B'.

(d) Shearing stress in pins at D and D'.

(e) Bearing stress between pins and plates at A, B, C, and D.

(f) Combined bending and direct stress in member BCD at a section 5 in. from D (where it begins to widen). At this section it is not dished.

(g) Average compressive stress in AB. AB is a column. The plate has been " dished " as shown to increase its radius of gyration. Compare the average compressive stress with the allowable P/A given by a suitable Rankine formula for a flat (not " dished ") member of this width and thickness.

In finding the forces acting on the members draw free-body diagrams, as shown in Fig. 446. Members AB and $A'B'$ are two force members (the force exerted by

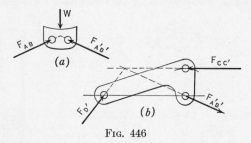

Fig. 446

each of them coincides in direction with the axis of the member). Member BCD is a " three force " member acted on by the three forces shown. These meet in a point. The directions of the forces at B and at C are known. A force polygon can be drawn for each of the free bodies.

5. A simple hoist is to be built for temporary use. Parts are available as shown in Fig. 447.

(a) What load, W, can two men hold if each exerts a force of 150 lb. on a crank? Neglect any frictional force.

(b) Calculate the torsional stresses in the shafts A, B, and C when this load is on the hoist.

(c) Each crank is keyed to shaft A with one key $2\frac{1}{2}$ in. long, $\frac{3}{8}$ in. square, sunk $\frac{3}{16}$ in. into shaft. Calculate the shearing and bearing stresses in the key.

(d) Calculate maximum bending and longitudinal shearing stress in beam D when W has the value found above. Assume weights as follows: drum and rope 700 lb., each bearing 20 lb., gear wheel on shaft C, 300 lb. Note that vertical forces exist between the gear wheel on shaft C and the pinion on shaft B. Assume that the effects of these forces are equally divided between beams D and E and result in a downward force at shaft C and an upward force at shaft B. The position of weight W along the drum should be taken as that which causes greatest load on beam D. In calculating the part of W carried by beam D, ignore the supporting effect of beam E on shaft C. One-inch-diameter holes are bored vertically through beam D for attaching bearings. To be safe, assume that such a hole may occur where bending moment is maximum.

6. A platform is to be built over a contractor's narrow-gage material track.   One proposed bent is shown in Fig. 448.   Adequate bracing will be used to insure sta-

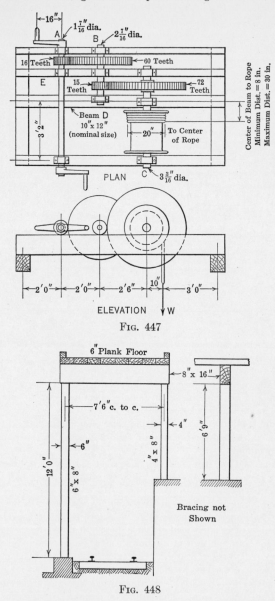

PLAN

ELEVATION   ↓W

Fig. 447

6″ Plank Floor

Fig. 448

bility, but it is not shown and it is assumed that it will not affect the stresses.   The bents will be 8 ft. apart.   Material will be Douglas fir, common grade.   Sizes shown in Fig. 448, are nominal.

The contractor wishes to know what load per square foot (on a width of 7 ft., 6 in.) is permissible.

State your answer to this inquiry, and submit all computations necessary for arriving at your conclusion. Also make a recommendation as to a change in size of one member to permit a larger load. Allowable stresses should be based on "occasionally wet but quickly dried " condition.

7. In a certain shop it is necessary to support loads of 3,500 and 14,000 lb. respectively. The arrangement shown in Fig. 449 is suggested. The beam A and bracket are welded together and the beam is bolted to a column at each end.

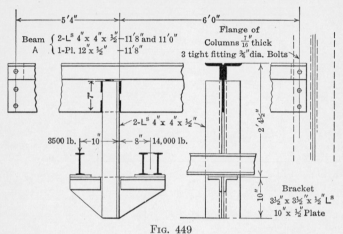

Fig. 449

Is this construction satisfactory as far as stresses are concerned? The following stresses should be considered:

(a) Tensile and compressive stresses in beam due to bending. (Is it necessary to reduce the allowable stress because of unsupported top flange of beam?)

(b) Shearing and bearing stresses in bolts connecting beam to columns.

(c) Stresses in vertical bracket angles.

(d) Shear and bending stresses in bottom cross plate of bracket. (The other ends of the I-beams which load the bracket are rigidly fastened so that the I-beams cannot move longitudinally.)

(e) Maximum load per inch in $\frac{5}{16}$-in. fillet weld connecting the vertical angles to the $\frac{1}{2}$-in. plate of the beam A. Each angle is attached with 12.5 in. of fillet in five 2.5-in. lengths, as shown.

8. A wooden frame building is to have columns spaced 12 ft. on centers in one direction and 16 ft. on centers in the other, as shown in Fig. 450. The second floor is to be designed to carry a live load of 100 lb. per sq. ft. The flooring is to be carried on joists and the joists on girders as shown. Joists are to be of western hemlock, select grade, spaced 16 in. on centers. Girders are to be of Douglas fir, select grade. In design of the floor system, weight of joists and girders is to be given whatever consideration it merits. Load is to be transmitted from the girders to the columns through cast-iron column caps, which are to be designed for the job. Load transmitted from column B to column A is 90,000 lb.

(a) Select joists of proper size, using stresses as given in Table XI. Assume weight of flooring at 5 lb. per sq. ft.

(b) Select girders of proper size to support the joists. Load on the girders may be treated as if uniformly distributed.

(c) Determine the necessary length, m, of the brackets on the column caps so that side grain compression on the girders will not be excessive.

(d) Design column A. It is to be of square cross-section, of Douglas fir, select grade.

(e) Calculate the change in elevation of the floor at the middle of the panel which occurs when the full live load is put on the floor. Assume that the deflection of the flooring between the joists is negligible and that no change occurs in the elevation of the lower end of columns A.

9. For loading materials at a factory, the arrangement illustrated in Fig. 451 is used. A hoist, carried on the lower flange of a 24-in., 100-lb. wide-flange beam is used to handle loads that come into a factory on railroad tracks beneath the hoist. Appropriate stops prevent the hoist load from coming within 2 ft. of either end of the beam, but it may have any intermediate position. The right-hand end of the beam is riveted to the flange of a

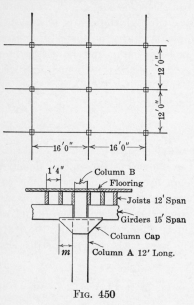

Fig. 450

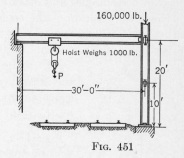

Fig. 451

20-in., 65.4-lb. I-beam used as a column and braced at midlength in the weak direction. In addition the column carries a nominally axial load of 160,000 lb.

(a) Determine the allowable hoist load, P, to accord with the New York City Building Code, 1938.

(b) What is the least number of ¾-in. rivets that may be used to connect the clip angles to the flange of the column?

APPENDIX A

CENTROID AND STATICAL MOMENT OF A PLANE AREA

The *centroid of a plane area* is a point which corresponds to the center of gravity of a thin homogeneous plate of the same shape. Such a plate will balance about any axis which passes through the center of gravity. If a piece of tin or cardboard, for example, is cut to the shape of an area whose centroid is to be located, it can be balanced on the sharp edge of a ruler (Fig. 452). The centroid lies on this axis. If two such axes are determined and marked, their intersection locates the center of gravity of the plate or the centroid of an area of the same shape.

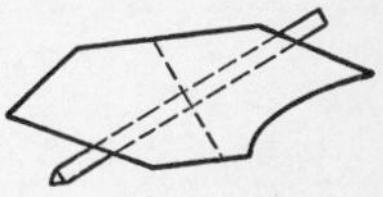

Fig. 452

Areas very commonly occur which may be divided into rectangles and other elementary shapes for which the position of the centroid is known. The statical moment with respect to a given axis for such an area is found by adding together the statical moments of all the component areas.

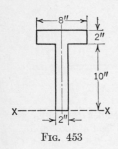

The distance from this axis to the centroid of the area may then be found by dividing the statical moment of the area with respect to this axis by the total area.

Example 1. Calculate the position of the centroid of the area shown in Fig. 453.

Solution: Since the area is symmetrical about the vertical axis shown, the centroid lies on this axis and it is only necessary to locate it on this axis. Assume a horizontal axis, X–X, through the lower edge of the area.

Fig. 453

$$Q = 10 \times 2 \times 5 + 8 \times 2 \times 11 = 100 + 176 = 276 \text{ in.}^3$$

$$\bar{y} = \frac{Q}{A} = \frac{276}{36} = 7.67 \text{ in. above axis } X\text{–}X$$

The position of the centroid of many elementary areas is found by integration.

Example 2. Calculate the distance to the centroid of a triangle from an axis through the apex parallel to the base.

Solution: The triangle in Fig. 454 represents any triangle. The base is b in. and the altitude h in. The shaded strip represents any strip parallel to the given axis, Y–Y, through the apex. Distance from the axis to this strip is x (which can have any value from zero to h). The length of the strip is, by similar triangles, $\frac{x}{h}\, b$.

383

The area dA is therefore $\dfrac{b}{h} x dx$.

$$Q = \int x dA = \frac{b}{h} \int_0^h x^2 dx = \frac{bx^3}{3\,h}\Big]_0^h = \frac{bh^2}{3}$$

$$\bar{x} = \frac{Q}{A} = \frac{bh^2}{3} \div \frac{bh}{2} = \frac{2}{3} h$$

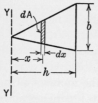

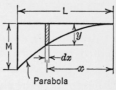

Parabola

FIG. 454   FIG. 455

Example 3.   An area which is often used in computing the deflection of beams by the area moment method is shown in Fig. 455.   The ordinate y at any distance x from the apex is $wx^2/2$, and at the other end $M = wL^2/2$.   Calculate the area and the distance from the small end to the centroid of the area.

Solution:

$$\frac{y}{M} = \frac{x^2}{L^2} \quad \text{or} \quad y = M\frac{x^2}{L^2}$$

Consider a thin vertical strip the height of which is y and the thickness of which is dx.   The sum of all such strips is the area shown.

$$A = \int_0^L y\,dx = \int_0^L \frac{Mx^2}{L^2}\,dx = \frac{Mx^3}{3\,L^2}\Big]_0^L = \frac{ML}{3}$$

or the area is $\frac{1}{3}$ the length times the maximum height.

To find the distance $\bar{x}$ to the centroid, first calculate the statical moment Q.

$$Q = \int_0^L x dA = \int_0^L \frac{Mx^3}{L^2}\,dx = \frac{Mx^4}{4\,L^2}\Big]_0^L = \frac{ML^2}{4}$$

$$\bar{x} = \frac{Q}{A} = \frac{ML^2}{4} \div \frac{ML}{3} = \frac{3}{4} L$$

APPENDIX B

THE MOMENT OF INERTIA OF A PLANE AREA

Let the area marked A in Fig. 456 represent any plane area and let the axis $X–X$ be any axis in the plane of the area. If the area is divided into small elementary areas (one of which is shown) and each elementary area is multiplied by the square of its distance from the given axis, then the sum of all these products is a quantity called the moment of inertia of the area with respect to the given axis. The units are inches raised to the fourth power, or in.[4], if all dimensions are in inches. The summing up of all the products can be performed by integration, and this sum may be represented as an integral. Thus,

$$I = \int y^2 dA$$

The proper limits must be given to the integral so that the operation indicated sums up $y^2 dA$ for all the elementary areas which compose the given area. Moment of inertia is always a plus quantity since y^2 is plus even though y is negative. An expression or formula for the moment of inertia of any of the common geometric areas with respect to some specified axis may be derived by integration.

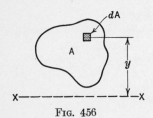

FIG. 456

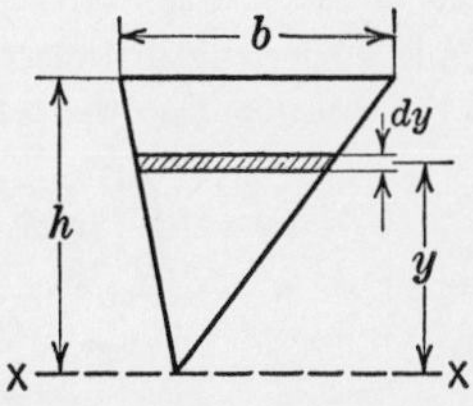

FIG. 457

Example. Calculate I for a triangle with respect to an axis through the vertex parallel to the base.

Solution: Fig. 457 represents any triangle, and the shaded strip represents any strip across this parallel to the axis. The width of this strip is $b\,\dfrac{y}{h}$, and consequently its area is $\dfrac{b}{h}y\,dy$.

$$I = \int y^2 dA = \frac{b}{h}\int_0^h y^3 dy = \frac{b}{h}\frac{y^4}{4}\Big]_0^h = \frac{bh^3}{4}$$

385

It should be noted that the moment of inertia of an area with respect to an axis does not equal the product of the area by the square of the distance from the axis to the centroid of the area.

Parallel Axis Theorem. A relation exists between I_0, the value of the moment of inertia of a plane area with respect to an axis through the centroid of the area, and I_x, the moment of inertia of the same area with respect to a parallel axis not through the centroid. This is expressed by

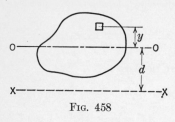

$$I_x = I_0 + Ad^2$$

FIG. 458

in which d is the distance between the axes.

Proof: The area in Fig. 458 represents any plane area. The axis $O\text{-}O$ is any axis through the centroid in the plane of the area, and the axis $X\text{-}X$ is a parallel axis. The area dA is any elementary area, its distance from axis $O\text{-}O$ being y, which is $+$ as shown, but is $-$ for any dA below axis $O\text{-}O$.

$$I_x = \int (d \pm y)^2 dA = \int (y^2 \pm 2\,yd + d^2)dA$$

$$= \int y^2 dA \pm 2\,d\int ydA + d^2\int dA$$

But $\int ydA$ is the statical moment of the area with respect to axis $O\text{-}O$. Since this is the centroidal axis, this statical moment is zero and

$$I_x = \int y^2 dA + d^2\int dA$$

Hence,

$$I_x = I_0 + Ad^2$$

This may be written $I_0 = I_x - Ad^2$, which shows that I with respect to a centroidal axis is less than I for any parallel axis.

Example. Calculate values of the moment of inertia with respect to a centroidal axis parallel to the base for a triangle, using value for I found in the previous example.
Solution:

$$I_0 = I_x - Ad^2 = \frac{bh^3}{4} - \frac{bh}{2} \times \left(\frac{2\,h}{3}\right)^2 = \frac{bh^3}{4} - \frac{2\,bh^3}{9} = \frac{bh^3}{36}$$

The value for I_0 for a triangle should be remembered.

I of Composite Areas. Many plane areas used in structural engineering can be divided into elementary shapes (rectangles, triangles, semicircles, etc.) for each of which an expression for I_0 is known or can be looked up. In such cases no integration is necessary to calculate the moment of inertia of the given area with respect to any axis.

Example. Using $I_0 = 1/12\ bd^3$ for a rectangle and $I_0 = 1/36\ bd^3$ for a triangle, calculate the moment of inertia of the area shown in Fig. 459 with respect to its horizontal centroidal axis.

Solution: The area will be divided into a rectangle and a triangle by the line shown. The distance from this line (axis 1–1) to the centroidal axis O–O of the whole area is

$$\bar{y} = \frac{+8 \times 12 \times 4 - 6 \times 9 \times 3}{8 \times 12 + 6 \times 9} = \frac{384 - 162}{96 + 54} = +\frac{222}{150} = +1.48 \text{ in.}$$

The plus sign indicates that the centroid is above the axis, 1–1.

For the rectangle, $\qquad I = \dfrac{1}{12}\ bd^3 = \dfrac{12 \times 8 \times 8 \times 8}{12} = \quad 512 \text{ in.}^4$

to " transfer " to axis O–O, add $\qquad Ad^2 = 96 \times 2.52^2 = \quad 609$

For the triangle, $\qquad I = \dfrac{1}{36}\ bd^3 = \dfrac{12 \times 9 \times 9 \times 9}{36} = \quad 243$

to " transfer " to axis O–O, add $\qquad Ad^2 = 54 \times 4.48^2 = 1{,}086$

Therefore I_0 for the whole area $\qquad = 2{,}450 \text{ in.}^4$

Radius of Gyration. The radius of gyration of an area with respect to a given axis is a distance found by the following equation:

$$r = \sqrt{\frac{I}{A}}$$

in which r is the radius of gyration and I is the moment of inertia of the area with respect to the given axis. It will be noted from the equation that, if I is given in in.^{4} and A is in in.^{2}, then r is in inches.

FIG. 459   FIG. 460

POLAR MOMENT OF INERTIA OF A PLANE AREA

If the moment of inertia is calculated with respect to an axis which is *perpendicular* to the plane of the area, the result is called the *polar* moment of inertia of the area with respect to the axis. In Fig. 460 the axis Z–Z represents an axis perpendicular to the plane of the given area.

Then, $I_z = \displaystyle\int r^2 dA$.

Since for any differential area $r^2 = x^2 + y^2$

$$\int r^2 dA = \int (x^2 + y^2)dA = \int x^2 dA + \int y^2 dA = I_x + I_y$$

Hence, the polar moment of inertia of a given area with respect to a given axis equals the sum of the two rectangular moments of inertia with respect to any two axes perpendicular to each other in the plane of the area, and intersecting at the foot of the polar axis.

The polar moment of inertia of a circle, with respect to an axis through the center, is used in the solution of problems involving stresses in circular shafting and an expression for this will now be derived.

In Fig. 461 the axis with reference to which the polar moment is wanted is perpendicular to the plane of the paper and passes through O, the center of the circle. The elementary area dA is taken in the form of a ring, the radius of which is r and the thickness of which is dr. The area $dA = 2\,\pi r dr$, and $r^2 dA = 2\,\pi r^3 dr$. Summing up this quantity for all the rings which compose the circle,

$$I_z = 2\,\pi \int_0^R r^3 dr = \frac{2\,\pi r^4}{4}\Bigg]_0^R = \frac{\pi R^4}{2}$$

It follows that the rectangular moment of inertia I_x or I_y is one-half this, or $I_x = \pi R^4/4$. For a " hollow circle " the moment of inertia with respect to an axis through the center equals the moment of inertia of a circle with the outer radius minus the moment of inertia of a circle with the inner radius.

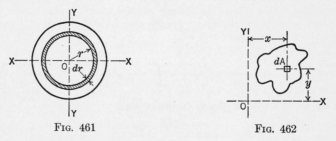

FIG. 461   FIG. 462

Product of Inertia of a Plane Area. The quantity $\int xy dA$ for a given area (Fig. 462) with respect to two rectangular axes is called the product of inertia with respect to the given pair of axes. If either axis is an axis of symmetry, then $\int xy dA$ is zero. Unlike moment of inertia the product of inertia with respect to a pair of axes may be negative. The symbol P_{xy} is commonly used for product of inertia.

In Fig. 463, X_0 and Y_0 are a pair of rectangular axes through the centroid of the area shown. X and Y are respectively parallel to and distant n and m from X_0 and Y_0. Let $\overline{P}_{xy}$ be the product of inertia with respect to the centroidal pair of axes.

Then $P_{xy} = \overline{P}_{xy} + mnA$ or $\overline{P}_{xy} = P_{xy} - mnA$, in which m and n may be positive or negative. This relation can be established in the same way as the similar theorem for moments of inertia.

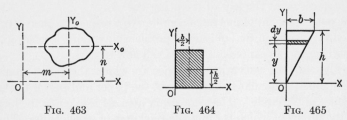

FIG. 463   FIG. 464   FIG. 465

Example. Determine the product of inertia of a rectangle (Fig. 464) with respect to axes coinciding with two intersecting sides.

Solution:

$$P_{xy} = \overline{P}_{xy} + mnA = 0 + \frac{b}{2} \times \frac{h}{2} \times bh = +\frac{b^2h^2}{4}$$

If the axes coincide with the top edge and left-hand side or with the bottom edge and the right-hand side of the rectangle, P_{xy} is negative.

Example. Determine the product of inertia for a right triangle with respect to the pair of centroidal axes parallel respectively to the base and altitude.

Solution: The value of P_{xy} will first be found with respect to a pair of axes one of which coincides with a side of the triangle and the other of which passes through the apex and is parallel to the base. For the area dA shown (Fig. 465) the area is $\frac{b}{h}y\,dy$.

$$P_{xy} = \int_0^h y \times \frac{b}{2\,h}y \times \frac{b}{h}y\,dy = \int_0^h \frac{b^2}{2\,h^2}y^3dy = \frac{b^2}{h^2} \times \frac{h^4}{8} = \frac{b^2h^2}{8}$$

With respect to a pair of parallel centroidal axes.

$$\overline{P}_{xy} = P_{xy} - mnA = \frac{b^2h^2}{8} - \frac{bh}{2} \times \frac{b}{3} \times \frac{2}{3}h = \frac{b^2h^2}{72}$$

If an area can be divided into simple shapes (triangles, rectangles, etc.) the product of inertia of the entire area with respect to a given pair of axes is the algebraic sum of the products of inertia with respect to the same pair of axes, of the several component simple shapes.

Principal Moments of Inertia: Principal Axes. The principal axes of inertia at any point of any given area are the two rectangular axes through that point with respect to which the values of I are a maximum and minimum, respectively. If the point is the centroid of the area, the axes are called the *principal centroidal axes*. When principal axes of inertia are mentioned without reference to any point, the axes referred to are centroidal axes. If an area has an axis of symmetry that axis is one

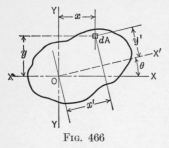

FIG. 466

of the principal axes. The two values of I with respect to the two principal axes are called the *principal moments of inertia*.

The inclination of the principal axes to any other rectangular axes is found by substituting values in an expression which is derived as shown below.

Fig. 466 represents any plane figure. OX and OX' represent two axes, the included angle being θ. A value of $I_{x'}$ is desired. It is evident that $y' = y \cos \theta - x \sin \theta$, and $x' = x \cos \theta + y \sin \theta$. Hence,

$$I_{x'} = \int y'^2 dA = \int (y \cos \theta - x \sin \theta)^2 dA$$

Expanding this, there results:

$$I_{x'} = I_x \cos^2 \theta + I_y \sin^2 \theta - 2 P_{xy} \sin \theta \cos \theta$$

Similarly,

$$I_{y'} = x^2 dA = (x \cos \theta + y \sin \theta) dA$$

Whence

$$I_{y'} = I_x \sin^2 \theta + I_y \cos^2 \theta + 2 P_{xy} \sin \theta \cos \theta$$

By the usual methods it may be found that the value of θ for which $I_{x'}$ is maximum or minimum is given by $\tan 2\theta = \dfrac{2 P_{xy}}{I_y - I_x}$.

The two values of θ resulting from this are 90° apart and give the directions of the axes through O for which I is respectively maximum and minimum. By substituting the values of θ found from this formula in the equations for $I_{x'}$ and $I_{y'}$ above, the values of the principal moments of inertia are found.

Example. The properties of a 5-in.-by-3-in.-by-$\frac{1}{2}$-in. angle are shown in Fig. 467(a). Determine the inclination of the principal axes of inertia and calculate the principal moments of inertia for this area.

Solution: The value of P_{xy} is first calculated. The area is divided into two rectangles by extending the upper edge of the horizontal flange. For each of these areas $P_{xy} = \overline{P}_{xy} + mnA$ in which $\overline{P}_{xy} = 0$. For entire area

$$P_{xy} = 0 + (4.5 \times 0.5) \times (-0.5) \times 1 + 0 + (3.0 \times 0.5) \times (-1.5) \times 0.75$$
$$= -1.125 - 1.6875 = -2.8125 \text{ in.}^4$$

The angle of inclination of the principal axes is found from

$$\tan 2\,\theta = \frac{2\,P_{xy}}{I_y - I_x} = \frac{-5.625}{2.58 - 9.45} = 0.819$$

Hence, $2\,\theta = 39° 19'$ and $\theta = 19° 40'$, as shown in Fig. 467 (b).

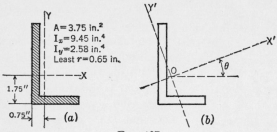

A=3.75 in.²
I_x=9.45 in.⁴
I_y=2.58 in.⁴
Least r=0.65 in.

1.75″

0.75″   (a)

(b)

FIG. 467

The principal moments of inertia are found as follows:

$$\begin{aligned}
I_{x'} &= I_x \cos^2 \theta + I_y \sin^2 \theta - 2\,P_{xy} \sin \theta \cos \theta \\
&= 9.45 \times 0.9417^2 + 2.58 \times 0.3364^2 + 2 \times 2.812 \times 0.3364 \times 0.9417 \\
&= 8.38 + 0.29 + 1.78 = 10.45 \text{ in.}^4 \\
I_{y'} &= I_x \sin^2 \theta + I_y \cos^2 \theta + 2\,P_{xy} \sin \theta \cos \theta \\
&= 9.45 \times 0.3364^2 + 2.58 \times 0.9417^2 - 2 \times 2.812 \times .3364 \times 0.9417 \\
&= 1.07 + 2.29 - 1.78 = 1.58 \text{ in.}^4
\end{aligned}$$

The above values of the principal moments of inertia can also be found by using the value of the minimum radius of gyration r and the cross-sectional area A as given in the steel handbooks.   Since

$$I_y = Ar^2 = 3.75 \times 0.65^2 = 1.58 \text{ in.}^4$$

and

$$I_x + I_y = I_{x'} + I_{y'}$$

then

$$9.45 + 2.58 = I_{x'} + 1.58, \text{ whence } I_{x'} = 10.45 \text{ in.}^4$$

APPENDIX C

TABLES

Tables II, III, IV, and V are complete except for the omissions noted. Table VI contains the unequal angles most commonly used in structural work.

Wide-flange beams (Table III) are arranged in groups, the beams in each group being rolled from the same set of rolls which are spread apart to roll the heavier sections. The beams of each group are designated by the *nominal* depth and flange width and the *actual* weight per foot, the *nominal* depth and flange width being the same for all beams of a group. For instance, all beams in the group at the top of page 395 (of which twenty are listed and eight omitted) are 14 in. × 16 in. beams, although varying in depth from 14.75 in. to 18.69 in.

Table XII, Physical Properties of Materials, is not exhaustive but includes widely used materials. Values given in this table are typical.

TABLE II

ELEMENTS OF AMERICAN STANDARD BEAMS

Depth of Beam	Weight per Foot	Area of Section	Width of Flange	Web Thickness	Axis 1–1			Axis 2–2		
					I	S	r	I	S	r
In.	Lb.	In.²	In.	In.	In.⁴	In.³	In.	In.⁴	In.³	In.
24	120.0	35.13	8.048	.798	3010.8	250.9	9.26	84.9	21.1	1.56
	7–24-in. beams omitted.									
	79.9	23.33	7.000	.500	2087.2	173.9	9.46	42.9	12.2	1.36
20	100.0	29.20	7.273	.873	1648.3	164.8	7.51	52.4	14.4	1.34
	6–20-in. beams omitted.									
	65.4	19.08	6.250	.500	1169.5	116.9	7.83	27.9	8.9	1.21
18	70.0	20.46	6.251	.711	917.5	101.9	6.70	24.5	7.8	1.09
	65.0	18.98	6.169	.629	877.7	97.5	6.80	23.4	7.6	1.11
	60.0	17.50	6.087	.547	837.8	93.1	6.92	22.3	7.3	1.13
	54.7	15.94	6.000	.460	795.5	88.4	7.07	21.2	7.1	1.15
15	75.0	21.85	6.278	.868	687.2	91.6	5.61	30.6	9.8	1.18
	70.0	20.38	6.180	.770	659.6	87.9	5.69	28.8	9.3	1.19
	65.0	18.91	6.082	.672	632.1	84.3	5.78	27.2	8.9	1.20
	60.8	17.68	6.000	.590	609.0	81.2	5.87	26.0	8.7	1.21
15	55.0	16.06	5.738	.648	508.7	67.8	5.63	17.0	5.9	1.03
	50.0	14.59	5.640	.550	481.1	64.2	5.74	16.0	5.7	1.05
	45.0	13.12	5.542	.452	453.6	60.5	5.88	15.0	5.4	1.07
	42.9	12.49	5.500	.410	441.8	58.9	5.95	14.6	5.3	1.08
12	55.0	16.04	5.600	.810	319.3	53.2	4.46	17.3	6.2	1.04
	50.0	14.57	5.477	.687	301.6	50.3	4.55	16.0	5.8	1.05
	45.0	13.10	5.355	.565	284.1	47.3	4.66	14.8	5.5	1.06
	40.8	11.84	5.250	.460	268.9	44.8	4.77	13.8	5.3	1.08
12	35.0	10.20	5.078	.428	227.0	37.8	4.72	10.0	3.9	0.99
	31.8	9.26	5.000	.350	215.8	36.0	4.83	9.5	3.8	1.01
10	40.0	11.69	5.091	.741	158.0	31.6	3.68	9.4	3.7	0.90
	35.0	10.22	4.944	.594	145.8	29.2	3.78	8.5	3.4	0.91
	30.0	8.75	4.797	.447	133.5	26.7	3.91	7.6	3.2	0.93
	25.4	7.38	4.660	.310	122.1	24.4	4.07	6.9	3.0	0.97
8	25.5	7.43	4.262	.532	68.1	17.0	3.03	4.7	2.2	0.80
	23.0	6.71	4.171	.441	64.2	16.0	3.09	4.4	2.1	0.81
	20.5	5.97	4.079	.349	60.2	15.1	3.18	4.0	2.0	0.82
	18.4	5.34	4.000	.270	56.9	14.2	3.26	3.8	1.9	0.84
7	20.0	5.83	3.860	.450	41.9	12.0	2.68	3.1	1.6	0.74
	17.5	5.09	3.755	.345	38.9	11.1	2.77	2.9	1.6	0.76
	15.3	4.43	3.660	.250	36.2	10.4	2.86	2.7	1.5	0.78
6	17.25	5.02	3.565	.465	26.0	8.7	2.28	2.3	1.3	0.68
	14.75	4.29	3.443	.343	23.8	7.9	2.36	2.1	1.2	0.69
	12.5	3.61	3.330	.230	21.8	7.3	2.46	1.8	1.1	0.72
5	14.75	4.29	3.284	.494	15.0	6.0	1.87	1.7	1.0	0.63
	12.25	3.56	3.137	.347	13.5	5.4	1.95	1.4	0.91	0.63
	10.0	2.87	3.000	.210	12.1	4.8	2.05	1.2	0.82	0.65
4	10.5	3.05	2.870	.400	7.1	3.5	1.52	1.0	0.70	0.57
	9.5	2.76	2.796	.326	6.7	3.3	1.56	0.91	0.65	0.58
	8.5	2.46	2.723	.253	6.3	3.2	1.60	0.83	0.61	0.58
	7.7	2.21	2.660	.190	6.0	3.0	1.64	0.77	0.58	0.59
3	7.5	2.17	2.509	.349	2.9	1.9	1.15	0.59	0.47	0.52
	6.5	1.88	2.411	.251	2.7	1.8	1.19	0.51	0.43	0.52
	5.7	1.64	2.330	.170	2.5	1.7	1.23	0.46	0.40	0.53

TABLE III

WIDE-FLANGE BEAMS

Elements of Sections

Depth of Section	Weight per Foot	Area of Section	Flange		Web Thickness	Axis 1–1			Axis 2–2		
			Width	Thickness		I	S	r	I	S	r
In.	Lb.	In.²	In.	In.	In.	In.⁴	In.³	In.	In.⁴	In.³	In.
36.72	300	88.17	16.655	1.680	.945	20290.2	1105.1	15.17	1225.2	147.1	3.73
		35 beams omitted		(depths	of 36″,	33″,	30″,	27″)			
24.72	160	47.04	14.091	1.135	.656	5110.3	413.5	10.42	492.6	69.9	3.23
24.56	150	44.10	14.063	1.055	.628	4733.5	385.5	10.36	452.5	64.3	3.20
24.41	140	41.16	14.029	.980	.594	4376.1	358.6	10.31	414.5	59.1	3.17
24.25	130	38.21	14.000	.900	.565	4009.5	330.7	10.24	375.2	53.6	3.13
24.31	120	35.29	12.088	.930	.556	3635.3	299.1	10.15	254.0	42.0	2.68
24.16	110	32.36	12.042	.855	.510	3315.0	274.4	10.12	229.1	38.0	2.66
24.00	100	29.43	12.000	.775	.468	2987.3	248.9	10.08	203.5	33.9	2.63
24.29	94	27.63	9.061	.872	.516	2683.0	220.9	9.85	102.2	22.6	1.92
24.16	87	25.58	9.025	.807	.480	2467.8	204.3	9.82	92.9	20.6	1.91
24.00	80	23.54	9.000	.727	.455	2229.7	185.8	9.73	82.4	18.3	1.87
23.87	74	21.77	8.975	.662	.430	2033.8	170.4	9.67	73.8	16.5	1.84
21.46	142	41.76	13.132	1.095	.659	3403.1	317.2	9.03	385.9	58.8	3.04
21.31	132	38.81	13.087	1.020	.614	3141.6	294.8	9.00	353.8	54.1	3.02
21.16	122	35.85	13.040	.945	.567	2883.2	272.5	8.97	322.1	49.4	3.00
21.00	112	32.93	13.000	.865	.527	2620.6	249.6	8.92	289.7	44.6	2.96
21.29	103	30.27	9.071	1.010	.608	2268.0	213.1	8.66	119.9	26.4	1.99
21.14	96	28.21	9.038	.935	.575	2088.9	197.6	8.60	109.3	24.2	1.97
21.00	89	26.15	9.000	.865	.537	1919.2	182.8	8.57	99.4	22.1	1.95
20.86	82	24.10	8.962	.795	.499	1752.4	168.0	8.53	89.6	20.0	1.93
21.24	73	21.46	8.295	.740	.455	1600.3	150.7	8.64	66.2	16.0	1.76
21.13	68	20.02	8.270	.685	.430	1478.3	139.9	8.59	60.4	14.6	1.74
21.00	63	18.52	8.250	.620	.410	1343.6	128.0	8.52	53.8	13.0	1.70
20.91	59	17.36	8.230	.575	.390	1246.8	119.3	8.47	49.2	12.0	1.68
18.64	124	36.45	11.889	1.071	.651	2227.1	239.0	7.82	281.9	47.4	2.78
18.48	114	33.51	11.833	.991	.595	2033.8	220.1	7.79	255.6	43.2	2.76
18.32	105	30.86	11.792	.911	.554	1852.5	202.2	7.75	231.0	39.2	2.73
18.16	96	28.22	11.750	.831	.512	1674.7	184.4	7.70	206.8	35.2	2.71
18.32	85	24.97	8.838	.911	.526	1429.9	156.1	7.57	99.4	22.5	2.00
18.16	77	22.63	8.787	.831	.475	1286.8	141.7	7.54	88.6	20.2	1.98
18.00	70	20.56	8.750	.751	.438	1153.9	128.2	7.49	78.5	17.9	1.95
17.87	64	18.80	8.715	.686	.403	1045.8	117.0	7.46	70.3	16.1	1.93
18.12	55	16.19	7.532	.630	.390	889.9	98.2	7.41	42.0	11.1	1.61
18.00	50	14.71	7.500	.570	.358	800.6	89.0	7.38	37.2	9.9	1.59
17.90	47	13.81	7.492	.520	.350	736.4	82.3	7.30	33.5	9.0	1.56
16.64	114	33.51	11.629	1.035	.631	1642.6	197.4	7.00	254.6	43.8	2.76
16.48	105	30.87	11.582	.955	.584	1497.5	181.7	6.96	230.7	39.8	2.73
16.32	96	28.22	11.533	.875	.535	1355.1	166.1	6.93	207.2	35.9	2.71
16.16	88	25.87	11.502	.795	.504	1222.6	151.3	6.87	185.2	32.2	2.67
16.32	78	22.92	8.586	.875	.529	1042.6	127.8	6.74	87.5	20.4	1.95
16.16	71	20.86	8.543	.795	.486	936.9	115.9	6.70	77.9	18.2	1.93
16.00	64	18.80	8.500	.715	.443	833.8	104.2	6.66	68.4	16.1	1.91
15.86	58	17.04	8.464	.645	.407	746.4	94.1	6.62	60.5	14.3	1.88
16.25	50	14.70	7.073	.628	.380	655.4	80.7	6.68	34.8	9.8	1.54
16.12	45	13.24	7.039	.563	.346	583.3	72.4	6.64	30.5	8.7	1.52
16.00	40	11.77	7.000	.503	.307	515.5	64.4	6.62	26.5	7.6	1.50
15.85	36	10.59	6.992	.428	.299	446.3	56.3	6.49	22.1	6.3	1.45

WIDE-FLANGE BEAMS (*Continued*)

Depth of Section	Weight per Foot	Area of Section	Flange		Web Thickness	Axis 1–1			Axis 2–2		
			Width	Thickness		I	S	r	I	S	r
In.	Lb.	In.²	In.	In.	In.	In.⁴	In.³	In.	In.⁴	In.³	In.
18.69	426	125.25	16.695	3.033	1.875	6610.3	707.4	7.26	2359.5	282.7	4.34

8 — 14 × 16 beams omitted.

17.00	300	88.20	16.175	2.188	1.355	4149.5	488.2	6.86	1546.0	191.2	4.19
16.81	287	84.37	16.130	2.093	1.310	3912.1	465.5	6.81	1466.5	181.8	4.17
16.62	273	80.22	16.065	1.998	1.245	3673.2	442.0	6.77	1382.9	172.2	4.15
16.50	264	77.63	16.025	1.938	1.205	3526.0	427.4	6.74	1331.2	166.1	4.14
16.37	255	74.98	15.990	1.873	1.170	3372.6	412.0	6.71	1278.1	159.9	4.13
16.25	246	72.33	15.945	1.813	1.125	3228.9	397.4	6.68	1226.6	153.9	4.12
16.12	237	69.69	15.910	1.748	1.090	3080.9	382.2	6.65	1174.8	147.7	4.11
16.00	228	67.06	15.865	1.688	1.045	2942.4	367.8	6.62	1124.8	141.8	4.10
15.87	219	64.36	15.825	1.623	1.005	2798.2	352.6	6.59	1073.2	135.6	4.08
15.75	211	62.07	15.800	1.563	.980	2671.4	339.2	6.56	1028.6	130.2	4.07
15.63	202	59.39	15.750	1.503	.930	2538.8	324.9	6.54	979.7	124.4	4.06
15.50	193	56.73	15.710	1.438	.890	2402.4	310.0	6.51	930.1	118.4	4.05
15.38	184	54.07	15.660	1.378	.840	2274.8	295.8	6.49	882.7	112.7	4.04
15.25	176	51.73	15.640	1.313	.820	2149.6	281.9	6.45	837.9	107.1	4.02
15.12	167	49.09	15.600	1.248	.780	2020.8	267.3	6.42	790.2	101.3	4.01
15.00	158	46.47	15.550	1.188	.730	1900.6	253.4	6.40	745.0	95.8	4.00
14.88	150	44.08	15.515	1.128	.695	1786.9	240.2	6.37	702.5	90.6	3.99
14.75	142	41.85	15.500	1.063	.680	1672.2	226.7	6.32	660.1	85.2	3.97
16.81	320	94.12	16.710	2.093	1.890	4141.7	492.8	6.63	1635.1	195.7	4.17
14.75	136	39.98	14.740	1.063	.660	1593.0	216.0	6.31	567.7	77.0	3.77
14.62	127	37.33	14.690	.998	.610	1476.7	202.0	6.29	527.6	71.8	3.76
14.50	119	34.99	14.650	.938	.570	1373.1	189.4	6.26	491.8	67.1	3.75
14.37	111	32.65	14.620	.873	.540	1266.5	176.3	6.23	454.9	62.2	3.73
14.25	103	30.26	14.575	.813	.495	1165.8	163.6	6.21	419.7	57.6	3.72
14.12	95	27.94	14.545	.748	.465	1063.5	150.6	6.17	383.7	52.8	3.71
14.00	87	25.56	14.500	.688	.420	966.9	138.1	6.15	349.7	48.2	3.70
14.18	84	24.71	12.023	.778	.451	928.4	130.9	6.13	225.5	37.5	3.02
14.06	78	22.94	12.000	.718	.428	851.2	121.1	6.09	206.9	34.5	3.00
14.19	74	21.76	10.072	.783	.450	796.8	112.3	6.05	133.5	26.5	2.48
14.06	68	20.00	10.040	.718	.418	724.1	103.0	6.02	121.2	24.1	2.46
13.91	61	17.94	10.000	.643	.378	641.5	92.2	5.98	107.3	21.5	2.45
14.06	58	17.06	8.098	.718	.406	597.9	85.0	5.92	63.7	15.7	1.93
13.94	53	15.59	8.062	.658	.370	542.1	77.8	5.90	57.5	14.3	1.92
13.81	48	14.11	8.031	.593	.339	484.9	70.2	5.86	51.3	12.8	1.91
13.68	43	12.65	8.000	.528	.308	429.0	62.7	5.82	45.1	11.3	1.89
14.24	42	12.34	6.801	.573	.338	432.2	60.7	5.92	28.1	8.3	1.51
14.12	38	11.17	6.776	.513	.313	385.3	54.6	5.87	24.6	7.3	1.49
14.00	34	10.00	6.750	.453	.287	339.2	48.5	5.83	21.3	6.3	1.46
13.86	30	8.81	6.733	.383	.270	289.6	41.8	5.73	17.5	5.2	1.41
14.38	190	55.86	12.670	1.736	1.060	1892.5	263.2	5.82	589.7	93.1	3.25
14.12	176	51.79	12.615	1.606	1.005	1712.5	242.6	5.75	538.4	85.4	3.22
13.88	161	47.38	12.515	1.486	.905	1541.8	222.2	5.70	486.2	77.7	3.20
13.62	147	43.24	12.450	1.356	.840	1374.4	201.8	5.64	436.8	70.2	3.18
13.38	133	39.11	12.365	1.236	.755	1221.2	182.5	5.59	389.9	63.1	3.16
13.12	120	35.31	12.320	1.106	.710	1071.7	163.4	5.51	345.1	56.0	3.13
12.88	106	31.19	12.230	.986	.620	930.7	144.5	5.46	300.9	49.2	3.11
12.75	99	29.09	12.190	.921	.580	858.5	134.7	5.43	278.2	45.7	3.09
12.62	92	27.06	12.155	.856	.545	788.9	125.0	5.40	256.4	42.2	3.08
12.50	85	24.98	12.105	.796	.495	723.3	115.7	5.38	235.5	38.9	3.07
12.38	79	23.22	12.080	.736	.470	663.0	107.1	5.34	216.4	35.8	3.05
12.25	72	21.16	12.040	.671	.430	597.4	97.5	5.31	195.3	32.4	3.04
12.12	65	19.11	12.000	.606	.390	533.4	88.0	5.28	174.6	29.1	3.02

38 beams omitted (depths of 12″, 10″, 8″).

8.19	21	6.18	5.272	.403	.252	73.8	18.0	3.45	9.13	3.5	1.22
8.09	19	5.59	5.264	.353	.244	64.7	16.0	3.40	7.87	3.0	1.19
8.00	17	5.00	5.250	.308	.230	56.4	14.1	3.36	6.72	2.6	1.16

TABLE IV

ELEMENTS OF AMERICAN STANDARD CHANNELS

Depth of Channel	Weight per Foot	Area of Section	Width of Flange	Web Thickness	Axis 1–1			Axis 2–2			
					I	S	r	I	S	r	y
In.	Lb.	In.²	In.	In.	In.⁴	In.³	In.	In.⁴	In.³	In.	In.
15	55.0	16.11	3.814	.814	429.0	57.2	5.16	12.1	4.1	0.87	0.82
	50.0	14.64	3.716	.716	401.4	53.6	5.24	11.2	3.8	0.87	0.80
	45.0	13.17	3.618	.618	373.9	49.8	5.33	10.3	3.6	0.88	0.79
	40.0	11.70	3.520	.520	346.3	46.2	5.44	9.3	3.4	0.89	0.78
	35.0	10.23	3.422	.422	318.7	42.5	5.58	8.4	3.2	0.91	0.79
	33.9	9.90	3.400	.400	312.6	41.7	5.62	8.2	3.2	0.91	0.79
12	40.0	11.73	3.415	.755	196.5	32.8	4.09	6.6	2.5	0.75	0.72
	35.0	10.26	3.292	.632	178.8	29.8	4.18	5.9	2.3	0.76	0.69
	30.0	8.79	3.170	.510	161.2	26.9	4.28	5.2	2.1	0.77	0.68
	25.0	7.32	3.047	.387	143.5	23.9	4.43	4.5	1.9	0.79	0.68
	20.7	6.03	2.940	.280	128.1	21.4	4.61	3.9	1.7	0.81	0.70
10	35.0	10.27	3.180	.820	115.2	23.0	3.34	4.6	1.9	0.67	0.69
	30.0	8.80	3.033	.673	103.0	20.6	3.42	4.0	1.7	0.67	0.65
	25.0	7.33	2.886	.526	90.7	18.1	3.52	3.4	1.5	0.68	0.62
	20.0	5.86	2.739	.379	78.5	15.7	3.66	2.8	1.3	0.70	0.61
	15.3	4.47	2.600	.240	66.9	13.4	3.87	2.3	1.2	0.72	0.64
9	25.0	7.33	2.812	.612	70.5	15.7	3.10	3.0	1.4	0.64	0.61
	20.0	5.86	2.648	.448	60.6	13.5	3.22	2.4	1.2	0.65	0.59
	15.0	4.39	2.485	.285	50.7	11.3	3.40	1.9	1.0	0.67	0.59
	13.4	3.89	2.430	.230	47.3	10.5	3.49	1.8	0.97	0.67	0.61
8	21.25	6.23	2.619	.579	47.6	11.9	2.77	2.2	1.1	0.60	0.59
	18.75	5.49	2.527	.487	43.7	10.9	2.82	2.0	1.0	0.60	0.57
	16.25	4.76	2.435	.395	39.8	9.9	2.89	1.8	0.94	0.61	0.56
	13.75	4.02	2.343	.303	35.8	9.0	2.99	1.5	0.86	0.62	0.56
	11.5	3.36	2.260	.220	32.3	8.1	3.10	1.3	0.79	0.63	0.58
7	19.75	5.79	2.509	.629	33.1	9.4	2.39	1.8	0.96	0.56	0.58
	17.25	5.05	2.404	.524	30.1	8.6	2.44	1.6	0.86	0.56	0.55
	14.75	4.32	2.299	.419	27.1	7.7	2.51	1.4	0.79	0.57	0.53
	12.25	3.58	2.194	.314	24.1	6.9	2.59	1.2	0.71	0.58	0.53
	9.8	2.85	2.090	.210	21.1	6.0	2.72	0.98	0.63	0.59	0.55
6	15.5	4.54	2.279	.559	19.5	6.5	2.07	1.3	0.73	0.53	0.55
	13.0	3.81	2.157	.437	17.3	5.8	2.13	1.1	0.65	0.53	0.52
	10.5	3.07	2.034	.314	15.1	5.0	2.22	0.87	0.57	0.53	0.50
	8.2	2.39	1.920	.200	13.0	4.3	2.34	0.70	0.50	0.54	0.52
5	11.5	3.36	2.032	.472	10.4	4.1	1.76	0.82	0.54	0.49	0.51
	9.0	2.63	1.885	.325	8.8	3.5	1.83	0.64	0.45	0.49	0.48
	6.7	1.95	1.750	.190	7.4	3.0	1.95	0.48	0.38	0.50	0.49
4	7.25	2.12	1.720	.320	4.5	2.3	1.47	0.44	0.35	0.46	0.46
	6.25	1.82	1.647	.247	4.1	2.1	1.50	0.38	0.32	0.45	0.46
	5.4	1.56	1.580	.180	3.8	1.9	1.56	0.32	0.29	0.45	0.46
3	6.0	1.75	1.596	.356	2.1	1.4	1.08	0.31	0.27	0.42	0.46
	5.0	1.46	1.498	.258	1.8	1.2	1.12	0.25	0.24	0.41	0.44
	4.1	1.19	1.410	.170	1.6	1.1	1.17	0.20	0.21	0.41	0.44

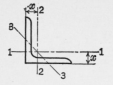

TABLE V

ELEMENTS OF EQUAL ANGLES

Size	Thickness	Weight per Foot	Area of Section	Axis 1–1 and Axis 2–2				Axis 3–3
				I	r	S	x	r min.
In.	In.	Lb.	In.^{2}	In.^{4}	In.	In.^{3}	In.	In.
8 × 8	1⅛	56.9	16.73	98.0	2.42	17.5	2.41	1.55
	1 1/16	54.0	15.87	93.5	2.43	16.7	2.39	1.56
	1	51.0	15.00	89.0	2.44	15.8	2.37	1.56
	15/16	48.1	14.12	84.3	2.44	14.9	2.34	1.56
	⅞	45.0	13.23	79.6	2.45	14.0	2.32	1.56
	13/16	42.0	12.34	74.7	2.46	13.1	2.30	1.57
	¾	38.9	11.44	69.7	2.47	12.2	2.28	1.57
	11/16	35.8	10.53	64.6	2.48	11.2	2.25	1.58
	⅝	32.7	9.61	59.4	2.49	10.3	2.23	1.58
	9/16	29.6	8.68	54.1	2.50	9.3	2.21	1.58
	½	26.4	7.75	48.6	2.51	8.4	2.19	1.58
6 × 6	1	37.4	11.00	35.5	1.80	8.6	1.86	1.16
	15/16	35.3	10.37	33.7	1.80	8.1	1.84	1.16
	⅞	33.1	9.73	31.9	1.81	7.6	1.82	1.17
	13/16	31.0	9.09	30.1	1.82	7.2	1.80	1.17
	¾	28.7	8.44	28.2	1.83	6.7	1.78	1.17
	11/16	26.5	7.78	26.2	1.83	6.2	1.75	1.17
	⅝	24.2	7.11	24.2	1.84	5.7	1.73	1.17
	9/16	21.9	6.43	22.1	1.85	5.1	1.71	1.18
	½	19.6	5.75	19.9	1.86	4.6	1.68	1.18
	7/16	17.2	5.06	17.7	1.87	4.1	1.66	1.19
	⅜	14.9	4.36	15.4	1.88	3.5	1.64	1.19
5 × 5	1	30.6	9.00	19.6	1.48	5.8	1.61	0.96
	15/16	28.9	8.50	18.7	1.48	5.5	1.59	0.96
	⅞	27.2	7.98	17.8	1.49	5.2	1.57	0.96
	13/16	25.4	7.47	16.8	1.50	4.9	1.55	0.97
	¾	23.6	6.94	15.7	1.50	4.5	1.52	0.97
	11/16	21.8	6.40	14.7	1.51	4.2	1.50	0.97
	⅝	20.0	5.86	13.6	1.52	3.9	1.48	0.97
	9/16	18.1	5.31	12.4	1.53	3.5	1.46	0.98
	½	16.2	4.75	11.3	1.54	3.2	1.43	0.98
	7/16	14.3	4.18	10.0	1.55	2.8	1.41	0.98
	⅜	12.3	3.61	8.7	1.56	2.4	1.39	0.99
4 × 4	13/16	19.9	5.84	8.1	1.18	3.0	1.29	0.77
	¾	18.5	5.44	7.7	1.19	2.8	1.27	0.77
	11/16	17.1	5.03	7.2	1.19	2.6	1.25	0.77
	⅝	15.7	4.61	6.7	1.20	2.4	1.23	0.77
	9/16	14.3	4.18	6.1	1.21	2.2	1.21	0.78
	½	12.8	3.75	5.6	1.22	2.0	1.18	0.78
	7/16	11.3	3.31	5.0	1.23	1.8	1.16	0.78
	⅜	9.8	2.86	4.4	1.23	1.5	1.14	0.79
	5/16	8.2	2.40	3.7	1.24	1.3	1.12	0.79
	¼	6.6	1.94	3.0	1.25	1.0	1.09	0.79
3½ × 3½	13/16	17.1	5.03	5.3	1.02	2.3	1.17	0.67
	¾	16.0	4.69	5.0	1.03	2.1	1.15	0.67
	11/16	14.8	4.34	4.7	1.04	2.0	1.12	0.67
	⅝	13.6	3.98	4.3	1.04	1.8	1.10	0.68
	9/16	12.4	3.62	4.0	1.05	1.6	1.08	0.68
	½	11.1	3.25	3.6	1.06	1.5	1.06	0.68
	7/16	9.8	2.87	3.3	1.07	1.3	1.04	0.68
	⅜	8.5	2.48	2.9	1.07	1.2	1.01	0.69
	5/16	7.2	2.09	2.5	1.08	0.98	0.99	0.69
	¼	5.8	1.69	2.0	1.09	0.79	0.97	0.69
3 × 3	⅝	11.5	3.36	2.6	0.88	1.3	0.98	0.57
	9/16	10.4	3.06	2.4	0.89	1.2	0.95	0.58
	½	9.4	2.75	2.2	0.90	1.1	0.93	0.58
	7/16	8.3	2.43	2.0	0.91	0.95	0.91	0.58
	⅜	7.2	2.11	1.8	0.91	0.83	0.89	0.58
	5/16	6.1	1.78	1.5	0.92	0.71	0.87	0.59
	¼	4.9	1.44	1.2	0.93	0.58	0.84	0.59

Smaller angles are rolled but not listed here.

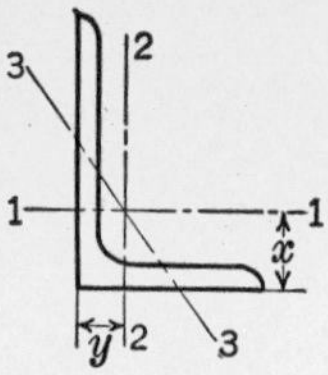

TABLE VI

Elements of Unequal Angles

Size	Thick-ness	Weight per Foot	Area of Section	Axis 1-1				Axis 2-2				Axis 3-3
				I	*S*	*r*	*x*	*I*	*S*	*r*	*y*	*r* min.
In.	In.	Lb.	In.²	In.⁴	In.³	In.	In.	In.⁴	In.³	In.	In.	In.
	1 1/8	49.3	14.48	88.9	16.8	2.48	2.70	42.5	9.9	1.71	1.70	1.28
	1 1/16	46.8	13.75	84.9	15.9	2.48	2.68	40.7	9.4	1.72	1.68	1.28
	1	44.2	13.00	80.8	15.1	2.49	2.65	38.8	8.9	1.73	1.65	1.28
	15/16	41.7	12.25	76.6	14.3	2.50	2.63	36.8	8.4	1.73	1.63	1.28
	7/8	39.1	11.48	72.3	13.4	2.51	2.61	34.9	7.9	1.74	1.61	1.28
8 × 6	13/16	36.5	10.72	67.9	12.5	2.52	2.59	32.8	7.4	1.75	1.59	1.29
	3/4	33.8	9.94	63.4	11.7	2.53	2.56	30.7	6.9	1.76	1.56	1.29
	11/16	31.2	9.15	58.8	10.8	2.54	2.54	28.6	6.4	1.77	1.54	1.29
	5/8	28.5	8.36	54.1	9.9	2.54	2.52	26.3	5.9	1.77	1.52	1.30
	9/16	25.7	7.56	49.3	8.9	2.55	2.50	24.0	5.3	1.78	1.50	1.30
	1/2	23.0	6.75	44.3	8.0	2.56	2.47	21.7	4.8	1.79	1.47	1.30
	7/16	20.2	5.93	39.2	7.1	2.57	2.45	19.3	4.2	1.80	1.45	1.30
	1	30.6	9.00	30.8	8.0	1.85	2.17	10.8	3.8	1.09	1.17	0.85
	15/16	28.9	8.50	29.3	7.6	1.86	2.14	10.3	3.6	1.10	1.14	0.85
	7/8	27.2	7.98	27.7	7.2	1.86	2.12	9.8	3.4	1.11	1.12	0.86
	13/16	25.4	7.47	26.1	6.7	1.87	2.10	9.2	3.2	1.11	1.10	0.86
	3/4	23.6	6.94	24.5	6.2	1.88	2.08	8.7	3.0	1.12	1.08	0.86
6 × 4	11/16	21.8	6.40	22.8	5.8	1.89	2.06	8.1	2.8	1.13	1.06	0.86
	5/8	20.0	5.86	21.1	5.3	1.90	2.03	7.5	2.5	1.13	1.03	0.86
	9/16	18.1	5.31	19.3	4.8	1.90	2.01	6.9	2.3	1.14	1.01	0.87
	1/2	16.2	4.75	17.4	4.3	1.91	1.99	6.3	2.1	1.15	0.99	0.87
	7/16	14.3	4.18	15.5	3.8	1.92	1.96	5.6	1.8	1.16	0.96	0.87
	3/8	12.3	3.61	13.5	3.3	1.93	1.94	4.9	1.6	1.17	0.94	0.88
	7/8	22.7	6.67	15.7	4.9	1.53	1.79	6.2	2.5	0.96	1.04	0.75
	13/16	21.3	6.25	14.8	4.6	1.54	1.77	5.9	2.4	0.97	1.02	0.75
	3/4	19.8	5.81	13.9	4.3	1.55	1.75	5.6	2.2	0.98	1.00	0.75
	11/16	18.3	5.37	13.0	4.0	1.56	1.72	5.2	2.1	0.98	0.97	0.75
	5/8	16.8	4.92	12.0	3.7	1.56	1.70	4.8	1.9	0.99	0.95	0.75
5 × 3½	9/16	15.2	4.47	11.0	3.3	1.57	1.68	4.4	1.7	1.00	0.93	0.75
	1/2	13.6	4.00	10.0	3.0	1.58	1.66	4.0	1.6	1.01	0.91	0.75
	7/16	12.0	3.53	8.9	2.6	1.59	1.63	3.6	1.4	1.01	0.88	0.76
	3/8	10.4	3.05	7.8	2.3	1.60	1.61	3.2	1.2	1.02	0.86	0.76
	5/16	8.7	2.56	6.6	1.9	1.61	1.59	2.7	1.0	1.03	0.84	0.76
	13/16	17.1	5.03	7.3	2.9	1.21	1.44	3.5	1.7	0.83	0.94	0.64
	3/4	16.0	4.69	6.9	2.7	1.22	1.42	3.3	1.6	0.84	0.92	0.64
	11/16	14.8	4.34	6.5	2.5	1.22	1.39	3.1	1.5	0.84	0.89	0.64
	5/8	13.6	3.98	6.0	2.3	1.23	1.37	2.9	1.4	0.85	0.87	0.64
	9/16	12.4	3.62	5.6	2.1	1.24	1.35	2.7	1.2	0.86	0.85	0.64
4 × 3	1/2	11.1	3.25	5.0	1.9	1.25	1.33	2.4	1.1	0.86	0.83	0.64
	7/16	9.8	2.87	4.5	1.7	1.25	1.30	2.2	1.0	0.87	0.80	0.64
	3/8	8.5	2.48	4.0	1.5	1.26	1.28	1.9	0.87	0.88	0.78	0.64
	5/16	7.2	2.09	3.4	1.2	1.27	1.26	1.7	0.74	0.89	0.76	0.65
	1/4	5.8	1.69	2.8	1.0	1.28	1.24	1.4	0.60	0.89	0.74	0.65
	9/16	9.5	2.78	2.3	1.2	0.91	1.02	1.4	0.82	0.72	0.77	0.52
	1/2	8.5	2.50	2.1	1.0	0.91	1.00	1.3	0.74	0.72	0.75	0.52
3 × 2½	7/16	7.6	2.21	1.9	0.93	0.92	0.98	1.2	0.66	0.73	0.73	0.52
	3/8	6.6	1.92	1.7	0.81	0.93	0.96	1.0	0.58	0.74	0.71	0.52
	5/16	5.6	1.62	1.4	0.69	0.94	0.93	0.90	0.49	0.74	0.68	0.53
	1/4	4.5	1.31	1.2	0.56	0.95	0.91	0.74	0.40	0.75	0.66	0.53

Many other unequal angles are rolled.

TABLE VII

U. S. STANDARD SCREW THREADS

Diameter and area at root of thread

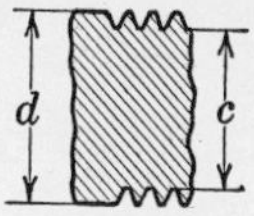

Diameter		Area		Diameter		Area	
Total d, In.	Net c, In.	Total Dia., d, Sq. In.	Net Dia., c, Sq. In.	Total d, In.	Net c, In.	Total Dia., d, Sq. In.	Net Dia., c, Sq. In.
¼	.185	.049	.027	2½	2.176	4.909	3.716
⅜	.294	.110	.068	2¾	2.426	5.940	4.619
½	.400	.196	.126	3	2.629	7.069	5.428
⅝	.507	.307	.202	3¼	2.879	8.296	6.509
¾	.620	.442	.302	3½	3.100	9.621	7.549
⅞	.731	.601	.419	3¾	3.317	11.045	8.641
1	.837	.785	.551	4	3.567	12.566	9.993
1⅛	.939	.994	.693	4¼	3.798	14.186	11.330
1¼	1.065	1.227	.890	4½	4.028	15.904	12.741
1⅜	1.158	1.485	1.054	4¾	4.256	17.721	14.221
1½	1.284	1.767	1.294	5	4.480	19.635	15.766
1⅝	1.389	2.074	1.515	5¼	4.730	21.648	17.574
1¾	1.491	2.405	1.744	5½	4.953	23.758	19.268
1⅞	1.616	2.761	2.049	5¾	5.203	25.967	21.262
2	1.712	3.142	2.300	6	5.423	28.274	23.095
2¼	1.962	3.976	3.021				

Thickness of standard nut equals nominal diameter of bolt.

TABLE VIII

STANDARD WELDED STEEL PIPE

(National Tube Company Standard)

Size, In.	Diameters, Inches		Thickness, Inches	Cross-section		Size, In.	Diameters, Inches		Thickness, Inches	Cross-section	
	External	Internal		Area of Metal, Sq. In.	Moment of Inertia, In.⁴*		External	Internal		Area of Metal, Sq. In.	Moment of Inertia, In.⁴*
⅛	.405	.269	.068	.072	.0011	5	5.563	5.047	.258	4.300	15.2
¼	.540	.364	.088	.125	.0033	6	6.625	6.065	.280	5.581	28.1
⅜	.675	.493	.091	.167	.0073	8	8.625	8.071	.277	7.265	63.3
½	.840	.622	.109	.250	.0171	8	8.625	7.981	.322	8.399	72.5
¾	1.050	.824	.113	.333	.0370	10	10.750	10.192	.279	9.178	125.8
1	1.315	1.049	.133	.494	.0873	10	10.750	10.136	.307	10.072	137.5
1¼	1.660	1.380	.140	.669	.195	10	10.750	10.020	.365	11.908	160.7
1½	1.900	1.610	.145	.799	.310	12	12.750	12.090	.330	12.876	248.5
2	2.375	2.067	.154	1.075	.666	12	12.750	12.000	.375	14.567	279.3
2½	2.875	2.469	.203	1.704	1.53	14 O.D.	14.000	13.250	.375	16.052	372.8
3	3.500	3.068	.216	2.228	3.02	15 O.D.	15.000	14.250	.375	17.230	461.0
3½	4.000	3.548	.226	2.680	4.79	16 O.D.	16.000	15.250	.375	18.408	562.1
4	4.500	4.026	.237	3.174	7.23						

*Rectangular moment of inertia with respect to a diameter.

TABLE IX

ALLOWABLE STRESSES — STRUCTURAL STEEL, CAST IRON AND MASONRY

(All stresses are given in pounds per square inch)

1. — STRUCTURAL STEEL FOR BUILDINGS

	A	B	C
Tension (net section)	20,000	18,000	16,000
Compression (on short lengths)	20,000	18,000	

(on gross section of columns)

$$A:\quad 17,000 - 0.485\frac{L^2}{r^2} \qquad B:\quad \frac{18,000}{1 + \dfrac{L^2}{18,000\, r^2}} \qquad C:\quad 16,000 - 70\,\frac{L}{r}$$

for $\dfrac{L}{r}$ not over 120.

Same as B for $\dfrac{L}{r}$ over 120.

	A	B	C
with a maximum of		15,000	14,000

$\dfrac{L}{r}$ not to exceed:

	A	B	C
for main compression members	120	120	120
for secondary members	200	200	150
Bending, (lateral deflection prevented)	20,000	18,000	16,000

Bending, compression flange

$$A:\quad \frac{22,500}{1 + \dfrac{L^2}{1,800\, b^2}} \qquad B:\quad \frac{20,000}{1 + \dfrac{L^2}{2,000\, b^2}} \qquad C:\quad 20,000 - 160\,\frac{L}{b}$$

$$A:\ \text{if } \frac{L}{b} > 15 \qquad B:\ \text{if } \frac{L}{b} > 15 \qquad C:\ \text{if } \frac{L}{b} > 25$$

	A	B	C
Bending, on extreme fibers of pins	30,000	27,000	25,000
Shearing, on pins	15,000	13,500	12,000
on power driven rivets	15,000	13,500	
on shop driven rivets	.....	.....	12,000
on field driven rivets	.....	.....	10,000
on turned bolts in reamed holes with a clearance not more than 1/50 of an inch	15,000	13,500	
on hand-driven rivets	.....	10,000	
on unfinished bolts	10,000	10,000	
on gross area of webs of beams	13,000	12,000	12,000
Bearing, on pins, power driven rivets in single shear	32,000*	24,000	
in double shear	40,000*1	30,000	
on pins and shop driven rivets	.....	.....	25,000
on field rivets	.....	.....	20,000

* If in reamed or drilled holes.   ¹Pins, 32,000.

Bearing, on hand driven rivets

in single shear.......		16,000
in double shear.....		20,000
on turned bolts in reamed		
holes		
in single shear.......	32,000	24,000
in double shear......	40,000	30,000
on unfinished bolts		
in single shear.......	20,000	16,000
in double shear......	25,000	20,000

Values given in column *A* are specified by the American Institute of Steel Construction (1936 specifications). Values in column *B* are from the New York City Building Code 1938. *A* and *B* are based on steel having an ultimate strength of 72,000 lb. per sq. in. Values in column *C* were widely specified from 1900 to 1930 and were based on steel having an ultimate strength of 65,000 lb. per sq. in. Because specifications contain restrictions and explanations which cannot be given in a brief table, original specifications should be used in actual design.

Cast Iron and Masonry; see Table I, p. 35.

TABLE X

Commercial Measurement of Lumber. Lumber is sold by *board foot* measure. A board foot is one-twelfth of a cubic foot; that is, a timber 12 in. by 12 in. by 12 ft. long contains 144 board feet. A board foot is usually assumed to weigh 4 lb.

Lumber dealers sell many standard sizes which are usually called by the nominal dimensions of the cross-section, as, for instance, a " two by four " or a " ten by twelve."

The nominal cross-sectional dimensions are commonly in multiples of 1 in. up to 4 in., above which they are in multiples of 2 in. The actual dimensions of lumber are less than the nominal dimensions because of shrinkage and the removal of wood by the saw and planer. For dressed lumber, dimensions of 4 in. or less may be $\frac{3}{8}$ in. scant. Larger dimensions may be $\frac{1}{2}$ in. less than nominal sizes.[1] The dimensions of rough (unplaned) lumber approach more nearly the nominal sizes, but are still somewhat scant. In calculations involving the strength of lumber the actual dressed sizes should be used. The number of board feet is based on nominal sizes, however.

[1] National Lumber Manufacturers' Association standards. Practice varies somewhat in different localities.

TABLE XI

ALLOWABLE STRESSES FOR LUMBER

Allowable stresses for lumber conforming to the basic provisions for select and common structural material of American lumber standards[1]

[As recommended by the Forest Products Laboratory, Forest Service, United States Department of Agriculture]

Species	Fiber stress in bending[2]									
	Continuously dry — All thicknesses		Occasionally wet but quickly dried				More or less continuously damp or wet			
			Material 4 in. and thinner		Material 5 in. and thicker		Material 4 in. and thinner		Material 5 in. and thicker	
	Select grade	Common grade	Select grade	Common grade	Select grade	Common grade	Select grade	Common grade	Select grade	Common grade
	Lb. per sq. in.	Lb. per sq. in.	Lb. per sq. in.	Lb. per sq. in.	Lb. per sq. in.	Lb. per sq. in.	Lb. per sq. in.	Lb. per sq. in.	Lb. per sq. in.	Lb. per sq. in.
Cypress, southern	1300	1040	980	830	1100	880	800	680	900	720
Douglas fir (western Washington and Oregon type)[3]	1600	1200	1233	983	1387	1040	948	756	1067	800
Douglas fir (dense)[3]	1750	1400	1349	1147	1517	1213	1037	882	1167	933
Fir, commercial white	1100	880	800	680	900	720	710	600	800	640
Hemlock, eastern	1100	880	800	680	900	720	710	600	800	640
Hemlock, western	1300	1040	980	830	1100	880	800	680	900	720
Hickory (true and pecan)	1900	1520	1330	1130	1500	1200	1070	910	1200	960
Oak, commercial red and white	1400	1120	1070	910	1200	960	890	760	1000	800
Pine, southern yellow[3]	1750	1200	1349	983	1517	1040	1037	756	1167	800
Pine, southern yellow (dense)[3]		1400		1147		1213		882		933
Pine, northern white, western white, western yellow, and sugar	900	720	710	600	800	640	670	570	750	600
Redwood	1200	960	890	760	1000	800	710	600	800	640
Spruce, red, white, and Sitka	1100	880	800	680	900	720	710	600	800	640

[1] American lumber standards: Basic provisions for American lumber standards grades are published by the United States Department of Commerce in Simplified Practice Recommendation No. 16, Lumber, revised July 1, 1926; specifications for grades conforming to American lumber standards are published in the 1927 Standards of the Amer. Soc. for Testing Materials, and in Amer. Ry. Engineering Assoc., Bul., vol. 30, No. 314, dated February, 1929.

[2] Stress in tension: The working stresses recommended for fiber stress in bending may be safely used for tension parallel to grain.

[3] Exact figures given: In order to preserve the exact numerical relations among working stresses for grades involving rate of growth and density requirements the values for Douglas fir (western Washington and Oregon type) and for southern yellow pine have not been rounded off, as have the values for the other species.

TABLE (Continued)

Allowable stresses for lumber conforming to the basic provisions for select and common structural material of American lumber standards

Species	Compression perpendicular to grain, select and common grades			Horizontal shear[4] — Not varied with conditions of exposure		Compression parallel to grain (short columns having ratio of length to least dimension of 11 or less)						Average modulus of elasticity[5] — Not varied with conditions of exposure or with grade
	Continuously dry	Occasionally wet but quickly dried	More or less continuously damp or wet	Select grade	Common grade	Continuously dry — Select grade	Continuously dry — Common grade	Occasionally wet but quickly dried — Select grade	Occasionally wet but quickly dried — Common grade	More or less continuously damp or wet — Select grade	More or less continuously damp or wet — Common grade	
	Lb. per sq. in.	Lb. per sq. in.	Lb. per sq. in.	Lb. per sq. in.	Lb. per sq. in.	Lb. per sq. in.	Lb. per sq. in.	Lb. per sq. in.	Lb. per sq. in.	Lb. per sq. in.	Lb. per sq. in.	Lb. per sq. in.
Cypress, southern	350	250	225	100	80	1100	880	1000	800	800	640	1,200,000
Douglas fir (western Washington and Oregon type)[3]	347[6]	240[6]	213[6]	90	72	1173	880	1067	800	907	680	1,600,000
Douglas fir (dense)[3]	379	262	233	105	84	1283	1027	1167	933	992	793	1,600,000
Fir, commercial white	300	225	200	70	56	700	560	700	560	600	480	1,100,000
Hemlock, eastern	300	225	200	70	56	700	560	700	560	600	480	1,100,000
Hemlock, western	300	225	200	75	60	900	720	900	720	800	640	1,400,000
Hickory (true and pecan)	600	400	350	140	112	1500	1200	1200	960	1000	800	1,800,000
Oak, commercial red and white	500	375	300	125	100	1000	800	900	720	800	640	1,500,000
Pine, southern yellow[3]	[6]	[6]	[6]		88		880		800		680	1,600,000
Pine, southern yellow (dense)[3]	379	262	233	128	103	1283	1027	1167	933	992	793	1,600,000
Pine, northern white, western white, western yellow, and sugar	250	150	125	85	68	750	600	750	600	650	520	1,000,000
Redwood	250	150	125	70	56	1000	800	900	720	750	600	1,200,000
Spruce, red, white, and Sitka	250	150	125	85	68	800	640	750	600	650	520	1,200,000

[3] Exact figures given: In order to preserve the exact numerical relations among working stresses for grades involving rate of growth and density requirements the values for Douglas fir (western Washington and Oregon type) and for southern yellow pine have not been rounded off, as have the values for the other species.

[4] Joint details: The shearing stresses for joint details may be taken for any grades as 50 per cent greater than the horizontal shear values for the Select grade.

[5] Factors to be applied to average modulus of elasticity values: The values for modulus of elasticity are average for species and not safe working stresses. They may be used as given for computing average deflection of beams. When it is desired to prevent sag in beams values one-half those given should be used. In figuring safe loads for long columns values one-third those given should be used.

[6] Working stresses for the common grade: The values given are for the select grade. Working stresses in compression perpendicular to grain for the common grades of Douglas fir (western Washington and Oregon type) and southern yellow pine are 325, 225, and 200, respectively, for continuously dry, occasionally wet but quickly dried, and more or less continuously damp or wet conditions.

TABLE XII

Physical Properties of Materials

Material	Weight Lb. per c.f.	Coefficient of Thermal Expansion, per Deg. F.	Ultimate Strength Tensile, Lb. per Sq. In.	Compressive, Lb. per Sq. In.	Elongation in Two Inches, Per Cent	Modulus of Elasticity, Lb. per Sq. In.
Ferrous Metals:						
Steel 0.15% C or less		0.0000061 –	45,000		30	30,000,000
0.20–0.30% C		0.0000073	60,000		25	(Often
0.40–0.60% C	490	average	75,000		20	29,000,000
0.70–0.85% C		0.0000065	110,000		10	or less)
1.00% C and over			105,000		small	
Cast Iron						
Gray	450	0.0000062	15,000 – 25,000	80,000 – 150,000	small	12,000,000
Malleable			35,000 – 58,000	80,000 – 150,000	15–4.5	25,000,000
Wrought Iron	480	0.0000067	45,000 – 50,000		40–20	27,000,000
Non-Ferrous Metals:						
Aluminum						
Annealed Sheets	165	0.0000123	12,000 – 15,000		30–20	10,000,000
Wire (Hard drawn)			25,000 – 55,000		8–2	
Copper						
Annealed	550	0.0000093	35,000		50	15,000,000
Wire (Hard drawn)			50,000		9	17,000,000
Brass (30% Zn)						
Cast	530	0.0000105	40,000	60,000	35	14,000,000
Rolled			60,000		5	
Bronze (10% Sn)	510	0.0000099	33,000	56,000	10	10,000,000
Duralumin						
Quenched and aged			55,000 – 65,000		20	10,000,000
Quenched, aged and rolled	174		75,000 – 80,000			
Non-metallic Materials:						
Stone or						
Gravel Concrete						
8¼ gal. water per sack of cement	150	0.000006		1,500*		2,000,000 –
7½ do.				2,000		4,000,000
6¾ do.				2,500		increasing
6 do.				3,000		with strength
Cinder concrete	110					
Lumber						
Southern pine (dense)	50			4,300		1,600,000
Douglas fir (coast)	40			3,900		1,600,000
Hemlock (western)	40			2,900		1,400,000
Spruce (red, white and Sitka)	33	0.000003		2,600		1,200,000
Cypress	48			3,900		1,200,000
White Oak	60			3,500		1,500,000

Values in the table are typical. For an individual specimen, the values (particularly those for strength, elongation and modulus of elasticity) may differ considerably from those given. Strengths and moduli of elasticity of lumber are for forces applied parallel to the grain.

* "Joint Code " values for 28-day concrete.

INDEX

% elong $= \dfrac{\text{elong at rupture}}{\text{ougen } L} \times 100$

% red area $= \dfrac{\text{total red. area}}{\text{original area}} \times 100$

$-\dfrac{6Ax}{L} = -\dfrac{wL^3}{4}$ unit, load

AREA $\dfrac{15}{16}" : 0.6903 \; "^2$

AREA $\dfrac{13}{16}" : 0.5185 \; "^2$

AREA $1\dfrac{1}{16} = .8866 \; "^2$

$\dfrac{6Ax}{L} = \dfrac{3}{8} PL^2$ conc center load not at center

$T = \dfrac{S_s J}{c}$ $\qquad J = \dfrac{\pi c^4}{2}$

$\theta = \dfrac{S_s L}{E_s c}$

$\theta = \dfrac{TL}{E_s J}$

AREA in load diag = load
ORDINATE in load diag = rate of loading
Resultant acts thru c.g.

$\dfrac{dM}{dx} = V$ $\qquad \dfrac{dV}{dx} =$ rate of loading

$M_2 - M_1 = $ area shear diag $\Big]_1^2$

$dF \text{(on horiz. strip)} = \dfrac{My}{I} dA = \dfrac{Sy}{c} dA$

$\int y \, dF = M_R \text{ N.A}$

$\int_{N.A}^{Top} dc = c$ $\qquad \int_{N.A}^{Top} y \, dc = C\bar{y}$